INDUSTRIAL WASTEWATER CONTROL

A Textbook and Reference Work

INDUSTRIAL WASTEWATER CONTROL

A Textbook and Reference Work

Edited by

C. FRED GURNHAM

Department of Civil Engineering
Illinois Institute of Technology
Chicago, Illinois

1965 ACADEMIC PRESS
NEW YORK AND LONDON

ACADEMIC PRESS, INC.
111 Fifth Avenue, New York, New York 10003

United Kingdom Edition published by
ACADEMIC PRESS, INC. (LONDON) LTD.
24/28 Oval Road, London NW1 7DD

LIBRARY OF CONGRESS CATALOG CARD NUMBER: 65-12767

Second Printing, 1971

PRINTED IN THE UNITED STATES OF AMERICA

LIST OF CONTRIBUTORS

Numbers in parentheses indicate the pages on which the authors' contributions begin.

R. J. AUSTIN, *American Oil Company, Whiting, Indiana* (285)

A. R. BALDEN, *Electrochemistry and Corrosion Department, Engineering Division, Chrysler Corporation, Detroit, Michigan* (453)

WALTER G. BELTER, *Division of Reactor Development and Technology, U. S. Atomic Energy Commission, Washington, D.C.* (429)

RUSSELL K. BLAINE,* *Formerly, Research Department, Hiram Walker and Sons, Inc., Peoria, Illinois* (147)

HENRY C. BRAMER, *Mellon Institute, Pittsburgh, Pennsylvania* (235)

L. W. CADWALLADER, *Potomac Electric Power Company, Washington, D.C.* (413)

H. F. ELKIN, *Sun Oil Company, Philadelphia, Pennsylvania* (285)

C. W. FISHER, *Koppers Company, Inc., Monroeville, Pennsylvania* (221)

D. GARDNER FOULKE, *Sel-Rex Corporation, Nutley, New Jersey* (339)

HARRY W. GEHM, *National Council for Stream Improvement (of the Pulp, Paper and Paperboard Industries) Inc., New York, New York* (357)

R. E. GREENFIELD, *Formerly, A. E. Staley Manufacturing Company, Decatur, Illinois* (121)

C. FRED GURNHAM, *Department of Civil Engineering, Illinois Institute of Technology, Chicago, Illinois* (1, 323)

ERNST P. HALL, *Consolidation Coal Company, Inc., Pittsburgh, Pennsylvania* (169)

LLOYD T. JENSEN, *The Great Western Sugar Company, Denver, Colorado* (133)

A. STANFORD JOHNSON,† *Oscar Mayer and Company, Madison, Wisconsin* (25)

* PRESENT ADDRESS: *Science Department, Regis School, Cedar Rapids, Iowa.*
† DECEASED.

v

C. J. LEWIS, *Colorado School of Mines Research Foundation, Inc., Golden, Colorado* (183)

RICHARD J. LUND, *Battelle Memorial Institute, Columbus, Ohio* (199)

WALTER A. MERCER, *Western Research Laboratory, National Canners Association, Berkeley, California* (97)

FRED O'FLAHERTY, *Tanner's Council Laboratory, University of Cincinnati, Cincinnati, Ohio* (395)

JOHN A. PETERS, *Fish and Wildlife Service, Bureau of Commercial Fisheries, Technological Laboratory, U. S. Department of the Interior, Gloucester, Massachusetts* (55)

JOSEPH W. SLAVIN, *Fish and Wildlife Service, Bureau of Commercial Fisheries, Technological Laboratory, U. S. Department of the Interior, Gloucester, Massachusetts* (55)

R. HOBART SOUTHER, *Greensboro, North Carolina* (375)

JOHN A. TALLMADGE, *School of Engineering, Yale University, New Haven, Connecticut* (255)

W. R. TAYLOR, *Diamond Alkali Company, Cleveland, Ohio* (305)

C. R. VIGSTEDT, *General Engineering Division, Armour and Company, Chicago, Illinois* (69)

CLIFFORD W. WATSON, JR., *Dairymen's League Co-operative Association, Inc., New York, New York* (81)

PREFACE

The pollution of streams is a matter of intense and increasing public concern. The wastewaters of industry, although only one cause of this pollution, receive a disproportionate fraction of the blame; hence control of industrial wastewaters has of necessity become a primary responsibility of company management.

Most leaders of industry have accepted the responsibility of controlling their discharges to minimize pollution. Perfection in pollution control cannot be achieved within a realistic cost pattern; so, as in most commercial ventures, an evaluation of opposing forces is necessary. One purpose of this book is to inform company officials as to what other plants, in their own and other industries, are doing to alleviate their problems of stream pollution.

An earlier book* on the principles of treatment, authored by the present editor, was well received by industry, educators, regulatory agencies, and others. Even before this went out of print, demand arose for a companion book written by industry people and covering the problems and activities of individual industries. "Industrial Wastewater Control" is the result.

The authors of the 24 basic chapters were chosen by the editor as outstanding experts in their fields. Many of the authors have represented their respective industries on the National Technical Task Committee on Industrial Wastes. Most are engineers or executives in the industries on which they have written. The exceptions, from the academic field or government, are nevertheless experts, in close touch with the industries they have discussed.

Any one of these chapters could have been expanded to a complete treatise. The editor has found his co-authors thoroughly cooperative in restraining themselves to the permissible space, yet covering the essential aspects. In general, each chapter describes the industry itself, characteristics of the industry wastewaters, methods of treatment and disposal, and significant trends. For the most part, practices described pertain to the United States.

To conserve space, reference lists have been kept brief. Each industry could be further documented, but literature searches are not difficult and are left to the reader.

*Gurnham, C. F., "Principles of Industrial Waste Treatment." Wiley, New York, 1955.

To the professors who will use this book as a text, two possibilities are suggested. The chapters may be studied in their present sequence, which was logically developed, or in any other sequence that may be preferred. Alternately, the professor may outline his course on the basis of treatment techniques or other rational order, and select chapters or portions of chapters to illustrate specific points.

The editor acknowledges with thanks the congenial acceptance by all his co-authors of his sometimes arbitrary demands, and their meeting of necessary deadlines without impairing the quality of their writing.

✿ ✿ ✿ ✿ ✿ ✿ ✿ ✿ ✿ ✿

Mr. A. Stanford Johnson, author of Chapter 2, on Meat, passed away in October, 1964. He was well recognized as an authority on wastewater control in the meat industry. His work for this book had been completed, except for final page proofreading, at the time of his death. The editor and co-authors, many of whom knew Mr. Johnson personally, were privileged to have been associated with him in this work, and will miss his cheerful cooperation in the future.

C. FRED GURNHAM

Chicago, Illinois
December, 1964

CONTENTS

FOOD PRODUCTS—ANIMAL

FOOD PRODUCTS—VEGETABLE

MINING

Chapter 1

INTRODUCTION

by C. FRED GURNHAM

Stream pollution control has become one of the principal problems facing modern civilization. The ill effects of pollution are in part economic, as in the added cost of purifying the water for municipal, industrial, or agricultural use. Pollution may make natural waters unfit as an environment for fish or other wildlife, and has caused extensive killings of fish on numerous occasions. Pollution of streams, lakes, and even coastal waters has rendered these natural resources unsuitable for recreation, preventing the enjoyment of swimming, boating, and similar waterside activities. Waters that are severely polluted may be esthetically offensive, to the eye or nose. The American public is aroused by the existence of pollution and its possible increase; the popular press has taken a stand for cleaner waters; and many governmental offices are actively engaged in the battle against polluted streams.

Industrial waste is one of the causes of stream pollution. It is roughly comparable, in its nationwide pollutional effect, with municipal sewage and other sanitary and domestic wastes. A third major source of contamination is agriculture, which discharges both excessive quantities of silt and chemicals leached or washed from the soil. Lesser amounts of pollution reach the streams from mining and construction activities, and from purely natural sources. In a particular locality or stream, any one of these waste origins may be the principal offender, causing offensive pollution.

Waterborne waste appears to be an inevitable result of nearly all manufacturing industries. Water is used for many purposes, often in large quantities, by industry; only a small fraction of the water used is distributed with the manufactured product. Most and frequently all of it must be discharged from the plant premises. Such discharges are inevitably contaminated with small amounts of all materials used in the plant: raw materials, unwanted substances accompanying the raw materials (dirt on vegetables, gangue with ores), manufactured products, intermediate products, by-products, and other substances used in the processing. Water is deliberately used to carry away some of these materials, others are of economic value but are unavoidably lost in the processing; whatever their origin, they contribute to pollution of the receiving waterway.

The correction or control of stream pollution, as far as it is related to industrial wastes, is a problem with many aspects. It should be attacked,

1

as it often has been, by cooperative effort of industry and stream regulatory authority. Engineers, chemists, biologists, and other experts are involved, both in evaluating and in solving the problem.

Industrial wastes are characterized by their differences rather than
their similarities. Each individual plant is an individual problem. There
are, of course, common parameters by which pollution can be evaluated;
there are treatment methods of somewhat general application; and, finally, there are similarities among the plants in any given industry. The
common parameters and treatments are briefly described in the remainder of this introductory chapter, and specific industries in the main
part of the book.

PARAMETERS OF POLLUTION

No natural water is pure. It inevitably carries, in dissolved or suspended form, at least traces of every material it has recently contacted:
earth, vegetation, animal life, and atmosphere; plus the chemical and
metabolic reaction products of these with each other, with the water itself, and with the organisms in or near the stream. The word "pollution"
should be applied only when impurities are present in objectionable concentrations, by the activities of civilized man.

Quantitative evaluation of stream pollution is based on the concentration of specific impurities or identifiable groups of impurities in the
stream. These concentrations are related, in turn, to the corresponding
concentrations in waters discharged into the stream, and to the relative
volumes of flow. Concentrations are usually reported in milligrams per
liter (mg/liter), which is practically identical with the now obsolete,
though often used, unit of parts per million (ppm). Flows are usually
stated in gallons per minute (gpm) or river flows in cubic feet per second (cfs); these and other volumetric or gravimetric flow rates are
readily converted from one to another. It is often desirable to express
pollution in total quantity rather than in concentration, for example, in
pounds of chloride discharged per day; this too is easily computed if concentration and flow rate are known.

The parameters or properties described below are those commonly
used in stream evaluation and the study of wastewaters (1).

RESIDUES (SOLIDS)

Residue on Evaporation. As the name implies, residue on evaporation,
formerly called "total solids," is the weight of impurity left when the
water is evaporated at 103°C. Because this test is so nonspecific, it has
little value except as one step toward a more complete analysis. Inor-

ganic and organic fractions may be roughly separated by igniting the residue at 600°C, which yields values for "fixed" and "volatile" residue. In interpreting both the primary evaporation and the later ignition, some knowledge of the characteristics of the impurities is important, as the analysis may be affected by such complications as hydrate formation or decomposition, breakdown of organic and certain inorganic compounds, and loss of significant materials by volatilization.

Total Suspended Matter. The total suspended matter, or nonfiltrable residue, is the dry weight of residue retained by an asbestos mat filter. This is obviously particulate matter, not dissolved impurities; though very fine particulate matter and colloidal solids may not be retained. A distinction between fixed and volatile suspended matter can be made by ignition.

Coarse and floating solids are impossible to sample in a representative manner; hence they should be avoided in the sample, but the sample man should report them. There is no reason to permit such wastes in an industrial or municipal effluent; hence they should not be significant. They occur, of course, in food processing plants, textile mills, and other industries, but are readily removed from the waste stream before discharge.

The principal objection to total suspended matter (as distinguished from its settleable fraction) is unesthetic appearance in the stream. It is, however, no different from silt and other natural suspended matter, unless the color is unusual. Suspended matter reduces light penetration into the stream water, affecting oxygen regeneration by photosynthesis.

Settleable Matter. The portion of total suspended matter which can be removed by quiescent settling is particularly significant. In a stream, settling tends to clarify the water, but at the expense of creating bottom deposits or sludge banks. If organic, these deposits may decompose with formation of objectionable odors; they also remove oxygen from the stream. If inorganic, they merely blanket the stream bottom; but this destroys bottom life and may upset the biological balance of the stream.

Deliberate removal of settleable matter by sedimentation, in specially designed equipment, is one of the most useful methods of waste treatment. It is used to remove settleable matter from the raw waste and, as well, settleable matter produced from nonsettleable contaminants during the waste treatment process, as by chemical precipitation, adsorption, or biological action.

Settleable matter can be determined on a volumetric basis, using an Imhoff cone or similar vessel. It is more often determined by weight, and is the difference between total suspended matter in the water before and after laboratory settling.

Dissolved Matter. Dissolved matter, or filtrable residue, in contrast to total suspended matter, is the portion of "residue" which passes through the asbestos mat, in solution or in fine suspension in the water. Individual components, which must be determined by specific tests, are usually more significant than the gross quantity of dissolved matter. In evaluating an industrial waste discharge or the effect of such a discharge on a stream, the test for dissolved matter has no significance unless it is used as a comparison with dissolved matter in the original stream or in the plant raw water.

Turbidity. Turbidity is a measure of the effect on light, and hence on appearance of the stream, caused by suspended and colloidal matter in the water. It has obvious esthetic significance, both in the stream itself and in any municipal water supplies taken from the stream. It may render the waters unsuitable for municipal supplies or for certain industrial uses, notably for food, beverage, and paper manufacture. The nature of the specific substance causing turbidity may be important for other reasons, as for its contribution to BOD load.

Oils. Oils and other floating films are highly objectionable in natural waters, for their unesthetic qualities and for actual damage to the waterway. They retard aeration of the stream, thus killing fish. Heavy oil films have been known to trap and kill waterfowl and land wildlife. Oily films coat bridge piers and other structures, leaving unsightly desposits, and are damaging to waterworks equipment. They may be difficult to remove from a water supply. Soluble or colloidal oils are less troublesome, except as chemical or biological action in the stream may release them as free oils.

COLOR, TASTE, AND ODOR

Color. Color occurs naturally in many streams, typically as a yellow or brown shade from swamp waters, or browns from iron-bearing waters. These and other colors may also be imparted by industrial effluents. Acid mine waters and natural drainage in mining regions often carry heavy iron discoloration, sometimes worsened by tannic acid and similar natural constituents of the water. Dye wastes from dyestuff manufacture, paper mills, and textile dyehouses may be spectacular and, of course, undesirable. The wastes of many industries are colored, hence conspicuous and objectionable to the public. Colored waters are not usable for public water supplies without treatment, which must often be elaborate and expensive. They may not be usable for certain industrial waters under any circumstances. Color itself is harmless, but it is not wanted by the public, and it may be an indication of more serious pollution such as a toxic substance.

Taste. Tastes caused by pollution are significant in potable waters and in waters used for fishing; in the latter, fish flesh often acquires and even concentrates taste-producing contaminants in the water. Many chemicals cause objectionable tastes, the most conspicuous being phenol and its derivatives. The medicinal taste of phenol is worsened by chlorination, a common process in water treatment. The limiting concentration for phenol, according to U.S. Public Health Service Drinking Water Standards, is 0.001 mg/liter, or only one part per billion. Phenols sometimes occur naturally, as by decomposition of tannin compounds in swamp waters; but their presence in water is generally blamed on such industries as coke and gas manufacture, petroleum refining, and the production of chemicals and plastics.

Odor. Odor may be a characteristic of the raw waste, or it may develop in the waste or the receiving stream by decomposition of other pollutants. Obviously, odors are esthetically offensive, even at an appreciable distance from their source. Commercial food preparation and similar operations cannot be conducted in an odorous environment. Some of the gases associated with odor may be physically damaging to structures, by causing chemical corrosion or discoloration of paint. Sulfide odors are the principal cause of complaint; these may form by reduction of sulfates, which exist in most waters, in the presence of decomposable organic wastes and anaerobic microorganisms. Adequate concentration of dissolved oxygen avoids anaerobic reactions, but cannot be maintained in an organically overloaded stream.

ACIDITY, ALKALINITY, AND pH

One of the most damaging characteristics of many industrial wastes, particularly from the inorganic industries, is their acid or alkali content. Either a high or a low pH may be damaging, causing fish kills and general sterility in natural streams, and inactivating the essential microorganisms in sewage treatment processes. Wastes of low pH are corrosive to steel and concrete structures in waterways or sewerage systems. Fortunately, it is not difficult to eliminate extremes of pH in wastewaters, by chemical neutralization. Adequate controls are available for this process, and the final effluent can be made suitable for discharge to either a stream or a sewer.

Acidity or alkalinity in a waste is determined by chemical titration to a specified pH, such as true neutrality at 7.0. More commonly, the phenolphthalein and methyl orange endpoints, approximately 8.3 and 4.0, respectively, are used. These titrations indicate the quantity of neutralizing material required for treatment; such material may preexist in the receiving stream or may be added as a part of waste treatment. Both acidity and alkalinity are customarily expressed in milligrams of calcium carbonate equivalent per liter.

The intensity of acid or alkaline quality is expressed by the pH value, which has a more direct relationship than acidity or alkalinity to most pollutional effects of the waste. Fish kills, for example, are caused by low pH rather than by a high concentration of titratable acidity. The measurement of pH is relatively simple, using either electrometric or colorimetric techniques. At the point of discharge, wastes should be near neutrality, usually in the range from 6 to 9, though this varies with the receiving stream or sewage.

DISSOLVED MATERIALS

Chlorides. Sodium chloride brines are waste products from a number of industries, particularly crude petroleum production and the manufacture of soda ash and other chemicals. Concentrations of chloride up to about 500 mg/liter are acceptable in most natural waters, with much higher quantities permissible in some, but uncontrolled discharge of brines would far surpass any reasonable limit in many streams. There is no practicable treatment to remove chlorides, so the usual solution to the problem is impoundment and carefully controlled release into streams that provide adequate dilution. Disposal to the ocean is feasible in some locations, disposal to deep underground formations in others, but chloride wastes remain one of the major unsolved problems of these industries.

Hardness. All natural waters contain some degree of hardness, caused primarily by the calcium and magnesium ions present. The concentration varies many fold in different parts of the United States, although in each area the people have generally become accustomed to and accept it. Some hardness is usually desirable, but any increase in hardness, such as may be caused by certain industrial wastes, may be resented and is, in fact, pollution. Hardness, in any degree, is expensive in that it causes scale, increases soap consumption, and forms precipitates or scums. When the hardness must be removed, either partially for municipal waters of excessive hardness or nearly completely for steam generation and many other industrial uses, the cost is greater for higher degrees of hardness. Industrial effluents that are sources of hardness include calcium chloride brines from many chemical industries, and wastes from lime-consuming industries, such as water treatment plants, pulp mills, and tanneries.

Surfactants. Surface-active chemicals, including the synthetic detergents, have been troublesome in sewage treatment plants and in natural streams, because of their ability to form froth. The problem has been worsened because the conventional alkyl benzene sulfonate surfactants are persistent, or refractory, in streams; despite their organic composition, they are broken down but slowly by natural stream organisms. The detergent manufacturing industry has recognized this problem, and has converted its entire production to biodegradable types of detergent. Frothing may continue until the surfactant properties are destroyed, but destruction will be accomplished in natural stream environments. Froth is not harmful, though it is unesthetic; perhaps, however, it serves a useful purpose as an indicator of domestic pollution.

Other Solutes. Almost every chemical or substance used in industry escapes in some degree with the wastewater, including raw materials, intermediates, final products, by-products, and processing substances. The most troublesome of these, in addition to those mentioned above, are probably sulfates, nitrates, ammonium compounds, and salts of the heavy metals. Organic dissolved matter will be considered separately. Any of these, or some other not mentioned, may be the critical contaminant in wastewaters from a particular industry.

RADIOACTIVITY

Radioactive wastes have great pollutional potential, though during the first two decades of the "Atomic Age" their points of discharge were relatively few. All aspects of radioactive materials, including disposal of their wastewaters, have been controlled by the Atomic Energy Commission; the potential hazards have been recognized, and protection of streams and other phases of the environment has been provided for. As radioisotopes are becoming more widely employed by industry and other users, the number of discharge points is increasing and monitoring becomes a greater problem.

The principal objection to radioactive effluents is based, of course, on their hazard to health because of high energy radiations. The danger is enhanced when the water is used internally, by drinking or by use in food preparation. It may be worsened if dispersed radioactive pollutants become concentrated, as by chemical precipitation or the action of living organisms, including microorganisms.

Three basic types of radioactive emissions are recognized, but in pollution control work it is simpler to compute exposure to total radiation or exposure to specific isotopes. These are discussed in the chapter on Atomic Energy. Food and air contacts are often of equal or greater significance.

In general, radioactivity cannot be destroyed, but radioactive wastes can be either disposed of by dilution to a degree that is safe, or concentrated and held in isolated, protected locations until they decay naturally. The choice of technique depends on the volume and concentration of waste and other factors.

ORGANIC POLLUTION

Organic wastes occur in a large number of industries, as well as in municipal and domestic sewages. Pollution of streams by organic matter is almost as serious as pollution by pathogenic microorganisms; the latter occur in sewages rather than industrial discharges, and are substantially eliminated by proper treatment, which usually includes chlorination.

Organic wastes are significant in streams because they are generally susceptible to biological degradation, which destroys them, but which consumes dissolved oxygen (DO) from the stream. Total depletion of DO leads to nuisance conditions, including bad odors and offensive appearance; even partial depletion may cause fish kills and render the stream unfit for its natural life forms.

It may be possible to evaluate organic wastes by measuring each significant constituent or compound present. However, in mixtures of components, such as comprise nearly all actual waste effluents, this is not feasible. Instead, it is the practice to evaluate general organic pollution, as by determination of the oxidizable carbon or measurement of the oxygen consuming power. The latter is generally accepted among sanitary engineers, in the form of BOD or COD tests. These are described below.

Dissolved Oxygen. The most generally accepted single criterion of pollution is the DO content of the stream. Under favorable nonpolluted conditions, this may approach the saturation value, or may even exceed saturation because of photosynthesis or oxygen generation in the stream.

The DO saturation value, significant though it is, is low; it depends on temperature, and is only 14 mg/liter at the freezing point, less at usual stream temperatures. This implies that the reserve of available DO, to take care of bio-oxidation of organic wastes, is not great and is easily depleted. Of course, oxygen is restored to the stream waters by photosynthesis, which is intermittent, and by absorption from the atmosphere, which is limited in rate. An overpolluted stream can thus become totally devoid of DO, a condition that is readily apparent to the public by dead fish, bad appearance, and offensive odors.

If about 2 mg/liter of DO can be maintained in all parts of the stream, nuisance conditions can be avoided. A higher concentration, perhaps 4–6 mg/liter, is necessary for a healthy population of game fish.

The determination of DO requires many precautions, to avoid changes during handling of the sample. The analysis must be performed, or at least carried to the point of chemical fixation, at the sampling site. The actual analysis involves absorption of the DO on freshly precipitated manganous hydroxide, release of an equivalent concentration of free iodine from iodide salt, and titration of the iodine with a standard reagent. Though complex, the whole procedure has been thoroughly standardized and is a simple routine to the sanitary chemist.

Biochemical Oxygen Demand. The major pollutional effect of organic wastes in a stream is their consumption of DO under the influence of living microorganisms in the stream environment. The rate and extent of oxygen depletion is customarily evaluated by the biochemical oxygen demand, or BOD, test. This is not a direct measure of organic content, but is a measure of its most significant pollutional characteristic, the capacity to consume oxygen. It is reported as milligrams (of oxygen) per liter.

The BOD test involves, first, a measurement of the DO initially present in a sample of water containing the waste under study. This may be a sample from the polluted stream or a batch of special water to which a known amount of waste has been added. Other samples of mixed water and waste are then incubated, in the presence of suitable microorganisms and nutrients and in an appropriate environment, usually for 5 days at 20°C. The remaining DO is then measured, the amount of DO consumed during the test is computed, and the oxygen requirements of the waste are reported as BOD. If all the DO is consumed during the incubation period, no quantitative report can be made; however, weaker dilutions of the waste can be arranged to produce usable data.

There are several possible interferences in the BOD test. Toxic materials invalidate it completely unless they can be detoxified or diluted to the point of negligible effect. Oxygen consumed by inorganic or reducing chemicals can be evaluated as an "Immediate Oxygen Demand," and need not then interfere with the slower biological reactions of organic contaminants.

In a polluted stream, biological decomposition of organic matter tends to deplete the DO, as shown by the BOD test. Simultaneously, as soon as the DO falls below saturation, reaeration from the atmosphere tends to replenish it, toward the saturation concentration. The resulting trend line of concentration depends on several factors; it is beyond the scope of this chapter, though well developed in specialized texts.

Because pollution by decomposable organic matter is so significant, industrial wastes are frequently compared with domestic wastes on a BOD basis. A "typical" municipal sewage contains about 0.17 lb of BOD per day for each person served. An industrial plant is therefore said to have a "population equivalent" equal to its daily pounds of BOD discharge divided by 0.17. It must be kept in mind that this concept of population equivalent applies only to BOD pollution and ignores pathogen count, suspended solids content, toxicity, and other parameters of pollution that either have no population equivalent or are neglected in favor of BOD.

Chemical Oxygen Demand. The BOD test is useful in many ways, but has the disadvantage that it requires 5 days for completion. Organic matter in wastewater can be evaluated in a few hours by the chemical oxygen demand or COD test. This does not duplicate the BOD test; it may or may not have a consistent ratio to the BOD. There is no fully acceptable substitute for the 5-day BOD test, but the COD test has considerable value nevertheless. Both tests measure organic matter, but certain types of organic compounds are resistant to each of the two tests, and not in the same manner.

The COD test is described, as are other special tests cited, in "Stand- and Methods" (2). Because of variation in response to the test among various types of contaminant, the recommended test conditions must be followed closely to get consistent and reproducible results, even though these results are somewhat arbitrary or empirical.

The test is based on treating the wastewater with a known amount of dichromate, digesting at an elevated temperature to oxidize the organic matter, and titrating the unconsumed dichromate. The oxygen equivalent of the dichromate destroyed is reported as the COD. Chlorides are the most significant source of error, because they react with dichromate; but a correction for chlorides can be made.

Toxicity. Many industrial wastes are toxic in the concentration at discharge, or even after dilution in the receiving stream. This can be a highly significant complaint, but toxicity is a property that is difficult to evaluate. Toxic wastes may affect human beings; toxic gases or fumes are especially hazardous to workers in sewers and at municipal or industrial waste treatment plants. More commonly, toxic substances in solution cause killings of fish or other aquatic organisms. The public, the sports-man in particular, is much aroused by such killings. Often the death of fish, even in large numbers, is a natural circumstance or is caused by oxygen depletion by municipal sewage; yet industry is usually the scapegoat for public censure. Industry, then, must be particularly careful to avoid releasing toxic wastes without adequate treatment. Many extensive fish kills have been ascribed to pesticidal chemicals washed from agricultural lands by natural drainage. It is a recurring debate whether this is the fault of industry for producing such materials or of the farmer for applying them; or, indeed, of the general public for demanding the large yields of agricultural products that can be achieved only by the use of pesticides.

Toxic wastes have also caused the death of domestic or wild animals that drink from the polluted stream; many industrial companies have paid for cows and other farm animals killed in this manner. In sewage treatment plants, toxic industrial wastes may inhibit or kill the useful microorganisms on which effective sewage treatment depends, as in activated sludge units or trickling filters. Toxic contaminants in a water prevent testing for BOD, unless they can be diluted to the extent of destroying toxicity without weakening the BOD concentration too far to measure. The COD test is used instead of BOD under these conditions, though it is not a direct substitute, as discussed above.

Toxicity is not a characteristic that can be measured in the conventional laboratory. Evaluation, except for single pure pollutants of known toxicity, is equivalent to a research study on the specific waste with various types of fish and other organisms. Such bioassays, using living organisms in aquaria, are expensive and not always conclusive. Study of naturally existing organisms in a given watercourse, by a trained biologist, gives an indication of the presence or absence of pollution, especially if carried out on several occasions, such as before and after establishment of a possible pollution source.

TREATMENT METHODS

Most industrial wastewaters must be discharged from the plant premises; only rarely is it possible to let them accumulate without discharge. To some degree, the receiving stream has a capacity for assimilating pollution, the degree depending on the ratio of dilution available, downstream uses of the water, and characteristics of the waste. It is reasonable and proper to utilize the stream's assimilative powers to the full, short of impairing its usefulness and esthetic quality. Such reasonable use for waste transport should not be considered as pollution.

A somewhat similar situation exists when industrial waste is discharged to a municipal sewer. This is often a convenient means of disposal, but it requires consideration of the possible effects. Most municipalities ban industrial wastes that are deleterious to the sewerage system, by corrosion of the sewers and plant equipment, or by interference with the sewage treatment plant and process. The industrial waste contaminants may be destroyed by the sewage treatment, they may disrupt the treatment, or they may simply flow unchanged through the sewerage system. In the last case, they are at least diluted by the municipal wastewater, prior to their release to a natural waterway.

If the assimilative capabilities of the stream or of the sewerage system are not adequate, the industrial waste should not be released in its original form. Treatment of the waste before discharge is then essential. Several techniques are available, some related to the processes of sewage treatment, others developed specifically for industrial waste. These are described in the balance of this chapter.

In-plant Measures

Any form of treatment of industrial waste, no matter how simple, is more expensive than the industry would like. The greater the volume of wastewater to be treated, and the greater the amount of contaminant to be removed or destroyed, the higher are the capital, labor, and material costs required. It is often economical, therefore, to eliminate or reduce the quantity of waste at its source in the manufacturing plant prior to treatment or, happily, in lieu of treatment. Several possible techniques exist, based largely on good engineering practices and common sense.

Process Change. It is not usual that the waste control engineer can request a change in his company's product or manufacturing process in order to ease his pollution problem, but several instances of this exist and it will probably become increasingly common as antipollution efforts continue. Examples are cited in subsequent chapters, and include substitution of process chemicals, modifications in process, and at least minor redesign of product. A related change, at great cost, has been the synthetic detergent industry's change-over from hard detergents to biodegradable materials, in order that domestic laundering wastes shall be less troublesome.

Material Recovery. Raw materials and products are of value to the manufacturer, but some fraction of each tends to be lost into the waste stream. This is an economic loss, and removal from the waste, to avoid pollution, is an added cost. To the extent that such substances can be salvaged for reuse in manufacturing or for some other purpose, there is an economic gain. Water is the most significant of such salvaged materials, and is discussed in the following paragraph. Other substances can also be recovered from waste, or intercepted before they enter the waste stream, for an economic gain. The recovery of by-products, in contrast to normal products, may also have merit, and has been profitable to some industries. Inexperienced planners, however, may over-rate the savings to be accomplished by small amounts of unusual by-products, alien to the industry's normal markets.

Water Reuse. Most industries use water, often in large quantities, for various processing purposes; yet little or none enters the final product. Thus most or all of it must be discharged as a pollution-bearing waste. Water is costly, and water of quality suitable for industry becomes scarcer every year. Sometimes, with only partial purification, spent water can be reused, once or several times, in the manufacturing process. Spent cooling water is particularly amenable to reuse, but even contaminated wastewaters may have salvage value.

Water unsuitable for direct reuse may be serviceable for a different purpose in which quality requirements are less strict. Final rinsing of a product may require nearly pure water, but the spent rinsewater may be usable for primary rinsing, or in a countercurrent series of rinses, without intermediate purification.

The purification of water for continuing use is sometimes performed in the process tank itself, in an "integrated" treatment system, which need not interfere with the manufacturing process.

Wastewater Collection. Usually the first step toward wastewater treatment is its collection from the several or many sources in the plant, and transport to a treatment site. Certain types of wastes should be kept separate until they reach the treatment plant or even some advanced stage of treatment; acid and cyanide wastes, for example, should be segregated for the sake of safety. Strong and weak wastes, otherwise similar, are often segregated for more economical treatment, perhaps to be blended after they become more nearly equal by treatment of the strong.

On the other hand, the mixing of wastes may provide partial treatment in itself, as by partial neutralization between acid and alkaline wastes. Mixing, too, provides equalization or leveling of fluctuations in flow or in composition. This leads to simpler treatment or better control of discharge.

Decisions between mixing or segregating of waste streams must be made on the basis of the several factors suggested above. In general, if treatment or discharge is facilitated by separate handling of certain wastes, separation should be maintained, but only as long as there is real benefit. As quickly as possible, the benefits of blending and equalization should be accepted.

PARTICULATE REMOVAL

The removal of particulate or suspended matter from a wastewater is usually an important part of its treatment. Because this is a less expensive operation than the chemical or biological operations needed for dissolved matter removal, it is widely used. Settling, flotation, and filtration are the most common techniques.

Settling. Settling, or sedimentation, is the least expensive of the physical treatments used to remove particulate matter. Several settling operations may be utilized in the processing of a given wastewater; for example, to remove heavy grit from raw waste, to remove finer suspended matter originally present, and finally to separate precipitates or sludges formed by chemical or biological treatment.

Settling is accomplished in ordinary lagoons, but more commonly special tanks are designed and built for the purpose. Design criteria are reasonably well established, and are discussed in standard texts on this subject.

An inevitable by-product of sedimentation is sludge. Removal of sludge from the settling basin may be intermittent, if the quantity is small; or continuous, usually by scraper mechanisms and pumps, when its volume is greater. Some heavy inorganic settled materials are solid or semisolid in nature, but most sludges are fluid slurries that require further dewatering prior to disposal. Disposal is often a problem, principally because of the land area required.

Particles lighter than water of course move upward rather than toward the bottom during sedimentation. They are removed by skimmers rather than scrapers. Many oils are in this category, and are recoverable by settling and skimming.

Flotation. Fine solids or particulate matter with a density close to that of water are not readily removable by simple settling. Some industries have found it practicable to accelerate the removal by floating the particles with minute air bubbles. The bubbles are created either by pressurizing the wastewater with air and subsequently releasing the pressure or by applying vacuum to air-saturated wastewater. In either case, the bubbles and solids or oils rise to the surface and are removed by skimming.

Filtration. Filtration is generally more expensive than settling as a means of removing suspended matter; but it may provide a more thorough removal, it takes less space, and it has certain special applications. Sludges produced by settling can be further dewatered by filtering, either on a sand bed or by mechanical equipment.

Filtration of raw wastes is not a common practice because of the large volume. Treated wastes may be filtered as a final treatment step if the discharge requirements are critical, as for effluents that are to be injected into porous underground formations.

Screening has some mechanical similarity to filtration, and is almost universally used as an early step in industrial waste treatment. It serves to remove coarse materials that might interfere with subsequent operations in the treatment. Screens range from coarse bar racks with 4- or 6-inch openings to fine screens of 40 mesh or smaller. Screens must be kept free from solids accumulations, lest their head loss become excessively high or their throughput low.

OTHER PHYSICAL TREATMENT

Heat treatment of wastes is expensive and unusual. It is sometimes employed, usually on special wastes or waste products of small volume, for purposes such as emulsion breaking or oxidation of organic matter.

Temperature control, usually by gentle heating, is a necessary part of certain biological treatments, such as anaerobic digestion of organic sludges and the aerobic or anaerobic fermentation of strong wastes.

Incineration of dewatered sludges is common in municipal sewage treatment, and may be utilized for organic industrial wastes. Incineration is, of course, commonly used for disposal of trash and other solid wastes, which are not specifically covered in this book.

Cooling of hot wastes may be necessary before their discharge to a stream or sewer. It is usually accomplished by spraying, cascading, or simple holding. This is a problem of considerable import in the power industry. Radioactive wastes may be stored for decay of radioactivity; above a certain minimum concentration, they require elaborate cooling equipment to dissipate the heat energy liberated spontaneously.

ADJUSTMENT OF pH

Wastes of excessively low or high pH require neutralization before their release to a natural stream or to a municipal sewer. Some plants, especially in the chemical industries, create both acid and alkali wastes, for which blending provides partial neutralization. For final pH adjustment, and sometimes for the whole task of neutralization, purchased chemicals must be used.

Acidic wastes can be neutralized with any of a number of basic chemicals. Caustic soda and sodium carbonate are somewhat expensive but extremely convenient; they are widely used by small plants or for treatments where small quantities are adequate. Lime is cheaper but somewhat less convenient, and is the most widely used alkaline reagent. It can be purchased as quicklime or slaked lime, high-calcium or dolomitic lime, and in several physical forms. Limestone and dolomitic limestone are cheaper yet, but less convenient to use and slower in reaction rate; they may become coated and inactive in certain wastes, and the extent to which they can raise the pH is limited. They are, however, widely used, sometimes as a roughing treatment to be followed by more effective reagents. The calcium and magnesium chemicals often form sludges, which require disposal.

Alkaline wastes are less of a problem than acid wastes, but nevertheless often require treatment. If acidic waste streams are not available or are not adequate to neutralize alkaline wastes, sulfuric acid is commonly employed. In some industries, carbon dioxide in the form of flue gas has been used to neutralize strong alkalinity in wastes.

Neutralization can be controlled by automatic instruments, and it is often desirable to record the pH of final effluent as it is discharged. The reagent chemicals can be fed automatically, in the form of solutions, slurries, or dry materials. If the reaction rate is slow, as in neutralization of waste acids with limestone, instrumentation and control design must take this factor into account.

Deliberate acidification of waste streams to a low pH, or alkalization to a high pH, is sometimes used as a special form of treatment. Oil emulsions may be destroyed, for example, by acidification. The pH must usually be restored close to neutrality before final discharge.

Oxidation and Reduction

Organic wastes and a few inorganic wastes can be destroyed or reduced in pollutional characteristics by oxidation. Biological oxidation is discussed in a later section. Chemically, oxidation can be accomplished by any of a number of oxidizing materials.

Aeration is the least costly means of oxidation, but is limited in its effectiveness. Few industrial wastes are adequately treated by aeration alone. Aeration is necessary in some types of biological treatment, and is an aid in chemical treatment with ferrous iron coagulants. Oxygen is more effective than air, but is rarely used because of its cost. High temperature, high pressure oxidation with air is used in sewage sludge destruction and for some industrial wastes; it is apt to increase in use.

Chlorination is the most common chemical oxidation procedure in industrial waste treatment. Because chlorine is costly, it should be used on concentrated rather than dilute wastes, except for final disinfection if that is needed. Hypochlorite salts and chlorine dioxide are used in special circumstances, but liquefied chlorine gas, available in pressure cylinders, is the most common reagent.

Ozone is used for oxidizing certain industrial wastes, notably phenols and cyanides. Permanganates and dichromates also have specific applications, but chlorine is the most widely used oxidation agent stronger than air.

The only significant application of chemical reduction to treat an industrial waste is in the conversion of chromate wastes to trivalent chromium, which is more easily precipitated. This is described in the chapter on Metal Finishing Products.

CHEMICAL PRECIPITATION

Chemicals are often added to an industrial waste for the specific purpose of precipitating a particular component. Metal ions, for example, are removed from solution by precipitation with alkaline reagents, and are then taken out of the waste stream by settling or filtration. In a similar manner, other components can be converted to volatile compounds by chemical treatment, and removed in an air or gas stream.

Chemical coagulation involves the precipitation of chemicals deliberately added to the wastewater in such a manner that the precipitate removes colloidal and finely divided contaminants. Iron salts, for example, are added to the waste, usually with lime, to form a precipitate of ferric hydroxide. As this precipitates, it agglomerates to large flocculant particles; as these settle, they entrap or otherwise remove fine particles that do not readily settle by themselves. This technique is used in many industries, especially for organic colloidal wastes, as from meat packing, canning, and petroleum refining.

OTHER CHEMICAL METHODS

Ion exchange is used to treat certain industrial wastes, especially if the contaminants are few and noninterfering, and if the recovered material has salvage value. Dilute rinsewaters from the metal processing industries can, in this manner, be recovered for their metal values and for reusable water.

Adsorption, usually by means of carbon, often serves to remove trace concentrations of particularly troublesome contaminants. Phenolic wastes from coke production and plastics manufacture can be treated by carbon to remove even fractions of a milligram per liter. Some adsorbed materials are recoverable, and the adsorbent regenerable; others are not.

In isolated examples, almost all the chemical engineer's unit operations are used for waste treatment. Distillation, evaporation, and extraction, for example, are employed in certain industries, though not common.

AEROBIC BIOLOGICAL TREATMENT

Dilute organic wastes, difficult or impossible to treat by physical or chemical methods alone, are often amenable to attack by microorganisms. These may be aerobic, in the presence of dissolved oxygen, or anaerobic. Certain nutrient elements must be present, notably nitrogen and phosphorus. The organic components are destroyed by metabolic processes, ending as innocuous materials. In aerobic systems, much of the carbon is removed as carbon dioxide, the hydrogen as water, and nitrogen and sulfur as nitrate ion or nitrogen gas and sulfate ion. Some of the waste is converted to cell tissue in the microorganisms; the excess appears as sludge.

Trickling Filters. A well-known technique for promoting contact among an industrial waste, the microorganisms that will consume it, and the oxygen needed for metabolism is the trickling filter. This is a bed of crushed rock or other suitable medium, through which the wastewater trickles, and through which air penetrates by natural or forced ventilation. Biological growths develop as a film on the medium, from microorganisms present in the wastewater or added in the form of domestic sewage or other culture. As the microorganisms grow, the organic wastes are consumed as food and metabolized to simpler and harmless compounds. Fragments of the film, containing dead and living organisms, slough off from time to time, and must be removed from the effluent, usually by settling.

A few organic wastes are not amenable to microbiological attack, but most compounds can, in time, develop a biological community that consumes them. Toxic materials, especially if they occur suddenly in the waste, interfere with or even kill the microorganisms, resulting in failure of the process. Equalization of the wastewater before treatment helps to prevent such shock dosages. Nutrient elements, if not present in the waste, can be added, either as chemicals or as domestic or sanitary sewage.

Activated Sludge. The activated sludge process brings the organic waste into contact with living microorganisms in large aeration tanks, in which the bacteria grow as flocculent suspended growths. Compressed air is supplied through diffuser plates or tubes as the source of oxygen.

Presettled organic waste flows continuously into the tank, for a detention and aeration period of several hours. Mixed liquor overflows at the same rate and is settled; a portion of the floc is returned to the aeration unit as seed.

Many modifications of the activated sludge process are used, in both sewage and industrial waste treatment. These include multiple units with various flow patterns, tapered distribution of air along a long tank, stepwise addition of the incoming waste, addition of inorganic flocs to the biological growths, intermediate clarifiers, and many other modifications of the basic process.

The activated sludge process often provides a smooth-running operation with excellent removal of organic matter from the waste. Many faults, however, can develop in the process. Shock loads of waste, abrupt variations in pH, temperature, and other environment factors, and the presence of toxic wastes are among the major causes of trouble. Nitrogen and phosphorus must be present; if they do not occur in the waste, sanitary sewage from the plant can be used as a source. Uniform feed and operating conditions encourage good activated sludge treatment, which is used by many organic industries.

Lagoons. Lagoons, holding ponds, or oxidation ponds provide several types of waste improvement, including biological removal of organic wastes. Equalization, sedimentation, and opportunity for self-treatment inevitably occur. Chemicals can be added, if desired, for further treatment.

The biological processes in a lagoon should be predominantly aerobic, for most satisfactory operation. Anaerobic conditions usually prevail in the bottom muds, but if the main part of the lagoon becomes anaerobic, bad odors and a poor degree of treatment result. Shallow lagoons and avoidance of overload are helpful in maintaining dissolved oxygen. Additions of sodium nitrate are used as a substitute or supplement for DO, but usually in emergency conditions only, to avoid odors.

Lagoons are used by many industries if land is available at reasonable cost. The lagoon may be suitable as sole treatment in some plants, but is better employed as final or polishing treatment of the waste before discharge.

Lagoons require a minimum of maintenance, but some control is desirable. They should be shallow, 3–6 ft in depth, for good DO control, and excessive plant growths should not be allowed. The banks should be kept clear of vegetation other than grasses. If sludge builds up, it can be removed; this is more common in inorganic settling lagoons. Lagoons are sometimes operated in series, to minimize short-circuiting of flow.

ANAEROBIC BIOLOGICAL TREATMENT

Although it is important to avoid anaerobic conditions in natural streams and in treatment plants that are supposedly aerobic, there are circumstances under which anaerobic microorganisms provide a useful part of treatment. As mentioned above, the bottom layers of aerobic lagoons are usually anaerobic, and may serve to decompose much organic matter even without nuisance. Deliberate anaerobic processing is used for treating many organic wastes.

In general, anaerobic degradation of organic matter is slower than aerobic oxidation, requiring days or weeks instead of hours. It is not practicable, therefore, to treat dilute wastes by anaerobic microorganisms because of the large tank volumes required. For strong wastes or waste fractions, anaerobic treatment is widely used. As a rule of thumb criterion, a 1% concentration of organic matter has been suggested as the minimum practical feed to an anaerobic process. This concentration is available in some organic industry wastes, in most organic sludges, and in many solid wastes such as garbage and food wastes.

Raw industrial wastes are sometimes treated by anaerobic fermentation of the whole waste, in large holding tanks. The effluent is rarely suitable for discharge, because of bad odor and high residual organics; but aerobic treatment may be employed for polishing it for release.

Settling tank sludges are often further processed by anaerobic digestion. The reduction in volume from raw waste to sludge makes this feasible. In digestion, much of the organic matter is gasified to methane and carbon dioxide, and the residual solids or humus are not objectionable in their nature. Temperature and pH controls are desirable for optimum digestion. The solids, after 1 to 2 months digestion, can be disposed of by dewatering and incineration or other methods.

ULTIMATE DISPOSAL

The final disposal of adequately treated wastewater usually presents no special problem. If it is indeed adequately treated, it may be simply discharged to the municipal sewer or a natural watercourse, or into a ditch leading to the watercourse. The sewer authorities may impose a fee, based usually on the total flow, the BOD content or chlorine demand, the quantity of water used in the plant, or some empirical parameter. Discharge to a river or lake may be through multiple outlets, to hasten the act of dilution; in a few instances, river water has been pumped into the treatment plant to assure adequate dilution at the moment of discharge.

Sludges are an unavoidable by-product of wastewater conditioning, and their disposal may present more serious problems. They include most of the pollutants removed by treatment, plus the treatment chemicals. If suitable and adequate land areas are available, sludges may be released simply as land fill; this is not usually possible.

Reduction in sludge volume eases the problem of its disposal, and is a common practice. It includes dewatering by thickening, filtration, or drying. Further reductions are accomplished by digestion of organic sludges, wet oxidation under high pressure and temperature, or incineration. Complete destruction cannot be accomplished, but disposal by dumping is usually possible after volume reduction and removal of putrescibility and other obnoxious features. Sludge disposal remains, however, a major factor of wastewater control.

REFERENCES

1. Gurnham, C. F., "Principles of Industrial Waste Treatment." Wiley, New York, 1955.
2. "Standard Methods for the Examination of Water and Wastewater," 11th ed. American Public Health Association, New York, 1960.

Food Products—Animal

Chapter 2

MEAT

by A. STANFORD JOHNSON

Meat industry wastewaters originate in the facilities for slaughtering animals and processing meat for the consumer. The wastewater sources include, in addition to the slaughtering and processing areas, the associated facilities such as stockyards, rendering, and livestock feed manufacture. The processing of hides is discussed in the chapter on Leather, and is therefore not described here. Meat canning, being a process similar to vegetable canning, is briefly discussed and the reader is referred to the chapter on Canned Foods for additional details. The processing of fish and poultry causes wastewater problems similar to those in the meat industry, and these are discussed in succeeding chapters. Some packing plants also operate refineries for inedible fats, but not usually on the same premises. Petroleum refining, a somewhat similar process, is covered in a special chapter.

THE MEAT INDUSTRY

In March, 1960, there were 3144 livestock slaughtering plants in the United States. Of these, 2967 slaughtered cattle and calves, 2381 slaughtered hogs, and 1215 slaughtered sheep and lambs. In 530 slaughtering plants operated under Federal inspection, cattle and calves were slaughtered in 486 of the plants, hogs in 266, and sheep and lambs in 211. By January, 1963, the number of Federally inspected slaughtering plants had risen to 563.

A slaughtering plant is a killing and dressing plant. Finished products include the fresh carcass and variety meats such as hearts, livers, kidneys, and tongues. In some slaughtering plants, various cuts of fresh meats are produced, rather than half and quarter carcasses. Hides, skins, and pelts are usually salted and shipped to tanners. The inedible viscera, trimmings, feet, and head bones are either shipped to a renderer or rendered on the premises.

A plant which both slaughters and processes fresh meat is called a packing plant. The killing and carcass trimming operations are similar to those in a slaughterhouse. Following chilling of the carcass, further trimming and cutting operations are carried out to produce various cuts of fresh meat and trimmings. The processing includes pickling, smoking, and canning of various meat cuts and sausage products. Packing plants also produce a number of by-products, ranging from lard and edible tallow to materials for animal feeds, glue, and soap manufacture.

In meat processing plants, fresh meat procured from a slaughtering plant is processed. There are approximately 1500 such establishments in the United States. Plants of this type do not usually have rendering facilities; inedible scrap such as bones and trimmings is sold to renderers.

The number of slaughtering, packing, and processing plants continues to increase. The total number of Federally inspected plants of all types increased from 1396 in 572 cities in 1960 to 1646 plants in 690 cities in 1963. In 1962, the greatest number of plants was located in the East and upper Midwest. California had 176, followed by Illinois with 150, Pennsylvania with 129, and New York with 115. All states except Alaska had at least one Federally inspected plant.

The total slaughter in 1962 included 26,083,300 cattle, 7,494,300 calves, 79,334,300 hogs, and 16,836,800 sheep and lambs, a total of 129,748,700 head of livestock. The industry sells more than $13 billion worth of meat products annually, and has a net worth in excess of $1.7 billion. The total number of employees is approximately 250,000, of which 75% are production workers.

ASSOCIATED FACILITIES

Stockyards are necessarily associated with slaughtering plants, and rendering facilities usually with slaughtering and packing plants; in addition, all types of plants have refrigeration equipment. The refrigeration generally requires water for the ultimate discharge of heat. Most plants generate their own steam for processing and heating, although in some larger cities this utility can be purchased. Plants having large steam generating capacity may also operate steam turbine generators for all or a portion of their electrical demand. Compressed air and vacuum systems are employed in most plants for operation of some plant equipment.

Plants which operate rendering facilities produce animal feeds. This product is sold in rail car, truck, and bag lots. A few plants have an extensive feed business with retail outlets; others sell to other feed manufacturers, doing little or no grinding and mixing on their own property.

It is common practice to operate a laundry for employees' work clothing, especially in Federally inspected plants. Garages for repair of cars and trucks, truck and rail car washing facilities, and shops for trades associated with maintenance of plant equipment are a part of most plant installations.

Water use in Federally inspected plants increased 37% from 1949 to 1959, whereas number of head slaughtered increased only 30%. A survey of 108 plants by the American Meat Institute indicated total fresh water intake in inspected plants to be 436 mgd. An additional 439 mgd is recirculated for cooling purposes. Of the fresh water intake, 60% came from wells and 40% from rivers and lakes.

Of these 108 plants, 100 treated more than 50% of the wastewater, and 47 treated 90–100%. Processes commonly used were screening, sedimentation, and gravity flotation. Secondary treatment included trickling filters, activated sludge, anaerobic contact, and stabilization ponds.

Discharge of industrial wastes to rivers and lakes accounted for 33% of the total wastewater; 54% was discharged to a municipal sewer system, and 6% to the ocean. The remaining 7% was not reported. Average consumption of water, by inclusion in the product and by evaporation loss, was 4% of the water intake.

WASTE CHARACTERISTICS

Wastewater characteristics vary, depending on facilities included in the plant, segregation of wastes from various sources, season, production or slaughter rate, diversion of cooling water, alertness of production supervision to waste prevention, and degree of treatment required for the wastewater. To control wastewater quantities and constituents, it is necessary that major sources be identified, and water use and sewer losses be controlled.

MAJOR SOURCES OF WASTEWATER

Slaughtering. Water use in slaughtering varies with type of animal slaughtered and degree of mechanization of the operation. Beef may be handled entirely on a chain conveyor, or eviscerating, hoof removal, and a portion of the skinning may be carried out with the animal on the floor, and the operation completed on a conveyor.

In the slaughtering area, the animal is killed and the carcass drained of blood. In beef slaughtering, the animal is skinned, the head, hoofs, plucks, and viscera are removed, the carcass is split, the head is removed and trimmed, and the carcass is washed prior to cooling. Hides are trimmed and salted for daily shipment to a tanner, or are trimmed, defleshed, and brine cured for later shipment. Hearts, kidneys, tongues, and brains are removed and chilled for sale as edible products. Paunch contents are emptied to the sewer. One stomach section may be rinsed, trimmed, and scalded, for sale as tripe. Intestines and windpipes may be washed, trimmed, and stripped of mucus, to produce casings. The inedible portions are collected for rendering.

Calf slaughtering is similar, except that the animal is usually not skinned on the kill floor. The hair is subjected to considerable washing before and after slaughtering.

Hog slaughtering differs from that of other livestock in that hair is removed without skinning the carcass. This is done by immersing the carcass in a scalding tub after bleeding. The carcass then enters a dehairing machine where hair and toenails are removed by mechanical scrapers and water sprays. Hair is flushed to the sewer or to hair processing equipment. Portions of the hog intestines may be processed to produce sausage casings and chitterlings. Hearts, kidneys, brains, and stomachs are variety meats, which are removed and washed prior to chilling.

Wastewater is generated in the slaughter area during production and during the cleanup operations following production.

After cooling, calves and sheep are sold as carcasses, and beef as halves or quarters. Hogs may be sold as half carcasses but are often cut up to yield hams, picnics, bacon bellies, loins, other meat cuts, and trimmings. Other carcasses may also yield various primal cuts of meat, trimmings, and bones, rather than be sold as whole carcasses. The cutting and boning rooms are not major sources of wastewater during production, but do yield wastewater during the nightly cleanup.

Processing. Production of sausage and smoked and canned meats generates wastewater in some processes. Smoked meat curing solution is dumped after the product is removed. The product is commonly washed by sprays before it is placed in the smokehouse.

Sausage production involves grinding, mixing, and stuffing into casings. Spilled product is a potential waste that may enter the sewer. Before smoking or cooking most sausage products, a spray wash is applied to remove meat from the casing exterior. Cooking may be done with steam or hot water. If hot water is used, a contaminated wastewater results. Following the cook, the product is chilled, usually by a water spray.

Some products are placed in metal molds or cans, cooked by immersion in a tank of heated water, and chilled by introducing cold water into the tank. These waters are discharged to the sewer. Aside from rinsing, cooking, and chilling, the primary wastewater source in processing originates in cleanup of the areas during break and lunch periods and following production. Major cleanup occurs on the second and third shifts, so does not coincide with the slaughtering unless the latter is a 2-shift operation. Washing of loaf forms, vats, barrels, and product racks is carried out after each use, during production hours.

Sanitary Sewage. Sanitary wastes are similar in character to domestic sewage. Sources include toilets and shower rooms, cafeteria kitchens, and the chemical laboratory. In a Federally inspected plant, sanitary sewage is required to be served by sewers separate from plant wastewater, to a point beyond the exterior wall of the building.

Associated Facilities. Nonmanufacturing facilities include stockyards; steam plant; refrigeration, compressed air, hot water, and vacuum equipment; and rendering areas.

(1) *Stockyards.* Stockyard wastes include manure and urine from animals. Water troughs are provided with a continuous flow. It is common to provide an overhead water spray system in hog pens to cool hogs in the summer. Bedding material, such as straw or wood shavings, is employed in beef and calf pens. Pens are cleaned by dry cleaning or by hosing the floor. Any bedding is usually removed by dry pickup prior to washing. If the yards have a roof, storm water does not become a factor. Without roofs, material that could be removed in dry pickup is washed to the sewers instead.

(2) *Utilities.* The refrigeration operation involves wasting heat to the atmosphere or to water, with or without a cooling tower. In some systems, the only water requirements are makeup water for evaporation losses and blowdown. Jacket water from compressors for refrigerant and air and from vacuum pumps is not contaminated.

Steam production results in boiler blowdown to the sewer. Some types of condensate and feedwater pumps are water cooled. If an exchanger is used for water conditioning, the regenerating rinsewater is discharged to the sewer. If a lime soda softening plant is used for either hot water or boiler feedwater, excess lime is discharged to the sewer.

(3) *By-products.* Rendering processes for edible and inedible by-products include wet and dry rendering and the low-temperature process. In wet rendering, product is ground and placed in a vertical cylindrical tank having a cone bottom. When filled with the proper charge, the cooker is sealed and live steam is introduced to raise the temperature and pressure of the contents to those of 40–60 psi steam. Cooking produces lard, tallow, or inedible grease, depending upon the raw material; and water and solids. After cooking, solids and water are blown to a tank for further processing, and lard or grease is blown to settling tanks.

In some plants, pressure is relieved through venting, and the lard or grease is decanted prior to discharging the solids and water. A water spray condenser may be used for odor control of the vent discharge, particularly in the rendering of inedible products.

The solids and water are centrifuged to separate solids from the water and entrained grease. The solids are discharged to a dryer for removal of the remaining water. Heat is applied by steam in a jacketed dryer or by gas burners that heat air introduced into the dryer. The operation can be batch or continuous. Vapors are vented to a water spray condenser. Control is necessary to prevent overloading or excessive vent line velocities, to minimize carry-over of fine dust from the dryer to the condensing water system.

Water-grease effluent from the first centrifuge is again centrifuged for further separation. The grease is discharged to settling tanks; the water is stored for feed to multiple effect evaporators. Evaporator effluent, called "stick," contains approximately 65% solids and is dried further. The stick must be mixed with other solids before drying to reduce the load on the agitator when it passes through the "glue" stage in drying. Vacuum is developed in the evaporators by a water jet which serves also as a condenser for vapors.

In dry rendering, raw material for inedible product is either ground or washed and ground, loaded into the cooker, heated, and mixed. Water is evaporated during cooking. The cooked grease and solids are discharged to a box with a perforated bottom to permit free grease to drain. The solids are pressed to remove additional grease. Vapors from the cook operation are vented to the atmosphere or, if odor control is necessary, to a water spray condenser. It is good practice to place a trap in the vapor lines to collect condensate and grease carry-over.

Low-temperature rendering is used for edible product. After removal of lard and defatted tissue by centrifuging, the residue is further rendered in either wet or dry cookers.

Blood collected by drains from the kill floor bleeding areas is usually processed further. One system consists of coagulation by heat in a thermal screw or tank, and screening on a 20 mesh vibrating screen. Solids from the screen are dried with other solids and stick or separately. Water from the screen can be economically evaporated for stick production. Beef blood can be processed in a patented system to produce a material used in the manufacture of plywood glue. Some plants store blood, with the addition of an anticoagulant, for shipment to other processors which produce blood by-products. Blood can also be dried by introduction of whole blood to a dry cooker, spray drying system, or rotary drum dryer.

Hair from hogs is washed in a flow-through tank, passed through a "picker" unit to remove toenails, and dried. Toenails are cooked in a dryer or dry rendered. Dried hair is compressed, baled, and sold. Hair can also be hydrolyzed by screening to remove water and cooking under pressure with lime in a wet or dry cooker. The cooked material must be dried to produce a powder that can be sold separately or mixed with other dried solids. During the summer season it may be uneconomical to save washed and dried hair. At these times, it is common to screen the dehairing machine discharge and to haul the hair to a land disposal site.

Some plants use selected material from the kill for production of gelatin, glue, and neat's-foot oil. These are no longer common processes, but they are sources of wastewater. Glue manufacture consists of washing raw materials, adding lime, rewashing, and cooking. After cooking, glue stock is separated, filtered, concentrated by evaporation, chilled, and dried. The washing operations produce wastewater with high BOD. The wash after liming requires neutralization with acid. Cooking produces tankwater and solids, which should be processed to produce tankage and not wasted to the sewer. Hide stock glue is extracted by hot water in open kettles prior to filtering. Gelatin production is a process similar to glue manufacture.

Production of stearines and neat's-foot oil from rendered fats and tallows is accomplished by lowering the temperature to crystallize the stearines and removing them in a press filter. Wastewater is not a great problem in this operation.

Control of Wastewater

Reductions in water use and in loss of organic materials to the plant sewer require careful analysis of production processes. Processing edible products necessitates use of potable water in sufficient quantity to properly wash the product and production equipment. The costs of water and wastewater treatment affect the net value of by-products and influence the economics of recovering individual products and the installation of water conservation devices.

Water Supply. The water supply should be at adequate pressure (70–80 psi) and the hot water supply at adequate temperature for proper washing with minimum quantities of water. The use of spring-loaded or foot-operated valves for intermittent wash operations is a necessity to minimize use. In many washing operations, use of water blasting at pressures up to 1200 psi or of steam jet nozzles reduces water use as much as 50%. Such units are portable, and are moved about the plant during cleanup to minimize equipment investment. Nozzles of proper design should be used on cleanup hoses to limit water use. Installation of orifices in distribution systems at various points of use is a better means of control than depending upon an operator setting a valve to limit water discharge.

Showering of sausage product for chilling requires well-placed nozzles to distribute the water on the product. Product which will have the casing removed prior to packaging can be cooled in a circulating system, where the water is chilled by a refrigeration unit. Similar circulating systems are applied to chilling canned and Saran tube products. Product temperature should be reduced by water chilling only to the point where it becomes more economical to chill in a refrigerated area.

The use of jacket water for cooling air and ammonia compressors and vacuum pumps can be limited by installation of temperature control valves to ensure that maximum temperature rise is attained. These valves are often a maintenance problem, however, and use of a circulating system is often more economical where units are centrally located and distribution costs are small. If neither of these methods is used, reuse of cooling water is possible by collecting it at a central point for pumping to areas where a potable water is not required. Such reuse includes washing of inedible viscera products and cattle paunch, condensing inedible rendering vapors, cleaning stockyards, makeup and flushing at the dehairing machine, makeup of scald tub water, showering in calf holding pens, and toilet flushing.

Water used in condensing ammonia in the refrigeration system remains potable and should be pumped to the plant distribution system.

Losses of Organic Matter. The greatest potential load of organic material to the wastewater is in rendering areas. Spills resulting from equipment failure or operator error can easily double the BOD of the raw waste. Wet rendering and blood processing areas should be drained to a sump. Spilled material can then be pumped back to the unprocessed product storage tank. This system needs a drain to the sewer to permit washing the area without the necessity of evaporating dilute water. The protein content of blood and tank water is approximately the equivalent of the BOD. Comparison of wastewater treatment cost per pound of BOD with net cost of evaporation per pound of protein determines the minimum concentration of protein water which can be economically evaporated. Usually, it is profitable to evaporate the first rinsewater from washing floors in tankwater and blood processing areas. Following the first rinse, the drain line to the sewer can be opened and remaining washwater drained to the sewer. The organic content of various waters from this area is illustrated by the following typical analyses:

	BOD, mg/liter	Suspended solids, mg/liter
Tankwater floor drainage	44,800	191,200
First cleanup rinse drainage	23,300	164,800
Cleanup water after first rinse	1,090	6,080

The water used in washing inedible viscera to remove manure prior to rendering is heavily laden with grease. Water drained from the perforated horizontal cylinder washer flows to a catch basin, equipped with sludge collector and skimmer mechanisms. Skimmings are rendered, and the sludge, primarily intestine contents, is discharged to the sewer. If subsequent wastewater treatment is required, the sludge may be screened prior to discharge to the sewer and the screenings disposed of with stockyards bedding. Catch basin effluent water has a BOD of 1000 mg/liter and contains 420 mg/liter grease. The influent contains 3500–4000 mg/liter total volatile solids, 200–300 mg/liter suspended solids, and 1300–2000 mg/liter grease.

Skimmings from the catch basin and from primary waste treatment units can be dry or wet rendered or rendered by centrifuging. Dry or wet rendering of skimmings requires concentration by decanting prior to rendering. The decanted water may have grease and total solids content as high as 4% each. Use of a centrifuge eliminates the need for a concentration tank and reduces grease in the discharged water to less than 1% and solids to less than 2.5%. In either case the water must be returned to the wastewater treatment plant, but with centrifuging the losses are reduced.

Rather than coagulating, screening, and evaporating the blood water and drying the screened solids and blood stick, the drying of whole blood results in fewer points of loss to sewers. Blood water has characteristics similar to tankwater; whole blood BOD approaches 100,000 mg/liter. Losses of either impose a serious shock load on a biological wastewater treatment process.

Vapor condenser water from rendering cookers, dryers, and evaporators contains 200–300 mg/liter volatile solids because of carry-over from the units. If cookers and dryers are loaded beyond capacity, greater quantities of grease and solids are discharged with the vapors. Frequent draining of vapor line traps is necessary to reduce carry-over. Vapor lines must slope down from the cooker and must be protected from cold air to prevent condensate from forming ahead of the condenser and draining back to the dry cooker. Water introduced into a cooker in this manner causes foaming and carry-over of grease.

The slaughtering area is the second important source of organic losses to the sewer. Blood drained from the animals should be collected in a trough or a curbed floor area equipped with a double drain system. Blood collected during the slaughter operation can be transported to the blood processing area by a pneumatic ejector, without clogging problems. Blood coagulates rapidly and clogs intakes if pumps are used to transport it. At breaks and after slaughter, the floor or trough is scraped with a rubber-bladed tool and rinsed briefly with water. The drain to the blood transporter is then closed, the drain to the sewer is opened, and cleanup is continued. As with the tankwater processing area, it is not economical to process all cleanup water. The blood transportation ejector and pipe lines are cleaned by flushing with water, which is discharged to the sewer. Double drains should be installed on the hog kill floor in the area between the dehairing machine and rosin dip or singer because blood drainage occurs at this point. Typical quantities of blood per animal are: hogs, 7 lb; beef, 30 lb; calves, 4 lb; and sheep, 2 lb. Wasting blood would increase the BOD of wastewater by at least 15%.

Following bleeding, the hog is immersed in the scalding tub to loosen hair and dirt on the carcass. The tub has a volume of 10–12 gal per hog per hour slaughter rate. In addition, a continuous maximum overflow of 2.5 gal per hog is used. At the end of the slaughter, the tank is emptied and cleaned. The tub water has the following characteristics:

Component	Concentration, mg/liter	Quantity, lb/100 hogs, at maximum slaughter rate
BOD	3650	11.2
Total volatile solids	5830	18.0
Suspended solids	7610	23.5

The tub is filled at night and the temperature is raised to 140°F. The fill and makeup water need not be potable, but cannot be polluted by inorganic or organic solids.

In the hog dehairing machine, a recirculating pump delivers 140°F water to sprays, which flush the hair from carcasses and scrapers to a drag conveyor in the bottom of the machine. Fresh water is used on the sprays in the final section of the washer, resulting in a continuous overflow of about 2.5 gal per hog, with the following characteristics:

Component	Concentration, mg/liter	Quantity, lb/100 hogs, at maximum slaughter rate
BOD	5070	10.1
Total solids	7280	14.6
Total volatile solids	6010	12.0
Suspended solids	4920	9.8
Total nitrogen	870	1.7

Neither the scald tub nor the dehairing machine flow rates are varied with the slaughter rates. When slaughter rate is reduced, concentrations are reduced; however, the pounds per hog does not vary greatly.

The hog carcass is further treated by shaving small areas, trimming off bruises, and showering, preparatory to opening the carcass. After the carcass is opened, the viscera are removed and placed on pans which travel parallel to the hog conveyor to permit inspection for disease.

On the return run, the empty pans must be sterilized by hot water and cooled. Water use can be reduced to 5 gal/hog by using four ¼-inch nozzles for the 180°F water, and four ⅛-inch nozzles for the cold water rinse. This produces satisfactory bacteria counts on the pans.

The neck area of slaughtered hogs contains blood clots that are removed by trimming with a knife or by a neck washer. Trimming removes more fat and thus represents loss of a potential edible product. Washing increases losses to the sewer. If a washer is used, a trap intercepts grease that can be collected for inedible rendering. The neck washing operation produces a wastewater having 500 mg/liter suspended solids, 5300 mg/liter total volatile solids, and 5000 mg/liter grease. The quantity of water used is 1.1 gal per hog. Grease and volatile solids losses to the sewer are each approximately 5 lb per 100 hogs, which may be eliminated by trimming blood clots and rendering the trimmings.

Viscera leaving the inspection pans are separated into edible and inedible items at tables. Sprays are used to flush the tables. Hearts, stomachs, and the lower digestive tracts are edible items.

Hog stomachs are opened on the kill floor and the contents (2.5 lb/hog) are flushed to the sewer. A spray is used to flush the table and a second spray flushes the stomach interior. Both should be foot-valve controlled rather than continuous streams. Stomachs then are placed in a tumbler washer for further washing.

Pork tongues and stomachs (tripe) are scalded to produce an edible product. The process consists of placing the product in a perforated rotating drum which is immersed to the drum axis in water. Hot water and steam are introduced to fill the tank and bring the temperature to the proper level. The drum rotates 5–10 minutes, the water is drained, and the tank is filled with cold water which runs until the discharge temperature is about 100°F. The tank is then drained and the product removed to a chill room. Discharge to the sewer is minor in terms of pounds per animal, although the waste is concentrated. Total volatile solids concentration from scalding stomachs is 11,600 mg/liter and the grease is 5200 mg/liter. The loss per batch is only 3¼ lb total volatile solids. Tongue scalding losses are less than one-half of those for stomachs.

Heart washing is done in a similar washer using two cold water rinses. Solids in the first rinse are high enough to make evaporation economical.

The second rinse is discharged to the sewer. As with stomachs and tongues, concentration of organic matter is high but small volumes make the pound loss of 2 lb total solids per batch negligible.

Portions of the lower digestive tract are separated for production of casings and chitterlings. Casing production is a source of concentrated wastewater. The mucus removed, like blood, has a high BOD and should be collected for rendering. Intestines are washed to remove manure, crushed to break the mucus membrane, and stripped. The stripper consists of two rotating drums, similar to a laundry wringer, which squeeze the mucus from the casing. Casings then drop into a tank of water before being wrung in a finishing machine where the mucus membrane is removed. The mucus or gut slime from hog casings is approximately 0.2 lb dry solids per hog. Water use in the soak tanks is approximately 5 gal per hog and has a BOD of 1500–2000 mg/liter. If the mucus is discharged with the soak tankwater, BOD is approximately 5000 mg/liter, and wastewater treatment screens may blind.

Chitterlings are flushed clean of manure. By installing limiting orifices and nozzles rather than drilled pipes on a commercial chitterling washer, it is possible to reduce water use from 130 to 70 gpm. The wastewater contains manure and broken pieces of chitterling.

Inedible portions of the viscera are commonly conveyed by water to a hasher or slicer. The material then goes into a perforated drum washer where sprays wash away manure. The product is drained prior to grinding and rendering. New plants use conveyors to transport the inedible material directly to the grinder, eliminating the hasher-washer water and the catch basin. It has been shown that the total value of rendered grease and solids is not adversely affected by eliminating washing, as the increased yield offsets any lowering of grease quality. The reduction in wastewater is notable. Pork hasher-washer effluent contains as much as 3700 mg/liter total volatile solids and 1900 mg/liter grease. Flow may be as much as 35 gal per hog. Reduction in volatile solids would be 107 lb per 100 hogs, and in grease 57 lb per 100 hogs. Approximately 75% of the grease would be recovered in the catch basin, but it would be more difficult to render because of the high water content, and would produce grease of lower quality.

In beef slaughtering, viscera pan washwater can be reduced to minimum levels as in the hog area. Pans are larger and require more nozzles. A major quantity of wastewater originates where the stomach or paunch is opened and washed. The paunch contains 65–80 lb of manure, which is removed by opening the paunch, emptying the contents to the sewer, placing the paunch over a frame, and washing the interior and exterior. The interior has a honeycomb surface and requires a great deal of washing to remove manure. In plants where attempts are made to reduce wastewater concentration, the paunch is emptied to a screw conveyor rather than to the sewer, to avoid leaching of soluble material from the manure. Water use in cleaning paunch is an high as 125 gal per head.

Washing portions of the paunch to produce edible tripe requires scalding and washing. The quantity of water used is 14 gal per head and waste characteristics are:

Component	Concentration, mg/liter	Quantity, lb/head
Total volatile solids	9360	1.12
Total nitrogen	1100	0.13
Grease	5220	0.62

After splitting, the beef carcass is showered and placed in the cooler. Water use at this point is 60 gal/head. The upper and lower digestive tracts of beef are processed similarly to hog casings.

Calf and sheep slaughter is similar to beef slaughter except that calves are commonly skinned in the cooler or by the purchaser. This requires that the hide be washed thoroughly before cooling. Spraying before slaughtering to loosen dirt on calves consumes 60 gal per head. The shower after slaughter requires 50 gal per head. Viscera pan wash is 24 gal per head. Casings are produced from portions of sheep intestines. Other offal items also may be cleaned, as is done in hog slaughter.

In manufacturing and boning areas, cleanup produces wastewater. To minimize losses to the sewer, all floor scraps should be picked up and placed in containers for delivery to the rendering department before water is used. Grease traps should be installed in smokehouse drains. All floor drains should have covers with small openings to prevent entrance of large solids.

Segregation of Wastewater. Sewers in the slaughter and packing plants include those for sanitary sewage, manure-laden water, manure-free water, and clear water. Following primary treatment, wastewaters are combined for secondary treatment. If wastewater is to be discharged to a receiving water after treatment, sanitary sewage and manure-laden sewage should be combined before primary treatment. If discharge is directly to a municipal sewer system with or without pretreatment, sanitary sewage should be discharged directly to the municipal sewer. Processing plants have no manure-laden water. Sewers include sanitary sewage, clear water, waters with low or no grease content, and waters with high grease content. Processing plants are most often located in urban areas, and discharge to municipal sewers. Wastewaters having grease contents which exceed the municipal standards should be separated for grease

TABLE I

SEGREGATION OF WASTEWATERS BY SOURCE

Manure-laden water

Stomach contents
Stomach washer
Paunch contents and washwater
Scald tub
Dehairing machine
Bleeding area cleanup
Stockyards
Meat scraps and tankage storage
   area
Smokehouse smokers, fans, ducts
Catch basin sludge

Tankwater and blood processing area
   cleanup water
Tankage dryer area
Calf showers
Plant laundry
Heart washer
Hair washer drainage
Casing selection
Evaporator and tankage dryer condenser
   water
Boiler blowdown and water softener lime
   waste

Manure-free, high grease water

Hasher-washer (catch basin effluent)
Edible and inedible cooker
   charging and cooking areas
Expeller and grease press room
Smokehouse cleanup
Sausage grind, mix, and stuff areas
Green meat boning areas
Can filling area
Loaf cook water
Edible and inedible grease
   settling and storage tank area

Lard packaging area
Barrel washer
Slaughter floor areas except bleeding and
   dehairing space
Casing stripper water (catch basin effluent)
Chitterling washwater (catch basin effluent)
Inedible grease and lard tank car cleaning
   tracks
Tripe washers
Tripe and tongue scalders

Manure-free, low grease water

Finished product chill showers
Coolers and freezers
Spice preparation area

Corridor and stairway areas and elevator
   pits
Finished product packaging

Clear water

Ice manufacture
Air aftercooler water
Canned product chill water
Brine from chill units
Storm water, yard and roof drains

Jacket water from ammonia and air compressors
   and vacuum pumps
Steam condenser water (if cooling tower is not
   used)
Steam condensate (if not returned to the boiler
   feed)

removal prior to discharge. In a slaughter plant, manure waters are separated from grease waters to permit recovery of a higher quality grease for rendering. Table I shows a suggested separation of wastewaters.

Clear water should be discharged to a storm drain system. This water, excluding the storm water, can be reused at a number of points, as has been mentioned. If desired, primary treatment plant effluent makes a suitable source for water for inedible cooker, dryer, and evaporator condensers. Condenser effluent should then be returned in a separate sewer to the primary plant effluent or to a separate settling tank in order not to increase the wastewater temperature beyond that needed for proper condensing.

QUANTITY AND CHARACTERISTICS OF WASTEWATER

Plant size, species slaughtered, amount of processing, reuse of water, wastewater segregation, by-product processes used, and number of by-products and offal items produced influence the quantity and characteristics of wastewater. Application of data from one plant to another without knowledge of the foregoing factors for each plant can be misleading. This is especially true for small plants where variability is more pronounced than among large plants. For example, a study of meat packing wastes reported in 1961 by Macon and Cote (2) included analyses of wastewater from 18 plants having slaughter rates ranging from 32 hogs and 1 beef to 449 hogs and 100 beef per day. The range in concentration, water use, BOD, and suspended solids was:

Flow, gal/head	152–1810
BOD, mg/liter	320–5440
BOD, lb/1000 lb live weight	1.9–27.6
Suspended solids, mg/liter	240–7220
Suspended solids, lb/1000 lb live weight	1.2–53.8
Total volatile solids, lb/1000 lb live weight	3.1–56.4

Some of the above plants slaughtered hogs only, some included rendering facilities, some separated clear water, and some recovered blood. The great range in all values illustrates the need for analysis of individual sources within a specific plant to properly control and segregate wastewater.

Table II describes flow and characteristics for manure-free wastewater sources (segregated as in Table I) from a packing plant. Data on some individual sources in slaughtering areas have been previously stated and are not repeated. Flow for the plant of Table II was 1500 gal/1000 lb live weight slaughtered (hogs, beef, calves, and sheep). Losses to the sewer per 1000 lb live weight slaughtered were: BOD, 14.6 lb; suspended solids, 11.2 lb; and grease, 7.8 lb. The manure-laden wastewater flow was 0.90 mgd. After screening, this contained 6900 lb each of BOD and suspended solids, making total flow and losses to the sewer per 1000 lb live weight slaughtered: flow, 2200 gpd; BOD, 19.9 lb; and suspended solids, 16.5 lb. This packing plant is large compared with the North Carolina plants described by Macon and Cote. Daily slaughter included 4000 hogs, 300 beef, and 300 calves at the time the study was made.

TABLE II

PACKING PLANT MANURE-FREE WASTEWATER CHARACTERISTICS, BY ORIGIN

Wastewater source	Flow, mgd	BOD		Suspended solids		Grease	
		mg/liter	lb/day	mg/liter	lb/day	mg/liter	lb/day
Catch basin effluent	1.045	1000	8,700	875	7,600	420	3,650
Slaughter, cut, inedible cooker charging area	0.245	2350	4,810	1680	3,440	2180	4,460
Cure box wash, bacon curing, bacon slicing, vat dump, salami mixing	0.193	1200	1,930	570	920	370	590
Salami mixing, sausage slicing and packaging	0.014	1220	140	1150	130	320	40
Boiled ham, boning, canned meats, pork sausage stuffing, large sausage stuffing	0.293	650	1,580	300	730	200	490
Beef boning, lard packaging, lard rendering, offal pack, hog cooler	0.020	1930	320	2350	390	2350	390
Vat wash, elevator vestibules	0.039	950	310	780	250	240	80
Sausage grind and mix, vein pumping, beef boning, pork trim, hog coolers	0.040	930	310	2100	700	330	110
Lard and meat scraps loading track, brine cure, elevator vestibules, hog cooler	0.015	2100	260	550	70	–	–
Smoked meats wash	0.036	1470	440	900	270	970	290
Total	1.940		18,800		14,500		10,100

Note: Some areas are drained by more than one stack and are thus repeated above.

In large slaughter and packing plants which segregate clear water, remove paunch manure by screening, and provide gravity separation of grease from the wastewater, the characteristics are less variable from plant to plant. Ranges of values for the combined wastewaters are:

Component	Range	Typical value
BOD, mg/liter	900–2500	1500
Suspended solids, mg/liter	900–3200	1200
Total volatile solids, mg/liter	1000–3100	1700
pH	7.1–7.4	7.2
Grease, mg/liter	600–2000	1200
Temperature, °F	75–95	90

Waste flow in terms of 1000 lb live weight slaughtered varies from 600 to 3500 gal. Flows in the lower portion of the range prevail for slaughter plants. Increased processing in packing plants increases the flow per unit of slaughter.

Variation. Wastewater quantities and characteristics are subject to seasonal, daily, and hourly variations, depending upon plant production levels. Slaughter is usually high between October and March. As illustrated in Fig. 1, variation in wastewater quantity is similar to but not as

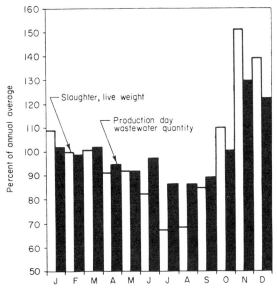

Fig. 1. Monthly variation in packing plant wastewater quantity and slaughter.

extreme as slaughter variations because of the leveling effect of processing. Variation in water use with slaughter rate is further illustrated in
Fig. 2, which shows the increased water use per head slaughtered as
slaughter rates fall below maximum levels. The concentrations of various
components increase during the months of heavy slaughter to 150% of
the levels during the summer, as shown in Table III.

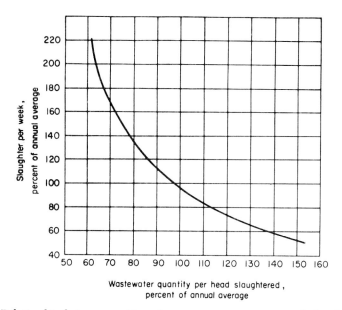

FIG. 2. Relationship between packing plant wastewater quantity and slaughter rate.

The day of the week effect on raw wastewater and primary effluent
characteristics is negligible on production days. On weekends with no
slaughter and little or no processing, the BOD and suspended solids
concentrations are reduced to less than half of production day levels.
Flow also is reduced, to less than 20% of that on production days. Stockyards, processes that carry over to Saturday, and weekend processing
account for the wastewater on weekends.

Hourly variations in wastewater as a result of shift operations are pronounced. Even in larger plants, the noon slaughter break is evident on
flow charts. Figure 3 illustrates the variations in flow, concentration, and
pounds of total volatile solids based on 2-hour composite samples. Between 6 AM and 10 PM, 86% of the volatile solids in the manure-free
wastewater of this packing plant reached the treatment facilities. Similar

TABLE III

MONTHLY VARIATION IN RAW PACKING PLANT WASTEWATER CHARACTERISTICS

| Month | Manure-free grease wastewater | | | Manure wastewater | |
	Total volatile solids	Suspended solids	Grease	Total volatile solids	Suspended solids
January	1506	1190	960	2500	1870
February	1690	1336	860	2136	1592
March	1378	1058	956	2000[a]	1450[a]
April	1490	850	552	1870	1370
May	1252	831	550	1778	1418
June	1200[a]	800[a]	550[a]	1750[a]	1400[a]
July	1290	863	592	1720	1400
August	1090	745	324	2170	2030
September	1374	934	457	2100	1630
October	1490	1320	710	2020	1785
November	1720	1218	662	2395	1984
December	1863	1518	739	2400[a]	1900[a]

Results given as milligrams per liter.
[a] Not sampled. Values estimated from slaughter and production levels.

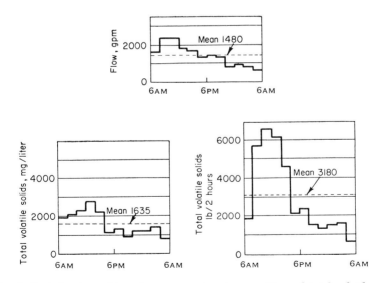

FIG. 3. Variation in packing plant raw wastewater quantity and total volatile solids by 2-hour intervals.

data for the manure wastewater showed 90% of the total volatile solids discharged in the 12-hour interval after start of slaughtering.

In analyzing wastewater samples, laboratory time can be reduced by using total volatile solids as a measure of BOD in raw and primary effluent samples. Differences between the two characteristics may be attributed to volatile solids in the water supply which do not contribute to BOD. Correlation of 40 daily values at one plant at several sampling points produced coefficients of correlation greater than 0.9 for the straight line of regression.

AMENABILITY TO TREATMENT

Meat industry wastes contain carbon, nitrogen, and phosphorus in proportions such that aerobic or anaerobic biological treatment is readily accomplished without the addition of nutrients. The velocity constant in the BOD reaction for the effluent of a trickling filter plant treating packing plant wastes tends to be higher than for raw domestic sewage.

EFFECT ON SEWERS AND RECEIVING WATERS

Wastewater can be discharged directly to a municipal sewer system without deleterious effect on sewer material or flow. With pipe slopes for proper velocity, solids do not accumulate in the sewer invert. Adequate grease removal is necessary prior to discharge, to prevent accumulations of grease on the sides and crown of the sewer. Usually, wastewaters having less than 400 mg/liter total ether-soluble matter do not create problems in maintaining sewer capacity.

Wastewater discharge to a receiving stream requires treatment to prevent solids accumulation on the stream bottom and floating material on the surface. The rapid decomposition of organic matter in the stream brings the dissolved oxygen minimum point closer to the point of wastewater discharge than for a similar load of domestic sewage. The nitrogen content of the wastewater provides nutrients for algae growth. The elevated temperature of both wastewater and clear cooling water may require special outlets for dispersal, to eliminate stratification in the receiving water. When adequate dilution or dispersal is not available, temperature stratification can be deleterious to fish life.

NUISANCE PROBLEMS

Operation of wastewater treatment facilities may create odor and insect nuisance problems unless control measures are taken. Solids removed by screening should be disposed of daily to reduce odors and eliminate fly breeding. Daily scum removal in all primary units and equalization tanks is necessary. On weekends, with the low rates of wastewater flow, septic conditions may develop, causing odor problems. If multiple units are available, odor can be reduced by taking one or more settling tanks out of service during warm weather weekends. Odors from trickling filters during low flow can be reduced by recirculation. Odors are less from a rotary distributor than from fixed nozzle application of wastes to the filter.

Sludge and wastewater lagoons do not cause unusual odor problems. The anaerobic units develop a heavy, dry scum that tends to limit odors. Aerobic stabilization ponds may present odor problems in northern climates when the ice cover first disappears in the spring. As in domestic sewage ponds which are not overloaded, odor problems are negligible.

Disposal of solids on land requires spreading in a thin layer on cropland, so that drying is rapid and odor and insect problems are eliminated. Disposal by landfill should be accompanied by proper covering procedures to reduce insect, rodent, and odor nuisance. If the solids have been digested, disposal for land fill does not require cover for nuisance control.

WASTE TREATMENT AND DISPOSAL

The treatment of wastewater is preferably handled in a municipal sewage treatment plant. Municipal regulations should limit grease content, or the municipal plant should provide adequate means of grease removal. In many communities, treatment by screening to remove manure solids, and gravity separation to reduce grease to 400 mg/liter, are the only pretreatments required prior to discharge to the public sewer. Application of a sewage service charge which includes surcharges for certain constitutents may make additional pretreatment at the packing plant economical. Some municipalities have adopted arbitrary limits for BOD, suspended solids, and other constituents, thus making pretreatment mandatory. Others, such as Omaha and South St. Paul, permit paunch manure to be discharged to the public sewer.

Discharge to a receiving stream requires treatment, the degree of which depends upon the dilution available. Discharge to small streams with little or no dilution or to lakes requires that effluent BOD be reduced to 20–40 mg/liter, requiring 85–95% removal of BOD.

Wastewater Treatment

Preliminary. Removal of grease or solids at the point of origin, for some major sources, has previously been described. The catch basin for treating inedible viscera washer discharge is a conventional settling basin with sludge and scum removal equipment. Detention times vary from

20 to 30 minutes. Design data can be determined approximately by measuring the time required for a scum-water interface to develop in a graduate filled with the sample. Stockyards wastewater may be screened at the site and the solids disposed of with the bedding. Stockyards wastewater, at plants where cattle pens are dry cleaned and hog pens are washed, contains up to 200 mg/liter BOD and 300 mg/liter suspended solids at peak periods, but less than 100 mg/liter BOD in 24-hour composite samples. This waste source could be connected directly to a municipal sewer with or without screening.

Primary Treatment. Gravity separation is the most common treatment of meat wastewaters. Typically, manure wastewater is screened prior to other treatment, although this is not a necessity. Screen mesh varies from 5 to 20 openings per inch; where secondary treatment is required, the larger openings are used. Where screens are the only treatment prior to discharge to a sewer, the finer mesh may be required to meet municipal regulations. In general, solids can be removed in sedimentation units more readily than by screens. As screen mesh becomes finer, maintenance costs increase and blinding becomes more of a problem.

Grit and scum removal from the manure wastewater can be accomplished in a settling tank having 15–45 minutes detention time. If screens are not used, manure solids also are collected in this unit. In primary sedimentation, surface settling rates up to 1000 gpd per sq ft and a detention time of 1.5 hours are used. Flocculation for 20 or more minutes prior to sedimentation improves removals. Treatment of manure-free wastewater for grease removal can be accomplished in sedimentation basins. Dissolved air flotation is often applied in treating either waste stream, with detention periods of 45–60 minutes and surface settling rates as high as 2500 gpd per sq ft.

Removals in primary units are shown in Table IV. Use of grit removal, flocculation, and sedimentation for manure-bearing wastewater reduces total volatile solids and BOD by 50%, and suspended solids by 75%. Dissolved air flotation applied to the manure-free wastes reduces BOD 40–60, suspended solids 50–70%, and grease 30–52%. The per cent removal of grease is dependent primarily upon influent concentration; effluent concentrations are similar, regardless of flow, for surface settling rates between 1900 and 2500 gpd per sq ft.

Chemical coagulation improves removals in primary treatment. Tests on manure wastewater show that alum increases removal of BOD 2.5 mg/liter and of grease 1.5 mg/liter for each milligram per liter of alum added. Polyelectrolytes also are being tested, and have the advantages of small chemical storage area and small feed equipment. Chemical treat-

TABLE IV

REMOVALS BY PRIMARY TREATMENT

Wastewater stream	Treatment units	Duration of test, days	Component	Influent, mg/liter	Effluent, mg/liter	Removal, %
Manure-bearing, after grit removal	Flocculation and sedimentation (520 gpd/sq ft)	5	BOD	1182	940	20.5
			Total volatile solids	1637	1307	20.2
			Suspended solids	978	471	51.8
Manure-bearing	Grit tank (40 minute detention), flocculation (80 minutes), and sedimentation (460 gpd/sq ft)	10	Total volatile solids	2019	939	53.6
			Suspended solids	1994	408	79.5
Manure-bearing, after grit removal	Dissolved air flotation (1900 gpd/sq ft)	16	BOD	923	766	17.6
			Suspended solids	738	556	24.7
			Grease	268	189	29.7
Manure-free	Dissolved air flotation (1840 gpd/sq ft)	25	BOD	1472	852	42.1
			Suspended solids	1055	547	48.1
			Grease	596	285	52.2
Manure-free	Dissolved air flotation	3 (during kill period only)	BOD	2008	820	59.2
			Suspended solids	1667	505	68.7
			Grease	1366	274	79.9
Manure-free	Dissolved air flotation (250 gpd/sq ft)	25	Suspended solids	1449	879	49.3
			Grease	933	459	50.9

ment can be varied with plant production levels, eliminating unused capacity in treatment units during periods of low production. Operating costs are high and investment is low.

Secondary Treatment. The use of trickling filters is a common method of secondary treatment in the meat industry. At loadings of 220 lb per 1000 cu ft, a 3-stage filter in West Fargo, North Dakota, produced overall BOD removal of 95%. A similar installation at Rochelle, Illinois, produces removals in excess of 95%. Removals on trickling filters tend to exceed those of the National Research Council curve (3) extrapolated to the higher loadings common in treating packing plant wastes. Figure 4

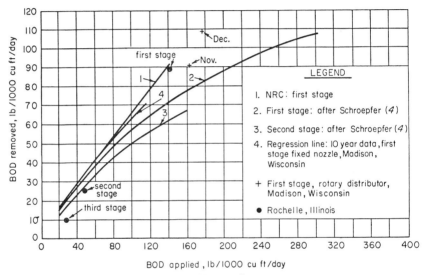

FIG. 4. Trickling filter performance curves.

shows the relationship between unit loading and removal. Curves 2 and 4 are design curves developed by the National Research Council and Schroepfer (4) for first stage filters. Curve 1 is a regression line for a fixed nozzle filter containing ¾- to 1½-inch rock. Also shown are average monthly data for a 3-stage filter at Rochelle, Illinois, and a single stage filter having 2½- to 4-inch rock. All data are for units that treat packing plant wastes exclusively. Removals include the final clarifier.

Provision for recirculation is necessary to maintain operation of distributor arms and to prevent freezing during periods of low flow. High recirculation rates on winter weekends may lower the waste temperature enough to cause freezing of the filters.

A hog slaughtering plant in Iowa is equipped with an activated sludge plant for treating wastewater. Retention in the aeration tank is 10 hours, based on the wastewater flow rate during production. No data are available on the loading or removals accomplished by this process.

The use of anaerobic ponds has become common in recent years. Present practice is to provide 3 ponds, the first and second being anaerobic and the third aerobic. Loadings on the first pond range from 300 to 1360 lb BOD per acre per day, with depths from 8 to 14 ft. If the bottom is above groundwater, greater depths are of advantage in reducing heat losses and making for easier solids removal by dragline. Up to 85% removal of BOD is accomplished in the first pond when loadings are 11 lb BOD/1000 cu ft. The second and third ponds are 3–5 ft deep, and have a combined area to provide a loading of 100–150 lb BOD per acre per day. Pond inlets should provide for adequate circulation. Inlet location at the pond center permits wind action to disperse solids in the second and third ponds. Some installations provide for addition of heat by underwater burners when anaerobic pond temperatures fall below 75°F. Overall removals in excess of 90% are accomplished on an annual average basis. During cold months, removals may fall to 70%. Normally, grease removal by gravity separation and solids removal by screening precede the anaerobic pond. In Louisiana, small abattoirs discharge all wastes, including blood and manure, directly to a 3-stage pond. A heavy layer of scum on the surface of the first lagoon improves operation.

The anaerobic contact process was developed under research sponsored by the American Meat Institute and George A. Hormel and Company. The process includes primary sedimentation for grease removal, and screening to remove large solids. The wastewater is then introduced into a digester maintained at 95°F. An equalizing tank is provided to level flow rates to the digester. The digester effluent is degassed by a 20-inch vacuum, and the solids are removed in a gravity separator for return to the digester. Digester gas is used to heat the influent to maintain temperature. If wastewater temperatures are 85°F or more and total volatile solids in the wastewater exceeds 1200 mg/liter, auxiliary heat is not required. The digester is equipped with a mixer and is loaded at 0.15–0.20 lb BOD per cu ft. The separator loading is 300 gpd per sq ft based on raw flow rate, and the sludge drawoff rate is 3 times the raw flow rate. Removals of 90% of the digester influent BOD are accomplished. Excess sludge volume for disposal is about 2% of the raw waste volume. The installation costs are approximately 70% of those for a trickling filter plant designed to accomplish similar removals.

Tertiary Treatment. Stabilization ponds are used following secondary treatment where they are required to increase the degree of treatment or to provide additional dependability. An anaerobic contact plant effluent in Minnesota is treated in 2 ponds operated in series. Depth is 3–4 feet and BOD loading averages 410 lb per day per acre on the total area of the 2 ponds. Removal of BOD averages 86%, with 45% of the removal accounted for by loss of water due to seepage.

Many secondary plant effluents are discharged to municipal sewers, where the wastewater is subjected to additional treatment in combination with municipal sewage. Industrial 2-stage trickling filter effluent is further treated in a municipal activated sludge plant in Wisconsin. Anaerobic contact plant effluent is mixed with domestic sewage and treated by trickling filters in Minnesota, and by activated sludge in Illinois.

Irrigation. Wastewater effluent from a trickling filter plant is disposed of by irrigation between April and December in Wisconsin. Loadings average 8000 gpd per acre, with BOD as high as 480 mg/liter and suspended solids of 280 mg/liter. Soil type and topography are important in this process. Soil must be well drained and the area must not be sloped to such an extent that runoff occurs. A crop such as canary grass, which accepts flooding and chlorides up to 2000 mg/liter, assists by transpiration of the water and utilization of the wastewater nitrogen.

Combined Treatment. Treatment of meat industry wastes in combination with municipal sewage is the practice in most cities. Chicago and Milwaukee at one time had large wastewater loads from packing plants, which they treated in activated sludge plants. In South St. Paul, Minnesota, the wastewater from packing plants makes up the major portion of the total flow to a municipal trickling filter plant. Many Iowa cities treat meat industry wastewater in municipal plants. Treatment processes used in these cities include primary treatment, trickling filters, and activated sludge. In some cities, such as Austin, Minnesota, special processes are installed to pretreat the industrial waste at the municipal plant before combining it with the sewage. The pretreatment requirements for meat wastewater range from none at South St. Paul to 85% removal of BOD at Madison, Wisconsin. Usual pretreatment requirements are screening and gravity separation of grease.

SOLIDS TREATMENT AND DISPOSAL

Sludge treatment is similar to that used in municipal plants. Quantities of sludge and skimmings are large because of the high solids content of the raw waste.

Quantities and Characteristics. Quantity of sludge varies with the degree of treatment, screen mesh, sump pumping practice, and production activity in the plant. At one plant in which BOD removal in the primary plant was 50%, sludge quantitites were 8 tons total solids (dry basis) per million gal of wastewater. The solids were 75% volatile, and the sludge was 5–6% solids. Secondary sludge from a trickling filter plant amounted to 1.6 tons total solids per million gal and was 75% volatile. The pH of the primary sludge was 6.5 and of secondary sludge was 7.0. Grease content of the primary sludge was 6000 mg/liter.

Screenings from a 5-mesh screen in a packing plant slaughtering beef, hogs, and calves amounted to 1.3 tons per million gal. The moisture content ranged from 81 to 85% and the wet weight was 31–34 lb per cu ft.

Treatment Processes. Digestion tanks can be loaded at 0.20 lb total volatile solids per cu ft if a mixer is used. Digested sludge can be disposed of in lagoons or dewatered by vacuum filters, and the cake hauled to disposal.

Lagooning of raw sludge is practiced without great nuisance problems. Plants at South St. Paul, Minnesota, and Rochelle, Illinois, discharge raw sludge into lagoons from a tower, by pneumatic ejector. In many lagoons it is necessary to decant liquid, which is then returned to the treatment process.

Most packing plants render skimmings removed from the manure-free wastewater. Other skimmings are handled with the sludges.

Ultimate Disposal of Solids. Sludge screenings and skimmings are disposed of on land, with or without prior treatment. Liquid sludge can be transported for spreading on land, or dewatering processes can be employed and the filter cake hauled to a land fill. Solids in lagoons must be removed and used for land fill, or new lagoons may be built if land area is available and the cost is less than cleaning.

At one plant, screenings are removed by a contractor who produces a composted fertilizer. The fertilizer value of screenings is low compared with commerical fertilizers. Nitrogen content is 1.1–1.8%; phosphoric acid, 0.25–0.74%; and soluble potash, 0.09–0.28%.

Cost of Treatment and Disposal

The investment in wastewater treatment facilities is dependent upon degree of treatment and the process used. Dietz and Clinebell (*1*) estimated costs for 3 secondary processes for plants of various sizes in 1964.

They considered a grit chamber, flocculator, sedimentation tank with sludge lagoons, 2-stage trickling filter, and aerobic ponds; an anaerobic contact plant followed by lagoons; and a 3-stage pond system with the first pond covered by foamed plastic bats and equipped with an underwater burner. Estimated construction costs and total annual costs including depreciation, interest, taxes, insurance, power, and labor are:

	0.5	1.5	2.5
Plant capacity, mgd			
Influent BOD, lb/day	5,000	12,000	15,000
Construction cost, $ per 100 lb BOD removed			
Trickling filters	12,000	7,500	3,740
Anaerobic contact	8,700	5,360	2,610
3-Stage ponds	4,450	2,380	1,840
Total annual cost, $ per 100 lb BOD removed per day			
Trickling filters	7.68	5.10	5.75
Anaerobic contact	6.25	4.15	4.39
3-Stage ponds	3.03	2.52	2.87

These costs are based on 90% removal of BOD, with annual costs based on 250 production days per year. If land area is available in the packing plant vicinity, the advantage of ponds is evident.

Studies on the use of alum to increase BOD removal by sedimentation showed that chemical costs ranged from $0.64 to $2.05 per 100 lb BOD removed over that possible by plain sedimentation, for increased removals of 50% and 78.5%, respectively. Cost of chemical feed equipment and possible increases in labor and quantity of sludge would further increase costs. The advantage of alum treatment is the small investment as compared with secondary treatment.

Sometimes the company prefers to have the municipality construct, own, and operate separate treatment facilities for the wastewater, and to make annual payments to the municipality to retire the capital investment and pay operating costs. This frees the company from the large investment and eliminates payment of real estate taxes and insurance on the treatment plant.

In municipal treatment of combined industrial wastes and domestic sewage, most municipalities obtain revenues from the general real estate tax levy. This is advantageous to the meat industry, as its assessed valuation is a smaller percentage of total municipal valuation than its wastewater quantity is of total sewage flow. Use of a sewage service charge based on volume and organic loading, with costs for unused treatment plant capacity collected from property taxes, is a more equitable method of obtaining municipal revenues. In some instances a contract is drawn, under which the meat industry agrees to make annual payments of amortization costs for the industrial portion of municipal plant capacity, and to pay the portion of operating expenses assignable to the industrial wastewater. The advantage of such a contract is that the industry does not incur costs for treatment plant expansion as a result of increased load from residential growth and the residents do not pay for additional capacity provided for the industry.

INDUSTRY TRENDS

During the 1950's and early 1960's, the meat industry abandoned many old packing plants in larger cities and built new slaughter or packing plants in small communities near the source of animal production. Increased mechanization in processing meat products has tended to reduce wastewater flow per unit of production. Increased reuse of water has had a similar effect. Reduction in value of edible and inedible fats and other by-products has reduced the complexity of rendering processes, which reduces losses to the sewer through equipment failure. At the same time, however, the low value of fats tends to make supervision more lax about losses to the sewers.

In designing new packing and slaughter plants, wastewater treatment facilities are an integral part of plant design. Industry-sponsored research has developed the anaerobic contact process and improved the application of ponds. Location of new plants in small communities has required the use of secondary and tertiary treatment of meat industry wastewater. The application of dissolved air flotation has reduced primary treatment tank sizes for removals equivalent to those by plain sedimentation.

Research needs in the area of wastewater treatment include an improved method of screenings disposal. Transportation to land disposal sites is becoming more costly, especially in larger cities. The solids removal system in the anaerobic contact process should be improved to reduce the pumping requirements for return sludge and to eliminate the occasional losses of solids to the effluent. Sludge disposal methods can also be improved. The use of secondary treatment has increased sludge quantities and, as with screenings, ultimate disposal of solids is becoming more costly. The improvement of primary treatment removals through the use of polyelectrolytes has not been explored to any great extent. Improvement of pond efficiency in cold weather is needed. The effect of equalization of flow on secondary processes has not been evaluated, particularly for trickling filters.

REFERENCES

1. Dietz, J. C., and Clinebell, P. W., "Anaerobic Stabilization." Engineering Institute on Industrial Wastes, Univ. of Wisconsin, February 1964.
2. Macon, J. A., and Cote, D. N., "Study of Meat Packing Wastes in North Carolina." Industrial Extension Service, School of Engineering, North Carolina State College, August 1961.
3. National Research Council, *Sewage Works J.* 18, 971 (1946).
4. Schroepfer, G. J., Lecture Outline, "Sewerage and Sewage Treatment." Dept. of Civil Engineering, Univ. of Minnesota, March 1951.

Chapter 3

FISH AND FISH PRODUCTS

by JOSEPH W. SLAVIN and JOHN A. PETERS

This chapter discusses the utilization and disposal of wastes produced during the handling and processing of fish, shellfish, and their industrial products. It describes the United States fishing industry, including the operations of commerical processing. This information is supplemented by details on the characteristics of wastes resulting from the production of fish fillets, shellfish, canned fish, precooked or breaded seafoods, and fish meal and oil. Included also is information on present waste disposal methods and on techniques now being advanced for future treatment of fish wastes. Although the wastes have some similarity to meat industry wastes, the differences are significant and therefore require special consideration.

THE FISHING INDUSTRY

The commercial fisheries of North America differ widely in regard to geographical location, types of materials produced, and processing methods employed. In 1962, the domestic catch of fish and shellfish amounted to 5.2 billion pounds, valued at 385 million dollars to the fishermen. About half was used for the manufacture of industrial products. The other half was marketed as fresh, frozen, or canned fish.

Major divisions of the fin fish and shellfish industry include groundfish, such as haddock, flounders, ocean perch, whiting, cod, pollock, and hake, primarily from New England and the middle Atlantic; menhaden, blue crab, and oysters, primarily from the middle Atlantic, Chesapeake, south Atlantic, and Gulf; shrimp, mullet, and red snapper from the south Atlantic and Gulf; carp, chubs, buffalo fish, catfish, lake herring, and yellow perch, from the Mississippi Valley and the Great Lakes; and tuna, salmon, halibut, king crab, dungeness crab, and oysters, from the Pacific coast and Alaska. Fresh and frozen products obtained from these fish and shellfish for human consumption consist of dressed fish, fish fillets, fish portions, and fish sticks; raw and precooked shrimp; crab, shrimp, oysters, clams, and lobsters marketed almost in their natural state; and canned products including tuna, salmon, mackerel, sardines, oysters, crab meat, and shrimp meat. Additional information on the production of

TABLE I

PRODUCTION OF FISH AND SHELLFISH IN 1961
(AS DELIVERED BY THE FISHING VESSEL)

Species or group	Volume, million lb	Value, million dollars
Salmon	310	52.0
Shrimp	175	51.7
Tuna	326	42.3
Groundfish[a]	585	34.1
Oysters (meats)	62	33.2
Menhaden	2315	25.6
Crabs	232	17.3
Lobsters (northern)	28	14.5
Clams	50	11.7
Halibut	53	8.4
Sardines[b]	156	2.9
Total—human food	2500	331
Total—industrial products	2700	31

[a] Includes haddock, cod, ocean perch, whiting, flounder, hake, and pollock.
[b] Includes small herring, brisling, sprats, and pilchards.

seafood is given in Table I. The table and the following discussion refer only to United States production and practices.

THE GROUNDFISH INDUSTRY

Groundfish, or bottom fish, are those fin fish that inhabit the bottom of the ocean and are caught by trawl gear. The most important species are haddock, cod, ocean perch, whiting, flounder, hake, and pollock. The fishery industry is centered in New England, as about 80% of the United States landings of these fish come from that area. The fish are caught in otter trawls fished from trawlers of 90–150 ft in length. In a typical commercial operation, the bag of fish is emptied on the deck of the vessel, sorted as to species and size, washed, and then iced in pens partitioned in the hold of the boat. Fish such as cod, haddock, and pollock are eviscerated on deck before being iced, whereas ocean perch, flounder, and whiting are stored whole. Vessels fishing for haddock, cod, and flounder stay at sea from 5 to 10 days each trip; those fishing for ocean perch stay out about 14 days.

Groundfish are usually processed at fish plants that are relatively small and that are centered in community fishing areas such as Boston, Gloucester, or New Bedford. Unloading from the vessel is accomplished by pughing the fish into a basket lowered through a hatch into the hold of the vessel. When filled, the basket is swung to the dock, and the fish are emptied into a weigh box, weighed, and pughed into a wooden tote box, which is moved into the processing plant. The handling of ocean perch at some of the larger plants has been mechanized to improve efficiency in handling and to maintain quality.

Processing operations include filleting, skinning, washing, packaging, weighing, and chilling or freezing. Equipment is available for carrying out many of these operations, but it is not automatic and therefore requires labor to operate. A substantial amount of manual labor is also used for filleting those fish that do not fall within the scope of existing filleting machines, and for packing, weighing, and transferring the product to the chiller or freezer. The amount of eviscerated fish handled daily in a groundfish plant of medium size may vary from 20,000 to 40,-000 lb.

Groundfish are used primarily for the production of fish fillets, which are marketed in the chilled or frozen state. Some haddock, cod, pollock, and other species are also sold as dressed fish, primarily for use in institutions or restaurants. Fresh fillets are generally marketed in tins of 20–30 lb capacity, packed in ice; the frozen products are retailed in 1, 5, or 10 lb cartons.

HALIBUT

Halibut is a member of the groundfish family, but it deserves separate treatment because of the different harvesting and processing methods employed. The major halibut fishery is centered in the Pacific Northwest. Alaska, Washington, and Oregon produce about 85% of the halibut landed annually in this country. The remaining amount is produced in the north Atlantic region.

The halibut is a large fish—those landed commercially vary from 20 to 80 lb. They are caught by means of baited long lines or set lines laid along the bottom of the sea. Halibut fishing vessels range from 50 to 80 ft in length and may land 30–50 tons of fish after 2–3 weeks on the fishing grounds. Commercial fishing on the Pacific coast is carried out from April or May until October under a quota established by the International Halibut Commission.

After being landed on the vessel, the halibut are dressed by removing the viscera and cutting away the gills. The halibut then are packed in ice in the fish hold. When the vessel reaches port, the fish are put into large metal or canvas baskets or are unloaded singly with a rope hoist and taken ashore for processing.

Halibut ordinarily are processed in relatively small plants. If the fish are not to be processed immediately, they are frozen and placed in frozen storage. The fish are marketed fresh or frozen, dressed (without the head), or as packaged flitches or steaks. The processing operations involve washing, cutting of the fish by machine or hand, packaging by hand, and freezing or storage with ice.

FRESH WATER FISH

Fresh water fish are produced from the Great Lakes, inland lakes such as the Red Lakes and the Boundary Lakes of Minnesota, and the Mississippi River and its tributaries. The major species include whitefish, lake trout, walleye, blue pike, lake herring, and various industrial fish. The catch from the Mississippi River consists primarily of carp, buffalo, sheepshead, catfish, and bullheads.

About half the fresh water fish produced in this country are caught by gill nets, haul seines, and trap nets. Pound nets are also employed in this fishery.

The processing plants are small and sometimes consist of merely a shed with running water and facilities for washing and cutting the fish. Most of the product is marketed fresh, either whole or dressed, in metropolitan areas. A very small quantity is filleted or packaged and frozen for sale in large retail markets.

TUNA

The principal center of the tuna industry is in southern California, although some species are landed in the north and middle Atlantic areas.

The major species of tuna consist of albacore, yellowfin, skipjack, and bluefin. They are caught by purse seine, hook and line, or trolling gear operated from vessels ranging up to 130 ft in length. The vessels are of modern design and have equipment for freezing the fish in brine as they are taken aboard. A large purse seiner may stay at sea for 3–4 weeks and may arrive in port with 300–350 tons of frozen tuna.

Tuna are marketed almost exclusively in the canned state. The fish are generally partially thawed aboard the vessel to facilitate separation during unloading. After being landed in the semifrozen condition, they are fully thawed with water in large tanks adjacent to the processing plant. The canneries are modern, and a considerable amount of mechanical equipment is employed in the processing operations. In California, cannery operations are carried out under the supervision of State fish inspectors, who check product quality and plant sanitation.

A typical processing operation involves butchering by hand to remove the viscera, spraying with fresh water, and placing the fish in wire baskets that are stacked into wheeled racks. The racks of fish are pushed into steam cookers, where they are subjected to temperatures of about 220°F for 2–8 hours; the exact period of time varies with the size of the fish.

After being cooked, the fish on the racks are placed in a room maintained at 60°–70°F to cool for 12–24 hours. The cooked product is conveyed to the cleaning tables, where manual labor is used to remove the head, to skin and split the fish, and to remove the backbone and tail. The halves are split into quarters, called loins, and the red meat is cut away from each piece. The cleaned loins are mechanically packed into cans of appropriate size, weighed, sealed, and retorted.

PACIFIC SALMON

Salmon hatch in streams or lakes, live their adult life in the ocean, and return to spawn at the same location where they were born. The 5 species found in the United States are chinook, sockeye, silver, pink, and chum.

Salmon are caught by seines, gill nets, and trolling gear. The vessels used in the fishery range from small trollers operated by individual fishermen to large barges maintained by the canneries. The fish are preserved by being stored in ice or in tanks containing sea water mechanically refrigerated to about 30°F.

The major portion of the salmon catch is canned, although some is marketed fresh or frozen. Many of the canneries are well equipped with machines for butchering the fish, for packing the meat into cans, and for weighing, sealing, and retorting the canned product.

SARDINES

In the United States, sardines include small herring, brisling, sprats, and pilchards. About 80% of the production is comprised of sea herring produced in Maine; the remainder consists of pilchards harvested primarily in California. The sardine industry is seasonal and is regulated by State law.

Fish used for the production of sardines are caught by purse seines, weirs, or trap nets. In Maine, the fish are left in the net for about 24 hours until the digestive tract is cleared. They are then transferred to a carrier boat by suction pumps and are salted down in the hold to retard spoilage. After being unloaded from the vessel, the fish are pumped into brining tanks and held until processed.

The canning of sardines is carried out at a number of small plants located along the coast. In Maine alone, about 34 plants are used to produce an annual pack of 2 million cases of product. A typical processing operation includes the usual precooking, cooling, can sealing, and retorting. A substantial amount of manual labor is used in the canning operation, particularly in packing the sardines into the cans.

SHELLFISH

The principal types of shellfish produced in this country consist of shrimp, scallops, oysters, clams, crabs, and lobsters. The shrimp and oyster industries deserve special mention because of the differences in processing operations and the types of wastes produced.

Shrimp. Brown, white, and pink shrimp comprise the bulk of the commercial shrimp fishery. The industry is located in the southern States and extends from Beaufort, North Carolina, to Brownsville, Texas. Almost all the shrimp landed in this area are caught by otter trawls fished from wooden vessels 50–70 ft in length.

Shrimp are marketed in several forms: fresh, frozen, breaded, canned, cured, and as specialty products. An increasing amount is being sold in the frozen state, whereas sales of canned shrimp are relatively constant.

The usual canning techniques are employed in producing canned shrimp. A typical processing operation includes washing and deicing the whole shrimp, removing the heads or shells, grading into different sizes, deveining, washing, blanching or precooking, packing into cans, weighing, can sealing, and retorting. There have been a number of improvments in the processing of canned shrimp within the past decade; at present, mechanical equipment is used for performing the washing, peeling, grading, and deveining operations. Manual labor is still used, however, in filling and weighing the cans.

Almost half the shrimp produced in this country is frozen raw with the shell on and is sold in bulk packages to wholesalers, institutional users, and processors of breaded shrimp. The processing operations include washing, grading into sizes, packaging, weighing, and freezing. Some plants produce frozen peeled and deveined shrimp for direct sale at consumer outlets. The processing of this product is the same as for the product with shell except for the additional peeling and deveining operations, which are carried out mechanically.

Oysters. The oyster is a bivalve mollusk that grows in shallow protected areas. It is harvested by hand gathering, tonging or raking, or by power dredges. The fishery is located within tidal waters and is subject to State control.

Oysters are marketed in the shell or as shucked refrigerated meats. Oyster meat is processed in accordance with sanitary regulations established by the U. S. Public Health Service and enforced by it and the State governments. The processing operations consist of hand shucking to remove the meat, washing in fresh water agitated with air, grading, and packing into metal or glass containers. The packaged meats are then chilled at least to 34°F.

MENHADEN

The menhaden is a small, oily fish that belongs to the herring family. In terms of annual landings, this fishery is the largest in the United States. The bulk of the landings is in the middle Atlantic area, but a significant quantity also comes from the Gulf of Mexico. The fishery is seasonal in nature, with fishing usually being carried out during the summer and fall.

Menhaden are caught by purse seines and then are pumped into the holds of carrier vessels 75–200 ft in length. Ice or other methods of preservation are not always used because many of the vessels stay at sea for only a day. On some larger vessels, however, refrigeration is now being used to preserve the fish during longer trips.

Menhaden are used for the manufacture of fish meal and oil. The process, called the wet reduction method, is carried out at about 30 plants located along the Atlantic coast and the Gulf of Mexico. Many of the plants are of modern construction and contain mechanical equipment for performing the various processing operations.

When the vessel returns to port, usually in the evening, the fish are pumped from the hold, washed, weighed automatically, and conveyed into the plant. The fish are cooked by steam in continuous cookers, then pressed to remove the oil and a substantial part of the water. The resulting press liquor is passed through vibrating screens to remove suspended solids and then centrifuged to separate the oil. The aqueous portion, called stickwater, is concentrated in evaporators, and put into storage tanks. It then is called condensed fish solubles. The fish material from which the water and oil have been pressed is known as press cake.

The press cake is conveyed directly from the presses to a rotary drier and is dried to about 10% moisture content. The dried material is mechanically transported to a scrap pile, where it is cooled. It then enters a hammer mill and is ground into meal. The meal is ordinarily weighed into burlap sacks for storage and shipment.

BREADED FISHERY PRODUCTS

The production of breaded fish and shellfish has increased greatly in recent years. About 200 million pounds of these convenience seafood items now is produced annually. The major products include fish sticks, raw breaded shrimp, and fish portions. They are usually packaged for direct consumer sale and marketed in the frozen state.

Plants used for the production of breaded seafoods are generally of modern design and are equipped with mechanical equipment for performing the various processing operations. Many of the firms employ the U. S. Department of Interior voluntary inspection service to maintain product quality and plant sanitation.

Fish sticks are rectangular, frozen portions of fish flesh that have been cut from blocks of frozen fish fillets, coated with batter, breaded, and precooked prior to being refrozen. The processing operations include cutting the sticks from the frozen block with band or gang saws or other types of cutting machines, and conveying the sticks through an automatic batter and breading machine, a continuous oil cooker, and an air cooler. The cooled product is usually packaged by hand prior to being frozen. In some of the more modern plants, however, the precooked and breaded sticks are frozen individually so that the product can be packed mechanically. The procedures used for other breaded seafoods are similar to those used in production of fish sticks.

THE FISHING VESSEL

Wastes originating on the fishing vessel vary according to the type of fishery in which it is engaged.

Menhaden make up the largest quantity of fish landed for industrial purposes such as the manufacture of fish meal, fish oil, and condensed fish solubles. The fish are commonly unloaded with centrifugal pumps. A dewatering screen is used at or near the discharge of the pump to separate the fish from the water used to make the fish flow to the pump suction line.

In the edible fish industry, ice used to cool the fish in the hold of the vessel is separated from the fish during or immediately after their being unloaded. During cleanup, large quantities of water are used to wash down the hold of the vessel. In the west coast tuna fishery, where the fish are usually frozen at sea, thawing is started on the return trip so the fish can be unloaded easily on reaching port. A brine solution is pumped through the storage wells to speed the thawing process.

Waste Characteristics. The wastes from the fishing vessel operation are made up of variable amounts of ice and large quantities of water or brine, both mingled to various degrees with fish slime, scales, blood, and oil. The proteinaceous materials predominate in most fisheries. In the menhaden fishery, oil is also present in the wastes from the fishing vessel.

The amount and compostion of waste vary greatly with season, length of time at sea, species of fish, and kind of refrigeration used (if any).

Waste Disposal. Often, wastes from the fishing vessel are pumped overboard into the harbor. In some ports, however, vessels are required to go outside the harbor to discharge wastes.

Effects of Wastes on Environment. Scales and other solids sink to the bottom; their effect on environment will be discussed under fillet plant wastes, since the latter contribute the greater share. The oily waste floats on the surface until it comes in contact with wharf pilings, commercial vessels, pleasure boats, and beaches, or is carried out to sea with the ebbing tide. Much of the proteinaceous slime and blood remains in suspension and is removed by the tide.

Trends. In the major fishery ports of the United States, primary concern is with control of wastes from the processing plants, as the quantities involved are much greater than from the vessels. It is anticipated, however, that once the plants have solved their waste disposal problems, the vessels will be required to discharge their wastes into the sewage systems.

THE FILLETING PLANT

The handling methods used in filleting plants vary, depending on species; but their contribution to liquid wastes is similar throughout the country. In many ports, the fish are sorted into size groups, deiced, and washed during unloading. Considerable quantities of water are used in these operations.

After being unloaded, the fish go either to the processing lines or, when landings are heavy, into storage pans, where they are held for 2–24 hours under a layer of fresh ice. Most species of fish are scaled en route to the processing line. This is a mechanical operation in which large quantities of water are used. The filleting and packaging operations do not contribute significantly to liquid wastes except for automatic filleting machines, which require continous streams of water flowing over the cutting knives and conveyor belts and, of course, during the cleanup operations when all equipment must be scrupulously scrubbed.

Waste Characteristics. Fillet plant wastes are similar to those from the fishing vessel—large quantities of water containing slime, blood, scales, fins, and pieces of viscera. The viscera, as such, do not enter into the wastewater from the plant. They are sent to the reduction plant for processing into fish meal or condensed fish solubles.

The scales are the largest constituent of wastewater. The scales on ocean perch amount to about 2% of the weight of the fish. A typical plant processes 8000 lb of ocean perch per hour; the flow of water in the scaler and other equipment amounts to 300 gal per minute, for an 8-hour total of 1280 lb of scales in 144,000 gal of water.

Waste Disposal. Although many ports are taking action to control disposal of wastes from fillet plants, the wastewater often is discharged, untreated, directly into the harbor. Efforts to improve industrial wastewater control are directly primarily toward connection of all plant drains to a trap or separator and thence to the city sewerage system. The separator may be a simple settling basin from which the solids are removed manually every few weeks. More elaborate systems incorporate a drag or screw conveyor to remove the settled solids, and a skimmer to remove the oil and bits of floating oily tissue such as liver. Another variation uses a rotating perforated drum; all wastewater flows through the screen, and the solids are removed from the screen by a scraper. In all systems, the solid wastes are collected and periodically hauled by truck to a reduction plant.

Effects of Waste on Environment. In some ports, the currents of water past the docks where wastes are discharged are quite rapid, and the solid materials are carried to sea and dispersed. In many others, however, almost stagnant conditions exist. The solids settle to the bottom of the harbor, where they are gradually broken down under anaerobic conditions. On decomposition, large bubbles of gases erupt from the water surface. Not only is there an odor problem, but there also is a paint problem, in that the gases tend to turn white paint to gray.

Trends. The trends are for municipal governments to enact legislation requiring filleting plants to treat their liquid wastes by separating the solids, and to discharge the wastewater into the city sewer. Although most companies recognize the need for improving the disposal of wastewater, the expense involved is large. An effective separator might cost $25,000, and this cost may be doubled when proper floor drains are installed in the plants and connected to the sewers.

It is expected that more effective waste control will come about in the future, though this will be difficult. The experience of one east coast port can be cited as an example of the type of problems experienced. All fish processing plants at this port were ordered to connect to the sewer lines within a 3-year period. At the end of this time, the industry had been unable to comply. Rather than force a complete shutdown of the fishery plants, the city granted a 1-year extension. During this period the plants were required, as a minimum, to have plans drawn up. At the expiration of the year's extension, several plants had installed separating equipment of varying design and effectiveness, but wastewater was still discharging into the harbor from some of the plants.

THE FISH MEAL PLANT

The fish meal plant receives its raw material from the industrial fishery, as menhaden or "trash" fish; from the filleting plant, as heads, frames, and viscera; and from the canning plant, as liquid from precooking retorts, viscera, and sometimes fish scrap and bones.

In general, only a small volume of wastewater comes from these plants. Those that handle industrial fish or gurry (as the fillet plant waste is termed) may hold the raw material in pen rooms, where liquid is squeezed out by the weight of the pile. Another source of wastewater, found only in a few of the oldest plants, is the press liquor that is not utilized in the reduction process.

Waste Characteristics. Composition of the waste from the pen rooms varies with the raw material but includes slime, blood, bits of viscera, and oil. The press liquor quantity and composition also vary greatly; a rough average might be: 800 lb of press liquor containing 40–80 lb of oil and 15–30 lb of protein from each ton of fish processed.

Waste Disposal. In modern plants, all "wastes," including pump water used during unloading of the vessel, enter the process: hence disposal is not a problem. In the older plants, juices from the pen room are discharged to the harbor, but the quantity is not great; however, where the press liquor is not utilized and is discharged to the harbor, the large quantity of protein and oil presents a serious problem.

Effects of Waste on Environment. In large fishing ports, waste from the fish meal plant mingles with the larger quantities of waste from the filleting plants and adds its small share to the general problem. The few plants dumping their press liquor into the harbors are in relatively sparsely populated areas, but even here the oil deposited on vessels, wharf pilings, and shore line, and the protein dispersed through the water are esthetically undesirable.

Trends. As with the filleting plants, the few fish meal plants involved are being required to stop disposing of wastes into the harbor. However, because the quantities are small, they are not being pressured as are the filleting plants.

THE FISH STICK PLANT

Wastewater from fish stick plants is confined almost entirely to the city water used during cleanup of the plant. This water carries the small quantities of fish flesh removed from saw blades, conveyor belts, and floors. In the early days of fish stick manufacture, at least one plant tried to dispose of its cooking fat via the city sewer. Complaints from the Sewer Department, which had to spend many hours reaming the solidified fat from the pipes, ended this practice.

Waste Characteristics. Protein is the prime solid material in the wastewater from fish stick plants. Small amounts of carbohydrate from the batter tanks and spilled breading also enter the waste stream.

Waste Disposal. In most plants, the wastewaters are disposed of in the city sewerage system. Some, which have been converted from filleting plants built out over the water, still use the harbor as a disposal system. The effects of this waste on the environment are negligible compared with wastes from other segments of the fishing industry. Where wastewater is being dumped into the harbor, the trend is to demand connection to the city sewer.

FISH CANNERIES

In tuna canneries, the water used in thawing the fish, the can washing solution, the can cooling water, and the water used during cleanup are the principal sources of wastewater. In other types of canneries, the fish are not ordinarily frozen; otherwise, the wastewater sources are the same as for tuna. Proteinaceous material, oil, and detergents from the can washer are the principal components of wastewater in all canneries.

Waste Disposal. The thawing, can washing, and can cooling waters from tuna canneries are generally dumped into the harbor. The cleanup water is screened to remove pieces of flesh and viscera and is then piped to the city sewers. In other types of canneries, waste disposal practices vary greatly. Salmon canneries in isolated sections of Alaska dump all wastes, including heads, tails, and viscera into the harbor. In the short 6-week operating season, great quantities accumulate. During the remainder of the year, the waste is dissipated by the tides and the carrion-eating gulls and other animals. Canneries in more populous sections dispose of their wastewater into the city sewer or harbor, or both, depending on local ordinances and convenience. The quantities generally are not large enough to constitute a prime nuisance.

The quantity of water used in thawing frozen tuna is large, and it is highly contaminated when it is dumped into the harbor. Its effect is similar to that cited for the wastes from filleting plants. Other types of canneries, too, have similar wastes, though varying in degree. As with all segments of the fishing industry, trends depend on the regulations and enforcement procedures applied by the cities and town affected.

Chapter 4

POULTRY AND EGGS

by C. R. VIGSTEDT

Poultry processing is a specialty segment of the meat industry. Although poultry plants bear a resemblance in general production sequences to meat processing plants, they have specific distinctions and problems, including the characteristics and treatment of wastewaters. Egg processing is not a major waste-producing industry, but is described in this chapter with poultry. Both industries have a tie-in with the dairy industry, especially in retail marketing. The industries are traditionally rural, but are becoming partially urbanized because of larger plants and mechanized operations located in areas where there is a readily available supply of birds. Wastewater treatment may be accomplished in complete plants on the manufacturer's premises, or by disposal to municipal facilities after appropriate pretreatment.

THE INDUSTRY

The poultry industry is a billion dollar annual business involving every state. The north central, midsouthern, eastern seaboard, and Pacific states are the major producers of turkeys, and the principal producers of chickens are the midsouthern states. The poultry industry is a growing business. The years since 1954 have seen a substantial increase in chicken slaughter and in turkey slaughter, as shown in Tables I and II. Chicken slaughter is almost exclusively restricted to broilers and fowl. A broiler is a young bird not over 12 weeks of age, while a fowl is 1 year old or over. Ducks, geese, and other poultry species produced are small in quantity

TABLE I

POULTRY PRODUCTION IN THE UNITED STATES

	Live weight, million lb		
Year	Broilers	Fowl	Turkeys
1961	5911	575	1550
1962	6000	600	1330
1963[a]	6240	600	1362

Based on U. S. Department of Agriculture statistics.
[a] Estimated from first 6 months of 1963.

69

as related to total poultry production, and the quantities have remained reasonably constant. Aggressive promotion, fast turnover, initially high return on investments, low costs, and attractive retail prices in relation to red meats have all contributed to the poultry industry's rapid growth.

The price of beef and pork, the red meats, can be correlated directly to the consumption of poultry. As beef and pork prices increase, the consumption of poultry generally rises, because poultry prices per pound have traditionally been below those of beef and pork. It is therefore of significance in the operation of a poultry processing facility to observe

TABLE II

POULTRY PRODUCTION AND CONSUMPTION IN THE UNITED STATES

	Turkeys				Broilers	
	Production		Domestic consumption			
Year	Million head	Million lb	Million lb	Lb per capita	Production, million head	Per capita consumption, lb
1955	66	818	818	5.0	—	—
1956	—	—	—	—	1344	17.3
1957	81	1034	990	5.9	—	—
1958	—	—	—	—	1660	22.0
1959	84	1123	1092	6.3	—	—
1960	—	—	—	—	1795	23.4
1961	107	1550	1386	7.5	1992	25.5
1962	92	1330	1328	7.1	1930	25.5
1963[a]	94	1362	1380	7.2	2008	26.2

Based on U. S. Department of Agriculture statistics.
[a] Estimated from first 6 months of 1963.

trends in consumer usage, federal controls, and other influences on the beef and pork industry, and to note their relationships to poultry. A further indication of the relationship of red meats to the poultry and egg industry is the per capita consumption shown in Table III for the 1952–1963 period.

The egg industry, while obviously closely associated with the poultry industry, is a separate processing and marketing business. Eggs are marketed as fresh shell eggs; frozen liquid eggs; frozen yolks, whites, or blends; and dried whole eggs, yolks, or whites. Egg production in 1962 totaled 174,367,000 cases, each case containing 360 eggs. Production has been moving from small farm flocks to large, efficient, integrated operations situated in low-cost producing areas, near major metropolitan areas. In integrated operations, all or part of the production processes, hatchery, feed mill, growers, layers, and processing are owned or controlled in the organization. Eggs are marketed as dairy products in food stores, and are used in commerical bakeries and for frozen prepared foods, confectionery products, dry mixes, salad dressing components, macaroni and noodles, and similar products.

TABLE III

EGGS, POULTRY, AND RED MEAT PER CAPITA CONSUMPTION

Year	Eggs, number per capita	Poultry, lb per capita			Red meats, lb per capita			
		Chicken	Turkey	Total	Beef and veal	Pork, without lard	Lamb and mutton	Total
1952	390	22.1	4.7	26.8	69.4	72.4	4.2	146
1953	379	21.9	4.8	26.7	87.1	63.5	4.7	155
1954	376	22.8	5.3	28.1	90.1	60.0	4.6	155
1955	371	21.3	5.0	26.3	91.4	66.8	4.6	163
1956	369	24.4	5.2	29.6	94.9	67.3	4.5	167
1957	362	25.5	5.9	31.4	93.4	61.1	4.2	159
1958	354	28.2	5.9	34.1	87.2	60.2	4.2	152
1959	352	28.9	6.3	35.2	87.1	67.6	4.8	160
1960	334	28.2	6.2	34.4	91.4	65.2	4.8	161
1961	325	30.3	7.5	37.8	93.7	62.3	5.1	161
1962	324	29.9	7.3	37.2	93.5	62.5	5.0	161
1963[a]	322	31.0	7.1	38.1	91.0	64.5	4.5	160

[a] Estimated from first 6 months of 1963.

PROCESSING PLANTS

The poultry processing plant is a highly mechanized high-production facility. Conveyor speeds of 35–50 turkeys per minute or 100 broilers per minute are common. The sequence of processing operations is: live bird receiving, killing, bleeding, plucking and eviscerating, chilling, and packing in ice or freezing for shipment. Inventories of live birds are kept low by scheduling incoming truck shipments in a manner to reduce holding time and inventory level. It is good practice to receive and process poultry on the same day, without hold-over of live birds. Storage of dressed ice-packed or frozen poultry is minimal also, with a significant reduction of holding inventory. Figure 1 shows the layout of a typical processing plant.

The U. S. Department of Agriculture has reported that, as of 1963, 892 poultry plants were operating under the Poultry Products Inspection Act, as follows:

Eviscerating plants	429
Further processing, such as canning, cooking, boning, and preparation of pies, dinners, or turkey rolls	298
Packaging or cutting up poultry not eviscerated at the plant	73
Eviscerating and canning	87
New York dressing only, not eviscerated	5

In addition, the Department reported that approximately 15%, or 1 billion lb of poultry, is processed annually under State or county inspections for intrastate consumption. The approximately 100 plants in this category are mostly producer-owned and are used solely for dressing of the producers' own poultry. Of the 429 inspected poultry plants, approximately 90 are exclusively for turkey processing and approximately 50 are for a combination of turkey and other poultry products.

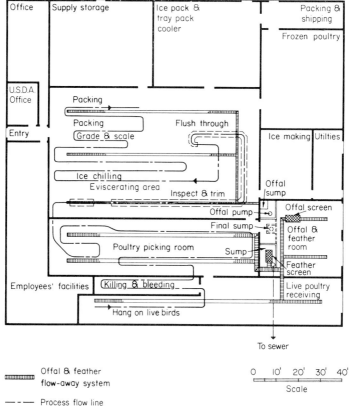

Fig. 1. Floor plan of a typical poultry processing plant.

The egg processing plant cannot be typified because any or all egg processing operations may be found in any location. The fresh shell egg is a complete food and package in itself. Processing consists of candling for blood spots and other inside defects, examination of the shell for defects, washing, grading, and cartoning. Hand methods are in general use; however, where quantity and quality permit, bulk candlers, sizers, and automatic cartoners are being installed. The per capita consumption of shell eggs has declined from 371 in 1955 to 324 in 1962.

The Department of Agriculture listed 326 shell egg plants under inspection and grading programs as of 1963. Many more operate outside Department control. The number of both plants and farm flocks is decreasing; conversely, the size of processing plants and laying flocks is increasing. As the industry becomes integrated, a smaller number of producers and processors will capture a larger share of the market. This condition has already developed in California, where 4 firms do a substantial portion of the business. Firms that are major factors in the shell egg business may be classified into 4 groups: independents, cooperatives, feed companies, and retail food chains. These groups are not restricted geographically. The extent of their activities overlaps and varies considerably.

Egg breaking operations consist of separating the yolks from the whites, which are then either frozen separately or blended to a customer's specifications and frozen. The breaking of eggs is, in part, a salvage operation of the shell egg business where cracked shells or otherwise substandard conditions are encountered. Further processing of eggs or yolks and whites through spray drying is common. These dried egg products are used by bakeries, home cake or bake mixes, and similar applications.

WASTE CHARACTERISTICS

Wastes are produced in a poultry processing plant from live poultry holding, killing, eviscerating and defeathering, and scalding and chilling. Contributions to waste flow additionally result from washup operations.

Blood Wastes. The major source of pollution in poultry processing is generally the waste blood, which contains feathers, dirt, and some manure. The majority of poultry processors attempt to recover free-draining blood. For good blood recovery, an area must be restricted to the collection of the blood, allowing for 2 minutes drainage time from the kill station. Even with the best of recovery practices, some blood is introduced into the plant sewer system. In addition, cleanup operations in the kill and bleed area send congealed blood and other matter to the plant sewers.

Approximately 6% of the poultry body weight is blood, 4% drainable in the bleeding area, leaving about 2% by weight in the bird. Tests have shown that chickens contain sufficient blood to equal a 5-day BOD of about 17.5 lb per 1000 chickens processed. In a good poultry plant operation, where blood wastes are carefully salvaged in the killing area, approximately 3–5 lb BOD per 1000 chickens may be sent to the plant wastes collectively from all operations.

Defeathering Wastes. In the customary processing progression, the next wastes result from defeathering operations. These wastewaters consist mainly of the continuous scalder overflow, continuous water spray flow from the defeathering machines, and final cleanup operations from dumping of scalder water and washdown of floors and equipment. Where the sudden release of water from a tank or vat might cause sewer overflow, it is good practice to provide a restricted drain opening.

Prior to entry into the defeathering machine, the bird is immersed in a scalder to relax feather follicles for easier feather removal. The scalder, operating on a continuous feed of approximately 1 quart of water per bird, therefore provides a steady flow to the plant sewer system. This waste is high in pollutional strength and contains feathers, some blood, and dirt.

Defeathering machines are equipped with beaters (rubber fingers) that force the feathers from the skin. Simultaneously with the beating, warm water is applied to lubricate the rubber fingers, to prevent epidermis removal, and to carry or "flow away" the feathers from the machine area. The continuous flow of water used in the defeathering machines is high in volume but relatively low in pollutional strength.

Flow-away System. The flow-away system is one in which head, feet, blood, trimmings, and other process wastes are flushed in a flume system to a central screening point. The screened materials are removed into containers or trucks and some of the liquid is reused through the flume system. Excess liquid or overflow is sent to the sewers. Only the defeathering area and the eviscerating area are equipped with flow-away systems; these are separate systems. Plants under Federal inspection generally use the flow-away system, which requires more water and has greater outflow than other types of feather and offal removal systems or methods.

Total Water Usage. The average total water usage for broiler, fowl, and junior turkey production is 6.25 gal per bird. The average usage for turkey production is 20 gal per bird. Both of these figures are based on production in Department of Agriculture inspected plants.

Waste Composition. The total waste composition that may be expected from an inspected plant on a weight basis is generally within the following limits:

	Wastewater composition, lb per 1000 birds
Total solids	20–27
Suspended solids	12–16
Settleable solids	8–11
Grease	1–2
5-Day BOD	22–31

Between 70 and 75% of the wastes are discharged during production hours.

Solid Wastes. Following defeathering, the eviscerating and cutting operations produce solid wastes consisting of feet, heads, inedible viscera, crops and windpipes, lungs, grit, sand, gravel, trimmings, grease, and blood. Lungs are generally removed by suction to a storage tank and then released to a flow-away system. In a hand removal operation, the lungs are discarded at the viscera trough with the remainder of the wastes.

WASTE DISPOSAL

The location of the poultry processing plant dictates the extent and method of waste treatment. In the search for a new plant site, the economics of waste disposal are an important factor. In locations where a municipal treatment plant is available, the plant pretreatment provisions depend on the municipal plant's available extra capacity and efficiency. In rural locations the treatment depends upon the State or Federal regulations covering the receiving stream or river.

PRETREATMENT

Regardless of the treatment system, pretreatment at the plant is necessary. The first pretreatment stage is the use of screens to remove the larger materials from the defeathering and eviscerating flow-away systems.

The reuse of water from the defeathering and eviscerating flow-away systems is controlled by U. S. Department of Agriculture regulations. These regulations allow the reuse of defeathering and eviscerating flow-away water for the removal of feathers, but flow-away water from either system may not be reused for eviscerating flow-away. Therefore, these two wastes are pretreated separately.

The feather flow-away wastes, which are high in water content, are passed over a screen of 20–50 mesh. This is generally a rotary or a vibrating screen from which the feathers are discharged directly to a container or into a conveyor. Water from this screening is collected in a sump; some is recirculated by pump and reintroduced into the flow-away flumes of the defeathering operations.

The offal flow-away wastes from the eviscerating area are discharged into a collection tank and are pumped over a rotary or vibrating screen of 20–50 mesh. The screened water is discharged into the feather water collection sump. Screened offal material is discharged to a bin or container for further disposal.

Primary Material Disposal. Feathers and offal, in plants not processing these materials further, are commonly removed by a truck trailer, in which the feathers and eviscerating wastes are separately compartmented. Where permitted, these materials may then be buried or incinerated. More often, poultry plants not further processing these primary waste materials sell the separated materials to rendering companies for further processing to feather meal, cracklings for animal feeds, and other by-products. Innovations and improvements in rendering have resulted in a market for primary waste materials in many locations.

Grease Removal. In addition to the screening of feathers and offal, the treatment of wastes should include grease removal. Wastes from all poultry plants contain grease that may be removed by skimming in a primary settling basin, by a grease trap, or by air flotation. The quantity of grease, the intended use of the recovered material, and the primary treatment facilities available dictate the removal method to be used. Grease content is 1–2 lb per 1000 birds.

After pretreatment, further processing of poultry plant wastes depends upon the availability of municipal facilities and the degree of pretreatment they require prior to discharge.

Analyses of poultry plant wastes were presented by Bolton (*1*) in 1958, and a summary of the average values is given in Table IV. Plants processing fowl (older chickens) generally produce the wastes of highest pollutional strength.

Egg processing plants have no special or unusual wastes because whole eggs, whites, or yolks introduced to sewers would be a loss of revenue. The only waste produced is egg shells, which are handled as common

TABLE IV
CHICKEN PROCESSING WASTE CHARACTERISTICS

Plant	Flow, gal per 1000 chickens			BOD, lb per 1000 chickens			Suspended solids, lb per 1000 chickens		
	Processing	Cleanup	Total	Processing	Cleanup	Total	Processing	Cleanup	Total
A	1,600	1,000	2,600	12.6	10.2	22.8	7.2	5.0	12.2
B	7,500	5,000	12,500	16.3	11.1	27.4	9.7	3.8	13.5
C	6,000	1,800	7,800	19.3	3.9	23.2	9.4	2.8	12.2
D	2,600	1,100	3,700	18.4	6.4	24.8	9.4	2.3	11.6
E	3,900	1,300	5,200	37.2	3.2	40.4	15.7	2.1	17.8

From Reference (1).

trash. Shells are accumulated in drums or directly in trucks and hauled to dumps.

COMPLETE TREATMENT OF POULTRY PROCESS WASTES

Methods available to the poultry processor for the complete treatment of his wastes are trickling filter, activated sludge, extended aeration, lagooning, land irrigation, sand filtration, and chemical treatment.

Settling Tanks. In all treatment systems, the floatable and sinkable materials must be separated in sedimentation tanks. The sludge requires additional handling by drying, lagooning, digestion, or burial. For each plant design, settling rates and sludge volumes are determined by laboratory tests. Some tests have indicated that 17–28% BOD removal and 30–65% suspended solids removal can be expected from settling. Although these values are wide, the range is important because extremes may be encountered.

Trickling Filters. Trickling filter systems in general, because of the high construction cost and operational requirements, are not often used where the processing plant is treating its own sewage. Trickling filter plant design for poultry wastes should not materially differ from standard practices for other biological wastes. The trickling filter plant should remove 75–95% of the BOD and 90–95% of the suspended solids. Where required, sand filtration may be used to provide a more highly purified effluent. At some plants, chlorination of the effluent is necessary.

Activated Sludge. The conditions outlined in regard to the trickling filter plant apply also to the activated sludge process. The construction costs of an activated sludge plant to obtain the same results as a trickling filter process are generally higher.

The extended aeration process is a modification of activated sludge and utilizes a 24-hour aeration or longer in the presence of activated sludge, followed by settling of the mixture. Part of the liquids discharged from the settled sludge tank are returned to the aerator. Lagooning may be required for additional purification of effluent before discharge into the natural waterway. The stream pollution regulations govern this action.

Lagoons. Lagoons or ponds are the most common type of waste treatment for poultry wastes. The lagoons generally require large areas of land and should be isolated from populated regions. Five-day BOD loadings vary from 20 to 150 lb per acre per day, depending upon State regulations. Generally, BOD loadings permitted in the northern states are lower than in the South. In northern areas where lagoons without heat are utilized, a retention of 3–4 months may be required during the winter because bacterial activity is limited by the cold. BOD loading is the key to sizing, but depth of liquid is also an important factor: 3 ft is considered normal, at less than 2 ft growth tends to be retarded, and at more than 4 ft the area tends to be overloaded. When properly operated, lagoons without aeration or agitation can be expected to provide 70–95% BOD reduction. Normal precautions must be taken to prevent undesirable odors and insect breeding.

Although lagooning is common, there is much still to be learned about it. Many states are running tests on mechanical agitation, heating of the aerobic ponds, and other experimental practices; and some industries, in connection with State authorities, are testing other types of modified lagooning designs to provide design data for future installations.

Irrigation and Crop Fertilization. The use of effluent for irrigation and crop fertilization has been tried, but the results of these trials have not been reported. There is not sufficient data for accurate design, but one approximation is the requirement of 1 acre of land for each 1000 birds slaughtered per week.

Sand Filtration. Sand filtration has been attempted, but tests have indicated that the filters were ineffective due to clogging by feathers and other solids.

Municipal Sewage Treatment. It is common practice in the treatment of poultry wastes for the producer to discharge his wastewaters to municipal treatment facilities. Industrial development committees from small rural towns in good livestock areas often attempt to attract poultry processors because jobs and revenue can be obtained from the plant. However, the town sewage treatment facilities are frequently found to be inadequate in capacity. The ability of the municipality to expand in time to meet the plant requirements then becomes a prime factor in site selection. The most common municipal facilities include either trickling filters or activated sludge units, and the handling of poultry wastes does not create any unusual problems.

INDUSTRY TRENDS

There is a continuation of breeding and nutrition research by poultry producers to develop poultry that will grow to a desired size consuming a minimum amount of feed. The trend to complete integration of hatcheries, feeds, growing, processing, and sales into one company or under one management is motivated for better control of raw materials and increased profits.

General trends in poultry manufacturing operations include reduction of inventory levels, reduction in total processing time, increase in hourly slaughter rate, decrease in man-hours per 1000 birds processed, and better use of feather and viscera by-products. Federal and State requirements have consistently increased the use of water per bird.

Although most poultry processing plants are geared to the production of whole birds, many manufacturers are turning to the addition of other operations. These operations, in·part, have been caused through U. S. Department of Agriculture regulations that prohibit the sale of birds with unwholesome parts, for example, broken bones, bruises, or skin discolorations, in the whole-bird market. Thus the dissection of birds into various parts, such as breasts, wings, and legs, has led to packaging of parts, manufacturing of parts into turkey rolls, and production of soup stocks and similar goods. Wastes from these operations are usually low in BOD and in treatment requirements.

Among poultry processors and Federal and State agencies, there is general alarm at the increase in water consumption. Reuse of process water without contamination of product is currently under heavy study. With outflows of 1,000,000 gal per day of treatable wastes, which is common for a poultry processor but which equals the total flow for a municipality of moderate size, the incentive for reduction is obvious. However, even with reduction in quantity of wastewater, the pollutional load remains constant per bird produced. The dilutional effect of plant wastes will undoubtedly be somewhat lessened in the future, increasing the treatment problem through the enforcement of water conservation.

REFERENCE

1. Bolton, J. M., *Purdue Univ. Proc. Ind. Waste Conf.* **13**, 109–125 (1958).

Chapter 5

DAIRY PRODUCTS

by CLIFFORD W. WATSON, JR.

The processing and manufacturing of dairy products is perhaps the most widespread of all industries in the United States. More than 20 million cows produce over 50 billion quarts of milk yearly. It is processed into fluid products such as homogenized pasteurized milk for immediate consumption or is manufactured into nonfat dry milk powder, cheese, and other less perishable products that may be stored. These manufactured products may later be used by the dairy industry or be shipped to the baking, candy, and other industries for use as an ingredient of their products. Wastes from the dairy industry resemble other food wastes, but have particular problems because of their susceptibility to biological attack.

THE DAIRY INDUSTRIES

Plants handling milk are classified as receiving, bottling, condensing, dry milk manufacturing, ice cream manufacturing, cheese making, and butter making. Other types of milk processing operations are of lesser importance.

Receiving. Milk is delivered from the farm to the receiving station in 10-gal cans. Upon receipt it is inspected and dumped from the cans into a weigh tank. The empty cans are rinsed, washed, sterilized, and returned. The weighed milk is pumped through a cooler to storage tanks where it is held for transport to a processing plant.

On many farms milk from the cows is placed directly into a refrigerated holding tank where it is cooled and held for transport to the processing plant.

Bottling. Raw milk received at the plant in 10-gal cans or tank trucks is cooled and pumped to storage tanks. Processing includes clarifying, pasteurizing, homogenizing, and filling into glass bottles, cardboard containers, metal cans, or polyethylene-lined corrugated cardboard containers. Some milk is separated and the resultant skim milk and cream are pasteurized and processed into such products as light cream, sour cream, half and half, fortified skim milk, chocolate drink, buttermilk, and, in some plants, cottage cheese. These are packaged in glass, metal, or card-board containers.

Condensing. Milk is received at the plant in 10-gal cans or tank trucks. Upon receipt it is cooled and pumped to storage tanks. Unsweetened evaporated milk is produced from whole milk. The milk is preheated, then evaporated under vacuum. The concentrated milk is homogenized by pumping it through a closely set valve that breaks up fat globules, thus keeping them in suspension. The product is filled into cans that are sealed and sterilized, packed in cardboard shipping containers, and stored at room temperature. Sweetened condensed milk is produced in a similar manner with sugar added. Condensed nonfat milk, whey, and buttermilk are similarly processed but are not homogenized.

Dry Milk Manufacturing. Milk received at the manufacturing plant is cooled and pumped to storage to await further processing. The whole milk is then preheated to about 90°F and centrifuged to separate the cream from the nonfat portion of the milk. The cream is pasteurized and stored for processing into such products as ice cream mix, or shipped to another processing plant. The nonfat portion is further heated and evap-orated under vacuum to a controlled percentage of solids. The concen-trated nonfat milk is then dried by either the roller process or the spray process.

Roller process powder is made by use of double drum driers, in which the concentrate is dried on rotating drums heated by steam. Con-centrate to be spray dried is preheated and pumped at high pressure through a small orifice into the drying chamber. Heated air flows into the chamber around the orifice and evaporates the moisture. Dried powder falls to the bottom of the chamber while vapor and hot air are removed through filters to the atmosphere. The dried powder produced by either process is collected, bagged, and stored to await shipment.

Ice Cream Manufacture. Ice cream mixes are made to formula by blending cream, condensed nonfat milk solids, liquid sugar, and flavor-ing, in varying quantities depending on the makeup of the final product. The prepared mix is pasteurized, homogenized, cooled, and pumped to freezers where the temperature is reduced to about 20°F. The frozen ice cream is packaged and stored in a −40°F room until hardened and ready for shipment.

Cheese Making. Whole milk cheeses such as cheddar are made from milk as received; whole milk is separated for production of nonfat milk cheese or cream cheese. The milk, which may be pasteurized, is run into vats. The process consists of souring and coagulating the milk by the addition of a starter and rennet, the starter being a lactic acid-producing bacterial culture, which varies with the cheese to be produced. The mixture is allowed to ripen at a controlled temperature until the proper acidity has developed. The curd is then cut with knives, and entrained whey is allowed to drain. The prepared curd is pressed to remove excess whey, and the pressed blocks of cheese are stored under controlled temperature and humidity for flavor development and further ripening. It is then packaged and placed in cold storage to await shipment. Processed cheese is made by grinding and melting the ripened cheese. It is heated to pasteurization temperature to halt the ripening process, and is packed while still hot.

Butter Making. Cream to be made into butter is pasteurized and may be ripened with a selected acid and a bacterial culture in preparation for churning. Churning at a temperature of 45–55°F produces butter granules from the butterfat in the cream. At the proper time buttermilk is drained from the churn, and the butter is washed, standardized for moisture and salt, and worked until it agglomerates into one mass. It is then removed from the churn and packaged for distribution.

The approximate compositions of processed and manufactured dairy products are shown in Table I. The wastes from milk plants consist of varying dilutions of these products.

SOURCES OF WASTE

Wastewaters from dairy plants fall into three categories: industrial waste, domestic waste, and spent uncontaminated waters. The last group includes water used in the refrigeration system for condensing, and water used for precooling various pasteurized products. Wastes in this category contain no milk solids. Industrial wastes from dairy plants consist of various dilutions of milk that enter the drainage system. These may be classified according to their source as follows:

Rinsewater and washwater from cans, tank trucks, equipment, product pipelines, and floors

Spillage, freeze-on, overflow, and leakage caused by improperly maintained equipment and poor operating practices

Entrainment from evaporators

By-products such as buttermilk, whey, and in some cases skim milk that cannot be utilized

Spoiled or damaged raw or manufactured products or by-products that cannot be salvaged for other uses

TABLE I

TYPICAL COMPOSITION OF COMMON DAIRY PRODUCTS

Dairy product	Butterfat	Protein	Milk sugar (lactose)	Added sugar	Ash	Acidity, as lactic	Total solids	Organic solids	BOD
Whole milk	3.9	3.2	5.1	0	0.7	—	12.9	12.2	10.3
Evaporated milk	7.9	6.7	10.1	0	1.4	—	26.1	24.7	20.8
Separated milk	0.1	3.3	5.3	0	0.8	—	9.5	8.7	7.2
Nonfat dry milk solids	0.9	36.9	50.5	0	8.1	—	96.4	88.3	73.7
Sweetened condensed separated milk	0.3	10.4	16.8	40	2.5	—	70.0	67.5	50.2
Buttermilk[a]	0.5	3.4	4.3	0	0.7	0.6	9.5	8.8	7.2
Whey[b]	0.3	0.9	4.9	0	0.6	0.2	6.9	6.3	3.5
Cheddar cheese	35.5	26.6	1.5	0	3.5	—	67.1	63.6	60.0
Cream	40.0	2.2	3.0	0	0.4	—	45.6	45.2	39.9
Ice cream mix	12.0	3.9	5.9	15	0.8	—	37.6	36.8	29.2

All values are given as percentages.
[a] Ripened cream buttermilk.
[b] American cheese whey.

The volume of industrial waste discharged by a dairy plant depends mainly on the availability of water and the care exercised by management in water conservation. A dry floor plant, using water conservation and waste saving practices, is the preferred method of operation now used in most modern plants. By employing such procedures, savings can be realized in the initial cost of water and in reduced cost of disposing of a smaller volume of waste.

Clear Water Segregation. Much of the water used in a milk plant remains uncontaminated after use; for example, condensing water and ammonia compressor jacket water from the refrigeration system, and cooling water from milk coolers, vat pasteurizers, and air-conditioning systems. To reduce volumetric load on the treatment system, these waters should be collected in a separate sewer and discharged directly to the receiving stream or storm sewer. Often this water may be reused in the plant, sometimes saving steam when used in another process requiring hot water.

Waste Prevention. Loss from leakage can be prevented by care in assembly of equipment, and by proper maintenance. When a leak occurs during an operation, a container should be available to catch the leaking material, preventing it from reaching the sewer. A leak at the rate of 1 drop per second will lose 2 quarts of product during a 10-hour operation, which shows the seriousness of leakage.

Overflow may occur where product flows into an open or vented piece of equipment. It can be prevented by the use of float operated or electronic level controls that shut off the flow or sound an alarm indicating that the vessel is reaching the full point.

Spillage is generally the result of careless handling or improper design or layout of equipment. This loss occurs primarily where product is dumped from one vessel into another as at a weigh can or other vat. Proper care in the dumping process eliminates most of these losses.

Freeze-on may occur wherever product is in contact with a refrigerated surface, as in a cooler or an ice cream freezer. Cans of milk trucked unprotected from the farm may also partially freeze in the winter. Proper controls or the use of ice water prevent freeze-on at coolers, and transport of cans in insulated vans prevents freezing.

Willful waste includes products such as whey, buttermilk, and separated nonfat milk that often have little or no commercial value and are frequently discarded. Although in the past this practice was commonplace, such high BOD products should never be allowed to enter the plant sewer system.

Residual waste is found in all plants. It consists of milk and milk products that cling to the surface of equipment or pipelines after they have been drained. For example, a can after being dumped may contain a residual of 5–6 oz of milk. A two-position drip saver on the can washer, with an atomizing rinse, removes half of this residual milk, thus reducing the pollutional load of can washwaters. Residual product may be removed from equipment and pipelines by draining after standing for a period of time, then flushing with water and collecting the first of the rinsewater for salvage. Such residual product can be disposed of by pasteurizing and returning to the farm for stock feed.

If care is not exercised in the operation of a vacuum pan, milk solids may become entrained in the vapor and carried over into the condenser water. This may be corrected by level controls and entrainment separators. Installation of entrainment separators at the Hershey Chocolate Company reduced the BOD of condenser water from a range of 30 to 90 mg/liter to 2, thus making a substantial reduction in pollution as well as a saving in product.

Pollutional Properties. Dairy wastes are composed almost wholly of organic matter, hence are high in oxygen demand. Milk is nature's most perfect food, and is a balanced food for bacteria and other microscopic organisms as well as for man. Dairy wastes in a stream are therefore consumed at a very rapid rate, causing depletion of oxygen and in some cases exhaustion resulting in evidence of serious pollution.

Milk wastes also contain nitrogen and phosphorus, which are excellent plant nutrients. In disposal by irrigation, this property has value in maintenance of a ground cover crop; however, in a stream the effect is detrimental. Algae and other aquatic plants are caused to grow profusely and, upon dying, the dead plants add taste and odor to the water. These are often not removed by water treatment processes preparing water for domestic use.

TREATMENT OF DAIRY WASTES

Settleable solids are not an important consideration in pollution by dairy wastes since all organic material is in a colloidal or dissolved state. Little or no BOD reduction can be effected by plain sedimentation. Detention in a primary settling tank causes the rapid conversion of lactose to lactic acid, which precipitates the casein. The acid effluent then becomes difficult to treat in the secondary process, and the casein will not digest due to the high acidity that has bactericidal qualities.

Although primary sedimentation is of little value in the treatment of dairy wastes, a grit removal chamber is essential. Sand and other gritty material washed from tank trucks can damage pumps in the treatment plant and interfere with the treatment processes.

Another important element in dairy waste treatment is equalization of flow. Volume and BOD of the waste vary greatly over a 24-hour period. To apply the waste uniformly to the treatment system, a balancing tank is necessary. This tank should be of sufficient capacity to hold surges while the waste is pumped out at a uniform rate. It is essential that wastes in this tank not become septic, so air is introduced through diffusers or other means to keep the raw wastes aerobic.

The treatment systems most effective for dairy wastes provide sufficient oxygen to biochemically oxidize the organic constituents. Treatment systems used extensively today are aeration or modified activated sludge, trickling filters, and irrigation. Lagooning has also met with some success.

Aeration. The heart of aeration treatment is the aeration tank. Aerobic microorganisms are fed organic material in the fresh waste and are supplied with oxygen taken from air, thus providing suitable environment and conditions for their growth and reproduction. The diffused air produces constant agitation that prevents sludge from settling and brings floc particles into intimate contact with the fresh wastes entering the tank.

Floc circulating in the aeration tank has a tendency to form clumps. This increases resistance to the transfer of oxygen into individual cells. The clumping may reach a point where the center of the floc particle is not able to obtain sufficient oxygen and becomes anaerobic. It is necessary, therefore, to maintain a high degree of agitation in the tank to keep the individual cells dispersed. This also exposes maximum cell surface and thus facilitates rapid oxygen utilization. Jet aerators, by shearing action, tend to break up floc particles and increase oxygen absorption. Figure 1 is a flow diagram of a typical aeration treatment plant in which sludge formed is recirculated to the aeration tank where it is continually oxidized and is eventually almost all burned up.

Treatment by oxidation has two distinct phases. The assimilation phase occurs as fresh milk wastes enter the aeration tank. During this phase the bacteria rapidly consume organic matter and require oxygen supplied at a high rate for a short time. In the second or endogenous phase, the bacteria receive no new food but digest the food ingested during assimilation. This requires considerably less oxygen over a longer period of time. Since autodigestion takes place continuously even during the assimilation phase, oxygen for it must be supplied during the full time of treatment.

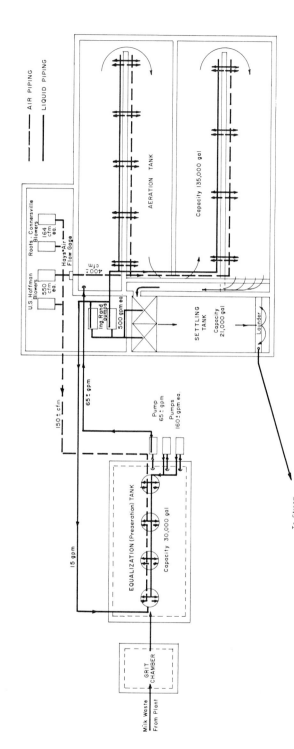

Fig. 1. Dairy waste treatment plant using aeration.

Research in the treatment of dairy wastes by oxidation has produced certain facts. Each pound (dry weight) of organic matter in dairy waste requires about 1.2 lb of oxygen for complete oxidation. Of the total solids present in nonfat dry milk, about 83.3% is organic; thus a unit weight of nonfat dry milk solids requires approximately a unit weight of oxygen. Of the oxygen required for complete oxidation, 37.5% or 0.45 lb/lb of organic matter is required during the assimilation phase. About 0.52 lb of new cell material (sludge) is formed from each pound of organic material added during the assimilation phase.

Endogenous respiration requires 62.5% of the required oxygen or 0.75 lb for each 0.52 lb of sludge formed. This is equal to 1.44 lb of oxygen/lb of ash-free sludge. During endogenous respiration at 90°F, sludge consumes itself at approximately 1% per hour; therefore, 0.0144 lb of oxygen per hour is required per pound of sludge in the aeration tank. Lower temperatures tend to slow this action.

The oxygen demand discussed above is COD; for dairy wastes this is approximately equal to the ultimate BOD. The 5-day BOD/COD ratio for dairy wastes is about 0.68.

Whey. The treatment of whey in aerobic systems has posed a problem. For biological growth a definite ratio of carbon to nitrogen must be maintained. Milk and milk wastes offer this balanced diet with a content of 51% lactose and 37% casein and albumin proteins. Whey contains only 13% protein which is insufficient for conversion to new cells. Consequently, surplus lactose remains in solution and is discharged untreated to the stream.

To treat whey aerobically, nitrogen supplement must be added. Pilot plant studies have shown that 22 lb of agricultural ammonium sulfate, an inexpensive nitrogen chemical, added to the aeration tank per 1000 lb of whey supplies the nitrogen necessary for a suitable protein-carbohydrate balance. Correction of pH may also be required, usually by addition of lime.

Aeration Problems. Foaming is the result of excess air applied during the endogenous phase, where the demand is only 10% of the assimilation phase. Reduction of the air supply approximately 3 hours after fresh waste addition has stopped may correct this condition.

Bulking may be caused by overloading because of insufficient time to complete the oxidation or insufficient air to take care of the excess organic material. An effective in-plant waste prevention program may overcome this problem.

An excess ratio of carbohydrate to protein may occur in wastes containing whey or in wastes from ice cream manufacture due to the added sugar. This becomes evident as a light sludge that is difficult to settle. Nitrogen supplement, as in the treatment of whey, helps correct this problem.

Trickling Filters. The trickling filter was one of the first methods attempted for the treatment of dairy wastes. Early experience indicated that strong dairy wastes applied to standard rate filters caused ponding, thus making the filter inoperative. Dilution was necessary, either by the addition of cooling and other clear waters, or by use of the high rate filter with recirculation of effluent from the secondary clarifier to the plant influent. A further modification of the high rate filter is the 2-stage unit.

Trebler developed a high rate 2-stage trickling filter in which the primary and secondary clarifiers are contained in a single circular tank divided with a transverse plate. The 2-stage filter consists of two concentric beds, the inner primary filter fed by two arms on the rotating distributor, and the outer secondary filter fed by two other arms on the same rotary distributor. Figure 2 shows a typical flow diagram for a 2-stage recirculating filter installation of this type.

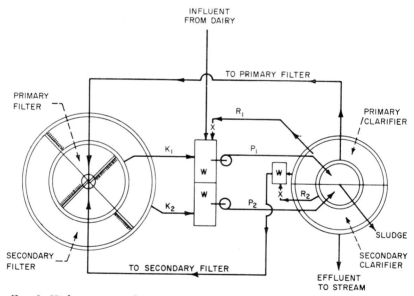

Fig. 2. High rate recirculating trickling filter. Symbols: K_1, primary filter effluent; K_2, secondary filter effluent; P_1, primary constant-volume pump discharge; P_2, secondary constant-volume pump discharge; R_1, primary recirculation effluent; R_2, secondary recirculation effluent; W, wet well; ×, float-controlled valve.

Problems have arisen with trickling filter treatment, usually because the lactose rapidly converts to lactic acid and reduces the pH of the holding or primary tank. This causes the casein to precipitate and also inhibits biological activity. Low activity, together with casein precipitation, causes filters to clog and does not permit development of the natural biological film. The results are odor and poor effluent from the treatment system. Aeration of the holding tank may improve operation of the filter, eliminating ponding and odors, and improve over-all treatment plant efficiency. It has been found that air applied at 0.25–0.5 cu ft/lb of BOD in the raw waste keeps the waste in a fresh condition and prevents lactic acid formation.

Irrigation. Where suitable land is available, irrigation as a means for disposal of milk wastes has been found feasible and is often the most economical and least troublesome method of treatment. Transpiration, evaporation, and, to a small degree, percolation take off the water. The organic constituents are consumed by bacteria naturally present in the earth, which convert them to carbon dioxide, water, and other products such as nitrates.

Two methods of irrigation are used, the spray type and the ridge and furrow type. Spray irrigation utilizes either a portable or a fixed piping system equipped with spray nozzles spaced along the pipe. The waste is generally collected in a sump from which it is pumped to the irrigation area. Ridge and furrow irrigation consists of a system of shallow ditches fed through gates from a header ditch in such a manner as to provide alternate flooding and rest periods.

Many factors must be taken into consideration in the design of an irrigation system of waste disposal. Most important are slope of ground (less than 6%), type of soil (clay, loam, sand, etc.), and type of cover crop. Other limiting factors include the rainfall, degree of cloudiness, and temperature. In spray irrigation, hydraulic loading and cation loading are the principal factors, and BOD is far less important than in biological treatment systems.

The area required for irrigation disposal depends on the volume of waste. Irrigation is a consumptive use of water, as about two-thirds of the water applied is lost through evaporation and transpiration. Organic material in the waste must also be considered. It is consumed by bacteria, mostly of the aerobic type and requiring oxygen. It is therefore necessary to provide a period of rest to allow the soil to take in air. As the liquid percolates through the soil it draws in air, making oxygen available for the aerobic process. If application of waste to the soil is continuous the available oxygen is consumed, causing anaerobiosis and accompanying malodors. To prevent this condition, irrigation piping should be moved every day or every second day. Ditches in ridge and furrow systems should be blocked off to give the area a period of rest at similar intervals of time.

Cation loading, particularly sodium, is significant in waste disposal by irrigation. Sodium occurs in milk, cleaning solutions, zeolite regeneration water, and cheese and butter plant wastes. The physical properties of soils are greatly influenced by the degree of saturation of clay and organic matter with sodium, and as the structure deteriorates, the soil becomes tight or impermeable to water and air. More than 65% sodium on a cation equivalent basis is generally unsatisfactory for disposal by irrigation. When high sodium exists, application of lime, calcium chloride, or gypsum is the generally recognized practice. Good drainage aids in the flushing out of concentrated salt solutions.

A hardy cover crop is important in an irrigation system. Reed canary grass has been found well suited to most conditions. Broome and Kentucky are the next best cover crops, although they generally will not endure ice cover from winter operation.

The permissible loading of irrigation systems is dependent on the type of soil, drainage, and cover crop. Experience with dairy wastes indicates variation in loading from 4000 to 30,000 gal per acre per day, and BOD strength from 25 to 2500 lb per acre per day. Studies of good operating irrigation systems indicate maximum detention in the holding tank for summertime operation should be from 1 to 2 hours. The tank should be flushed frequently to prevent scum accumulations that cause odors. A ¼ inch screen should be placed at the wet well to catch solids that may clog sprinkler heads. The screen should be cleaned daily.

Domestic wastes should be excluded from irrigation systems because the solid matter may clog sprays and, secondly, where sprayed acreage is used for the grazing of domestic animals there is the possibility of spreading pathogenic organisms.

Lagooning. Stabilization lagoons are used extensively for treatment of domestic wastes, and some of these installations have successfully treated combinations of domestic and dairy wastes. Since 1955, lagoons have been used to treat dairy wastes alone. Aerobic lagoons or oxidation ponds are designed to have a large surface area per unit volume. Oxygen is introduced into the liquid by natural or mechanical aeration and by photosynthesis. BOD loading is important and must be controlled so the oxygen demand of waste decomposition does not exceed the ability of the reoxygenation processes to supply the necessary oxygen. The State

TABLE II

MISSOURI STATE STANDARDS FOR LAGOONS

Type of plant	Population equivalent per 1000 lb milk received	Lagoon loading, pop. equiv. per acre of water surface	BOD, lb per acre of water surface
Cheese plant[a]	16	400	64
Receiving station[b]	4	300	48
Creamery[b]	6	400	64
General dairy[a, b]	10	350	56

[a] Whey excluded.
[b] Good waste prevention practiced.

of Missouri has set up standards for lagoons for the treatment of dairy wastes; these are shown in Table II.

Other Treatment Systems. Many methods have been attempted in the quest to find a less costly system for dairy waste treatment, but except for aerobic biological systems all have failed to provide satisfactory treatment. Septic tanks with relatively long detention times were used for many years by smaller plants but rarely with success. They have also been used as primary treatment before stone or sand filters. Conversion of lactose to lactic acid occurs rapidly, causing the precipitation of casein. The acid condition inhibits proteolysis, so the accumulated sludge does not digest. It is ultimately carried out with the effluent, causing odorous sludge banks in stream bottoms. Where the septic tank is used with filters, the escaping solids rapidly clog the pores and cause filters to fail and to create obnoxious odors. The acid septic tank effluent also inhibits the biological growths necessary for efficient operation. For these several reasons septic tanks are not suitable for the treatment of dairy wastes.

Chemical precipitation has been used as a means of dairy waste treatment. Lime has been used to raise the pH, and ferrous sulfate or other coagulating chemicals to cause a precipitate. This precipitate, however, removes only material in colloidal suspension and does not alter the composition of the dissolved solids. The cost of chemicals, the cost of labor to handle the chemicals, and the sludge make this process unattractive. Under the best conditions BOD reductions of only 40–50% are realized.

There is a tendency in the dairy industry to consolidate smaller inefficient operations into larger and more automated operations. Of necessity, receiving and manufacturing operations are located in the country areas and today even processing operations are moving out nearer the supply of milk in a location central to the area of distribution. Treatment for the wastes from these larger plants is a necessity. The trend in treatment is toward the aeration-type system that will provide a high degree of BOD removal, thus eliminating the problem of stream pollution.

REFERENCES

1. Dairy Industry Committee, "Waste Prevention in the Dairy Industry; Report of the Waste Task Committee," 1950.
2. Lawton, G. W., Englebert, L. E., Rohlich, G. A., and Porges, N., *Univ. Wisconsin Engr. Expt. Sta. Res. Rept.* **15**, 1960.
3. McKee, F. J., *Sewage Ind. Wastes* **29**, 157–164 (1957).
4. U. S. Dept. Agr. Handbook No. 176, "Dairy Waste Treatment by Aeration—Theory, Design, Construction, and Operation," 1960.
5. U. S. Public Health Service Publ. No. 298, "An Industrial Waste Guide to the Milk Processing Industry," revised 1959.
6. Zack, S. I., *Sewage Ind. Wastes* **28**, 1009–1019 (1956).

Food Products—Vegetable

Chapter 6

CANNED FOODS

by WALTER A. MERCER

A remarkable expansion of the canning industry in the United States came during the decade of the 1860's. Processing plants for fruits and vegetables sprang up in Ohio, Indiana, Illinois, and California. At the beginning of the Civil War the Federal government commandeered nearly all of the canned foods to feed the soldiers in the camps and in the fields. At the close of the war, production of canned foods had increased sixfold.

Similarly, during World Wars I and II dependence on canned fruits and vegetables was accentuated. This dependence on canned foods during wartime emergencies was carried over into peacetime periods. Today, the public consumes the full production capacity of a multimillion dollar industry, geographically distributed throughout the United States and its territories, and producing a wide variety of canned fruits and vegetables in both metal and glass containers. Production of canned fruits and vegetables has doubled during the last 25 years.

In numerical terms, the modern canning industry comprises about 2200 plants, operated by about 1800 separate companies. These canning plants are located in 49 of the 50 states, as well as in Puerto Rico and other United States possessions.

Although the modern canning industry is highly mechanized, more than 300,000 workers are employed during the peak of the canning season. Wages and salaries total more than $600 million per year. Thousands of other persons are employed in allied industries that sell materials to the canning industry or distribute its products. For example, the canning industry is the nation's third largest user of steel, the quantity of steel used for cans, machinery, and other canning equipment being exceeded only by the totals for the automobile and the construction industries.

VOLUME OF CANNED FOOD PRODUCTION

Approximately half the nation's vegetable crops and nearly half the fruit production is used by the canning industry. About 80% of all tomatoes harvested in the United States are canned; 75% of the beets; 65% of the green peas; and more than 50% of the sweet corn. Large proportions of the catch of certain fish are canned: 99% of the tuna, 90% of the sardines, and 85% of the salmon.

Canners customarily measure their production by the case, which may contain as few as 6 large cans or as many as 96 small cans, or their equivalent in glass. Annual production for the 1963 season was more than 750 million actual cases, containing about 26 billion containers of food, and having a retail value of $5.2 billion.

CANNING PROCEDURES

Details of commercial canning practices vary with the nature of the food, but certain basic operations are common to practically all canned fruit and vegetable products.

Preliminary Preparations. Fruits and vegetables are harvested into bins, boxes, or hampers, and delivered by truck from the fields to the cannery. At the cannery one of the most important steps in commercial procedure is the thorough cleaning of the raw foods. The methods of cleaning vary with the nature of the food, but all foods must be freed from adhering soil, dried juices, insects, and chemical residues.

With certain raw foods, such as leafy vegetables, washing with water is usually preceded by dry cleaning procedures. Small stones, sand, and other fine debris are mechanically removed by the application of revolving or agitating screens. Strong blasts of air may be used to remove dry leaves and chaff from certain raw foods. Green peas are passed through flotation units to separate stones and the pealike berries of a weed that is picked up by the pea vine harvester. Both fruits and vegetables are subjected to high pressure water sprays while being conveyed on moving belts or passed through screens.

Preparations for Canning. After being thoroughly cleaned, the raw product is further prepared for canning. Some fruits and vegetables are sorted for size and maturity. Sorting for size is done by a series of moving screens having different mesh sizes or by passing the raw foods over rollers spaced at different intervals. Separation of fruits and tomatoes into groups according to color and degree of ripeness is done by hand. Vegetables such as peas and lima beans can be separated into portions having more or less maturity by passing them through flotation units using salt solution. Separation on the basis of specific gravity is done continuously and automatically by machinery.

Trimming to remove blemishes or other undesirable portions of the raw foods must be done by hand. Usually women are employed for this purpose and they become exceedingly skillful in locating and removing defects.

Fruits such as pears, apples, and peaches must be peeled and cored or pitted in preparation for canning. Mechanical means are generally used to remove the skins of pears and apples and to cut the peeled fruit into halves or slices. Peaches and apricots are halved before peeling and the pits are removed. Machines are now widely used in these operations. The halves are belt conveyed to peelers where they are treated with hot dilute caustic solution, applied either by immersion of the fruit or by flooding solution over the halves turned skin side up on a moving belt. Tomatoes to be canned whole are peeled by use of hot caustic. The lye is recirculated and maintained at strength by addition of concentrated sodium hydroxide. At the end of each work shift, the caustic solution is released to the sewer. The heating and recirculating system is then cleaned and recharged with new solution.

After caustic treatment, the fruit halves or whole tomatoes are subjected to high pressure water sprays to remove skin and excess caustic. Following this wash the raw product is again inspected and blemishes are removed. Inedible pieces are discarded as waste. The raw product trimmings, discarded pieces, and any spillage on the floor are accumulated on belts and finally in gutters and conveyed in water to the waste screening operation which separates suspended material from liquid waste.

Blanching of Raw Foods. Green vegetables are immersed in hot water or exposed to live steam in the blanching operation, in order to expel air and gases, to inactivate enzymes that cause undesirable flavor or color changes, and to wilt products such as spinach so they are more easily filled into the cans.

The water used for blanching is retained for the length of the canning shift, usually 8 hours, with as little fresh water added as possible. Over this period of use, leaching of sugars, starches, and other soluble materials from the raw fruits and vegetables causes the blanch water to become a highly concentrated solution. Usually the blanch waters are responsible for the largest portion of the soluble components in the liquid wastes. Caustic peeling solutions also are strong wastes.

Final Operations. Raw fruits and vegetables are transported to and from the various operations prior to can filling largely by means of moving belts. However, hydraulic conveying by flumes or pumps is increasing in use. Either of these hydraulic means of conveying the fruits and vegetables requires the use of water, which then becomes a part of the liquid waste. Belt conveyers must be continuously washed and lubricated with water sprays, also contributing to the composite waste flow.

In the final operations, the fruits and vegetables are conveyed to the canning department where they are given a last inspection and placed into cans or jars. The containers are conveyed to machines that automatically dispense sirup over the fruit, brine over the vegetables, and juice over the whole tomatoes. Passage of the cans or jars through a steam-heated box exhausts air from the contents and raises the temperature, in order to provide a vacuum in the container after the cover is sealed in place. Air may also be exhausted from the container just before the cover is sealed. After heat processing, the cans or jars are cooled with large volumes of clean water.

CHARACTERISTICS OF FOOD CANNING WASTES

Waste materials that originate in fruit and vegetable canning operations fall into two general classes: solid materials, such as trimmings, pits, peels, leaves, stems, and defective whole pieces, that are discarded within the plant; and liquid materials consisting of sugars, starches, and other carbohydrates leached from fruits and vegetables and carried in solution in the wash or flume waters used within the plant.

Solid wastes that collect within the cannery are carried from the plant by either belt systems or water flumes. With the latter, suspended solids must be removed by passing the water over a screen. With the exception of water used for production of steam and the comparatively little water that enters the product as brine or sirup, all water used in food canning enters the waste system. Wastewater leaving the canning plant contains organic matter and must be recognized and handled as a waste material requiring treatment. However, water used to cool the heat-processed cans or jars contains only minor amounts of organic matter, and treatment is unnecessary if this water can have a separate means of disposal.

Amount of Solid Waste and Possibilities of Utilization

The quantities of solid waste material from the canning of typical fruits and vegetables are given in Table I. In some instances, almost half the raw tonnage received at the cannery must eventually be handled as solid waste. Because this represents a substantial percentage of the raw product purchased from the grower, recovery of usable by-products from fruit and vegetable waste solids has always been an enticing proposition.

The fact that utilization has not been practiced more extensively is due to the seasonal nature of fruit and vegetable canning operations; the perishable nature of the waste, which requires that it be immediately converted into a stable form; the reluctance of food processors to assume additional responsibilities during their intensive operating periods; the small financial return, which may not equal the costs of conversion; and

TABLE I

AMOUNT OF SOLID WASTE
PER RAW TON OF TYPICAL FRUITS AND VEGETABLES

	Fruits			
	Apples	Berries	Peaches	Pears
Avg. season, weeks	13	6	4	8
Tons of raw fruit received:				
Per plant, avg. season	3137	845	1249	6059
Per plant, max. day	46	47	85	139
Tons of solid waste produced:				
Per plant, avg. season	1462	45	132	2765
Per plant, max. day	19	4	20	55
Avg. tons of waste per raw ton	0.47	0.05	0.11	0.46

	Vegetables			
	Asparagus	Beets	Corn	Peas
Avg. season, weeks	6	8	6	6
Tons of raw vegetable received:				
Per plant, avg. season	859	4772	5349	5108
Per plant, max. day	35	126	253	213
Tons of solid waste produced:				
Per plant, avg. season	260	1831	3845	389
Per plant, max. day	12	42	178	16
Avg. tons of waste per raw ton	0.30	0.38	0.72	0.08

the recent realization that pesticides used during the growing season may remain as residues concentrated in the peel and other discarded tissues. Utilization of dehydrated solid wastes as animal feed is largely confined to tomato waste and, to a limited extent, asparagus and spinach wastes. At the present time only tomato waste is utilized by drying.

Dehydration of tomato waste must be preceded by pressing to remove as much moisture as possible. No corresponding equipment has yet been perfected for the pressing of untreated pear, peach, and apricot solids. These fruit wastes do not provide the fibrous material required for juice extraction by pressing. For this reason their dehydration as a means of waste utilization is apparently not feasible at this time. Assuming that mechanical problems involved in pressing and dehydrating a fruit waste could be solved, and sale of finished product assured, a break-even cost picture would be possible only where the operation could be continuous. This would require an accumulated supply of fruit solids. In many areas this does not seem possible, because accumulated fruit solids quickly ferment, with development of odors which might become a public nuisance.

Ensilage from Fruit Waste Solids. In one reported attempt, the preparation of ensilage from pear waste was successful. From 8 to 20% of finely chopped alfalfa hay was mixed with the pear solids, and the mixture was delivered into a trench silo. One of the problems reported was drainage of juice from the silo. No other successful installations are known.

Production of Alcohol from Fruit Wastes. Production of alcohol from fruit wastes is technically possible, and sporadic attempts at this method of utilization have been made. One apparently successful operation using pear waste has been reported; however, the necessary facilities were already available for the production of fruit brandies from other fruits.

The disposal of still slops from alcohol production would be of major concern in many areas. The slops or bottoms are high in organic content and pollution-producing properties. A major disadvantage would be the seasonal nature of cannery operations producing the fruit wastes, as year round use of distillery facilities is an economic necessity. Further discussion is presented in the chapter on Fermentation Products.

Other Uses of Solid Wastes. Efforts have been made to produce a sirup base and a dry cake or pellet from pear waste to be used as cattle feed. These investigations have been on a pilot scale, although large amounts of pear solids were used. The procedure consisted of mixing the waste at a temperature of about 93°F with 0.35% calcium carbonate to produce gelatin from the pectins. After a 1-hour cure the gel was squeezed in a rack-and-cloth press. The press cake was dried in a rotary dryer.

In one experiment it was proposed that the press juice be refined for reuse as a canning sirup. For this it had to be clarified and its color removed. The press juice was acidified and passed through a cation exchange treatment in a hydrogen cycle to remove the calcium added in gelatinization of the raw stock. The juice was then boiled and treated with gelatin at the rate of 2–3 oz per 100 gal of juice. Flocculated collodial materials were then removed by carbon filtration. Commercial attempts to utilize fruit waste by this method have not been reported and are not known to be in use.

The production of a canning sirup as described above requires that the raw waste be from sound, edible fruit. This could not completely solve the disposal problem because much of the fruit waste consists of inedible portions and unsound fruit. One large scale attempt has been made to develop a practical process for converting pear waste solids into a soluble molasses and a dried pellet for cattle feed. It is a matter of record that the operation was technically successful on a pilot plant scale. However, when the operation was taken over by a privately financed concern, it was soon discontinued. It is assumed that an unfavorable economic situation was the cause for discontinuance.

Because of inadequate economic and technical information regarding methods of utilization of cannery waste solids, waste material has been disposed of by the most inexpensive and troublefree method available to each canner under his own set of circumstances.

METHODS OF DISPOSAL FOR SOLID WASTES

Methods available for disposal of solid waste and liquid waste are entirely different. It is therefore necessary to collect the two types of waste separately within the plant or to separate them by screening when the two are combined.

REMOVAL OF SOLIDS BY SCREENING

The composite waste flow from fruit and vegetable canning operations is composed of two types of solids, the particulate or suspended solids and the soluble or colloidal matter. Regardless of the ultimate method of disposal, suspended solids should be removed by screening the composite waste flow. Failure to screen the waste may cause unsightly conditions in streams because of solid materials that form floating scum or bottom sludge; unnecessary overload on oxidation ponds or digesters, if such treatment is used; or clogging of sewer lines, filters, and distributors if discharge is to a sewage treatment plant. Screening is required by most states and municipalities as a pollution control measure, regardless of the means of disposal of the liquid portion of the waste. Intentional maceration, grinding, or comminution of suspended solids, in order to pass more of the solids through a regulation sized screen, is neither desirable nor allowed.

Screen Types in General Use. The size, shape, and general nature of the solid particles to be removed from the composite waste flow have a definite influence on the efficiency and effectiveness of the screening operation. All screens require attention in order to prevent occlusion or blinding of the mesh openings and the flooding over of unscreened effluent. Three types of screens are in general use for removing solid waste.

(1) *Rotary drum screens.* These are revolving drums covered with a screen cloth which ranges in fineness from 6 to 10 openings per linear inch. The composite waste flow enters the screen through an open end

of the drum; liquids pass through the screen and solids are retained on the inside of the cloth. The solids may be washed from the cloth by water sprays as the drum revolves upward and over a refuse conveyer. In other types, the drum retains the solids on the screen and delivers them by gravity flow into a screw conveyer or bucket elevator.

(2) *Vibrating table screens.* Flat, agitating screens are now widely used for removal of solids from canning wastes. Finer screen cloths can be used than would be possible with drum screens, and 20–40 openings per linear inch are common. A definite advantage for these screens is the possible adjustment of amplitude of vibration, making possible more effective screening of solids that differ in size and nature.

(3) *Gyrating circular screens.* Circular screens having a 3-way gyrating motion have been used successfully for screening dry materials such as sand, gravel, grain, and similar products. They also show promise for wet screening operations. Among the advantages claimed are that no special foundation or support is required, that unscreened materials do not spill over, and that the 3-way vibration allows the use of finer screen cloths and removal of more suspended solids.

GENERALLY USED METHODS FOR DISPOSAL OF SOLID WASTES

In most plants the waste solids from fruit and vegetable canning are a liability to the canner. In urban areas the canner must pay on a weight or volume basis to have the wastes removed from the plant. Because of the inadequacy of economic and technical information regarding methods of utilization, the canner or hauler disposes of the wastes by the least expensive method available to him under his circumstances. Often, however, thought and ingenuity can lessen the costs of disposal for solid wastes.

Land Fill Disposal. Burial of solid wastes in land fill operations is widely used. This method of disposal requires little ground area, but the site must be most carefully selected. Generally, land unsuitable for other purposes must be used, because a period of years is required for stabilization of a completed fill. This is particularly true of fills containing fruit solids. Furthermore, seepage of liquids into wells and streams must be prevented. Other serious problems are the prevention of fly breeding and odor production from the open face of the fill. An earthen cover must follow as closely as possible the filling operation.

New or expanded land fill operations for the disposal of cannery waste solids may be impossible in areas undergoing urban expansion. Publicity concerning water pollution and odor problems resulting from land fill operations has alerted many city and county governments to the nuisance potential in this method of disposal. Operation sites and permits may be obtainable only in localities at distances that result in prohibitive hauling costs.

Land Spreading of Waste Solids. A second method of land disposal involves spreading the waste material in a thin layer over the land surface. It must then be worked into the soil before odor production or fly breeding can result.

Although this method of disposal is still used in some semi-urban areas, compliance with city and county regulations governing these operations has become more and more difficult. As the urban areas expand, it is expected that disposal sites farther removed from these areas must be used. Consequently, the cost of this method of disposal will eventually become prohibitive.

Incineration of Waste Solids. In a few instances, comparatively dry waste solids have been burned. Some consideration has been given to the possibility of using waste solids as supplemental fuel for steam production. Partial predrying of solids by use of stack gases has been contemplated.

It is believed that incineration of waste solids cannot now be considered as a method of disposal. Assuming that the method had economic advantages, which is doubtful, regulations concerning air pollution abatement would prevent incineration on a scale necessary to solve the disposal problem.

Feeding of Fresh Wastes to Animals. Disposal of wet waste solids by feeding to animals has been widespread. This, of course, is not possible in some areas of the country. When considered as a means of disposal for cannery waste, a number of major objections are involved. Sites where feeding operations could be carried out are usually distant from the location of the canneries concerned. Hearings on new permits for such operations usually bring forth much opposition from residents near the intended site of operation.

Delivery of wet waste to farms already in existence often involves prohibitive hauling costs. Other disadvantages result from the lack of balanced nutrients in fruit wastes and the seasonal nature of cannery operations.

Disposal of Ground Solids to City Sewers. From the canners' standpoint, the most convenient method of disposal for solid waste would be discharge to a sewage treatment plant. However, where this is not now permitted it is doubtful that future permission can be obtained. A number of cities now find their sewage effluents do not meet the standards set by water pollution control agencies. The failure to provide adequate treatment is more pronounced during the season when cannery liquid wastes are discharged into the sewers.

Assuming that solid wastes were discharged into the sewers, the organic loading on treatment facilities would be increased by approximately 60–70%. Appropriate increases would be required in treatment facilities. In view of the emphasis now being placed on pollution abatement, it does not seem possible that cannery solid wastes will be taken into the sewers.

Specialized Methods of Handling Waste Solids

The growing complexity of the problems arising from waste disposal in urban or semi-urban areas has necessitated consideration and use of specialized methods of disposal. In some cases more research is needed on these methods.

Ocean Disposal of Solids. Cannery waste solids are being barged out to sea from one area in the West. Approximately 70,000 cubic yards of fruit, tomato, and vegetable solids are collected by a scavenger company from a community of canneries and accumulated in a concrete sump. From the sump the solids are bulldozed into a hammer mill for breaking up the larger pieces of fruit and the peach pits. Following this, the solids are pumped into a converted oil barge which, when loaded, is towed to a disposal area about 26 miles beyond the nearest point on the mainland.

The mechanics of disposal at sea consist of pumping the waste material from the barge at a rate of discharge prescribed by the pollution control agency. The speed and direction of the barge are also prescribed.

A monitoring program was required by the pollution control agency. This was carried out by sampling the ocean at various depths and distances behind the barge. All regulatory agencies concerned with the operation are pleased with this method of disposal. The results of all tests indicate that the discharge creates only momentary changes in the water.

Inclusion of Comminuted Solids in Spray-Irrigated Liquid Wastes. Limited studies have been made on the inclusion of comminuted solids in liquid waste disposal by spray irrigation. Where the location of the cannery has made this method successful, the need for screening and handling of solid wastes has been eliminated. Experience with spray irrigation of solid waste has shown that the concentration of solids in the water is not a factor in harmful effects on soil or cover crops. The hydraulic loading is the determining factor. More experimentation must be done to solve problems in connection with comminution of the solids. A more detailed cost analysis must also be made.

Composting of Solid Wastes. High rate aerobic composting as a method of disposal for fruit waste solids is under investigation and is receiving much attention.

Since fruit solids are 80–90% moisture, dry moisture-absorbent materials must be mixed with the wastes. Of the materials tested, rice hulls, sawdust, and composted municipal garbage have performed satisfactorily. High rate aerobic composting is attained only when the initial moisture content of the mixture is controlled within the range of 65–70%. Adequate aeration must then be provided in order to prevent slow, anaerobic, malodorous decomposition.

On a weight basis, the usual mixing ratio is 2 parts wet solids to 1 part dry material. With the optimum moisture balance and adequate aeration, the compost process begins quickly and is evidenced by a rise in temperature to a level of 150°–160° F. Although the initial pH level is on the acidic side, the production of ammonia in the final stages of the compost process causes an elevation in pH to about 8.5. When stabilization of the process has been attained and the compost is dried, it may be recycled as the dry material for new lots of wet fruit solids.

SOURCE, VOLUME, AND CHARACTERISTICS OF LIQUID WASTES

The point of origin within the canning plant, the volumes discharged, and the characteristics of liquid wastes vary greatly among the different products packed, among canners of the same product, and from day to day in the same plant. However, it is possible to make some generalizations on an industry-wide and average-canning basis.

The annual production of more than 750 million cases of canned food requires about 36 billion gal of water—an approximate average use of 50 gal per case of food. The daily waste flow from fruit and vegetable canneries ranges from 400,000 to 4,000,000 gal, with the average flow being in the vicinity of 1.5 million gal for western operations and approximately 500,000 gal per day for the average operation on a national basis. Although much of this required volume of water is reclaimed from previous uses, the industry is entirely dependent on the availability of adequate water of good quality.

Should the 36 billion gal of clean water used by the canning industry be discharged without treatment, its treatment potential would be equal to 300 billion gal of domestic sewage. In terms of BOD, the organic load carried by this volume of liquid is estimated to be 500 million pounds. This represents the potential pollution load should the wastes be discharged to streams. Fortunately, only a small fraction of the total load is discharged without treatment.

EXAMPLES OF WASTE SOURCES, VOLUMES, AND CHARACTERISTICS

Because of the production variables which affect the origin and volume of liquid wastes, it is possible to give data only for typical operations. Table II shows the sources and estimated average volumes of wastewa-

TABLE II

SOURCES AND ESTIMATED VOLUMES OF WASTEWATERS
FROM PROCESSING STEPS IN CANNING OF FRUITS

Operation	Waste flow, gal.		Per cent of total flow
	per hour	per ton	
Peeling	1,200	48	2
Spray washing	11,000	385	17
Sorting, slicing, etc.	3,000	120	5
Exhausting of cans	1,200	48	2
Processing	600	24	1
Cooling of cans	24,000	945	37
Plant cleanup	21,000	840	33
Box washing	1,960	70	3
Total	63,960	2480	100

ters from processing steps in the canning of fruits. The volumes given are those which result if only fresh water is used in all operations and no attempt is made to reuse water. These volumes can be considerably reduced if, for example, can cooling waters are recirculated as cooling waters or reclaimed for use in product washing.

Generally, it can be assumed that the canning of most fruits and vegetables produces a liquid waste approximately 10 times the strength of domestic sewage when expressed in terms of BOD. Table III gives more specific information regarding the strength of wastes from the canning of individual fruits. Table IV gives similar information for individual vegetables.

As already stated, the volume and character of both the solid and liquid wastes from the canning of fruits and vegetables vary widely with the kind of raw product being processed and with the methods employed in the individual canning plants. Aside from factors beyond the direct

TABLE III

VOLUME AND CONCENTRATION OF TYPICAL FRUIT CANNING WASTES

Fruit product	Waste volume, gal/case	5-day BOD, mg/liter	Suspended solids, mg/liter
Apples	25–40	1680–5530	300–600
Apricots	57–80	200–1020	200–400
Cherries	12–40	700–2100	200–600
Cranberries	10–20	500–2250	100–250
Peaches	45–60	1200–2800	450–750

control of the canner, such as the kind and ripeness of the fruit, variations in the volume and character of the wastes are caused by differences in the extent of hydraulic conveying of raw product, in methods of in-plant transport of solid wastes, in the extent of screening of the composite wastes, in equipment maintenance, and in the general orderliness and good housekeeping within the plant.

Because of these wide variations in individual canning operations, the information given herein should not be relied on in evaluation of an existing waste flow or in designing waste treatment systems. Each can-

TABLE IV

VOLUME AND CONCENTRATION OF VEGETABLE CANNING WASTES

Product	Waste volume, gal/case	5-day BOD, mg/liter	Suspended solids, mg/liter
Asparagus	70	16–100	30–180
Beans, baked	35	925–1440	225
Beans, green or wax	26–44	160–600	60–150
Beans, kidney	18-20	1030–2500	140
Beans, lima, dried	17–29	1740–2880	160–600
Beans, lima, fresh	50–257	190–450	420
Beets	27–70	1580–7600	740–2220
Carrots	23	520–3030	1830
Corn, cream style	24–29	620–2900	300–675
Corn, whole kernel	25–70	1120–6300	300–4000
Mushrooms	6,600	76–850	50–240
Peas	14–75	380–4700	270–400
Potatoes, sweet	82	1500–5600	400–2500
Potatoes, white	—	200–2900	990–1180
Pumpkin	20–50	1500–6880	785–1960
Sauerkraut	3–18	1400–6300	60–630
Spinach	160	280–730	90–580
Squash	20	4000–11000	3000
Tomatoes	3–100	180–4000	140–2000

nery waste problem needs special study. Significant reductions can be made in the strength and volume of canning wastes by institution of waste prevention and water saving practices.

POLLUTION AND NUISANCE EFFECTS OF LIQUID WASTES

Wide variations in the nature of food canning wastes allow only generalizations about the pollution and nuisance effects that may result when these wastes are discharged to streams. The usual high concentration of soluble solids in liquid wastes causes rapid and abundant microbial growth in the receiving waters under normal stream conditions. The ability of the stream to assimilate the waste without showing evidence of pollution depends largely on the relationship between volume or flow of waste discharged and volume or flow of the receiving water.

Starches and sugars present in food canning wastes are readily utilized by aerobic types of microorganisms. This utilization requires that dissolved oxygen be taken from the water. The most common and expected pollution effect is depletion of the oxygen concentration to a level at which fish life is killed. If utilization of oxygen continues without replenishment, anaerobic decomposition of the waste begins, with production of odors, discoloration of the stream, and other nuisance conditions.

Even though liquid wastes are screened as effectively as possible under cannery operating conditions, the suspended solids concentration is usually high. This is particularly true of fruit canning wastes and some vegetable wastes. Gaseous fermentation of wastes in the stream causes flocculation and agglomeration of suspended solids, which are brought to the surface by entrained gases and form a scum blanket. In addition to being unsightly, the floating scum may become a site for fly breeding and odor production.

Under some conditions, a receiving stream may be adversely affected by the pH of canning wastes. Fruit canning may produce an acid waste unless the fruit is lye-peeled. In the latter case, the composite liquid waste flow may be highly alkaline. Other nuisance problems may result from the color of the liquid waste. For example, beet canning waste imparts a brilliant red color to the receiving stream unless it is highly diluted. Occasionally the high temperature of a canning waste may reduce the oxygen concentration of the receiving water and cause significant changes in its natural biological flora.

An important point to consider in the discharge of fruit and vegetable canning wastes to streams is that such wastes do not constitute a direct health problem. Unless domestic sewage is added to these wastes they do not contain microorganisms infectious to human beings or animals. The wastes become health factors only when improperly handled.

WASTE PREVENTION AND REDUCTION

The prevention of waste in food canning is of considerable economic importance. With the exception of inedible portions of the food, any discharge of raw product to waste is costly, not only because of actual product loss, but also because acquisition and operation of waste disposal and treatment equipment is expensive.

In-plant practices can reduce the strength and volume of the liquid waste. In general, solid food wastes should not be hydraulically conveyed in gutters or flumes. Leaching of soluble materials from water-transported solids can significantly increase the organic strength of the liquid waste. Abrasion of solid materials passing over vibrating separatory screens causes finely divided solids to be added to the liquid waste. For these reasons, solid refuse should be collected at the points of origin and conveyed by belt or other means to a pickup station outside the plant.

A study of water usage in a food plant always reveals that more water is used than is necessary, and that the composite waste flow includes clean waters that could be discharged without treatment. Any reduction in the volume of waste flow is a saving in disposal and treatment costs. Often, trouble in sewage treatment plants receiving cannery wastes is the result of hydraulic overloading and not of organic strength of the wastes. When liquid wastes are discharged to a land disposal system, such as an oxidation pond, reduction in volume results in extended retention time in a given storage area and, consequently, a higher degree of waste stabilization.

Reuse of water is an effective means of reducing the volume of liquid wastes. Several basic procedures for conserving water can be used in all canneries. These include the elimination of waste by use of automatic shutoff valves on water hoses, use of high pressure sprays for cleanup rather than low pressure sprays, and elimination of excessive overflow from soaking and washing tanks. Significant savings of water can be accomplished by substitution of mechanical conveyors for water flumes, and by selection of equipment more efficient in design and operation.

In a typical food canning operation, the largest single use of water is that required to cool the heat-processed cans. Where water shortage is not a problem, cooling water should be separated from the composite waste flow. It may then be discharged without treatment to storm sewers or to a waterway.

Where segregation and separate disposal of the cooling water is not possible, it should be reused as a means of reducing the volume of liquid waste. The most efficient method of reuse, after cooling and chlorinating the water, is recirculation for can cooling.

When can cooling water is not recirculated, it may be considered for reuse in the following operations: in caustic or water peeling baths, for removal of caustic after peeling, as a primary wash of the raw product, for canning belt lubrication, and for plant cleanup operations.

METHODS OF TREATMENT AND DISPOSAL FOR LIQUID WASTES

In the treatment and disposal of liquid waste from food canning, one of three general objectives must be accomplished: (1) the waste must be suitable for discharge to a stream without causing pollution, (2) a land disposal system must be provided that will prevent nuisance problems due to excessive odor production, or (3) arrangements must be made to discharge the waste to a community sewage treatment plant.

Local regulations and conditions prescribe treatment and disposal practices. However, certain methods have been developed and are in general use throughout the canning industry. Arranged in the order of their frequency of use, the types of treatment are as follows: treatment in municipal sewage systems; land disposal in the form of impounding lagoons or irrigation systems; biological and chemical treatment, either preparatory to disposal by other means or as the only treatment.

Treatment in Sewage Plants. Discharge of screened raw cannery wastes into a municipal sewage treatment plant is the most desirable disposal method if satisfactory arrangements can be made. However, the seasonal nature of cannery operations and the high pollutional strength of the wastes may cause serious problems. The nature of the pollutants in the cannery waste may also upset normal sewage treatment processes. The sugars and sugarlike compounds in liquid wastes from fruit canning require a biological process for stabilization, which is not desirable for the complete stabilization of domestic sewage. In some phases of stabilization, the two are directly antagonistic. It has been observed that, in cities where the volume of domestic sewage is not large enough to give high dilution of the cannery waste, attempts to treat the combined wastes are not effective. However, many canners are discharging wastes to large municipal systems where treatment is completely satisfactory.

In contemplating the discharge of cannery waste to a municipal system the following factors should be considered by both canner and municipality.

(1) *Type of treatment process used by the sewage plant.* Activated sludge treatment processes, in particular, are reported to be adversely affected by cannery waste in high concentration.

(2) *Volume of cannery waste.* The relationship between the volume of cannery waste and the volume of domestic sewage should be considered; that is, whether dilution of the cannery waste will be high enough to prevent harm to the treatment process.

(3) *Capacity of the sewage plant.* The seasonal production of cannery wastes means that consideration must be given to the costs of increasing plant capacity for use during the season, in relation to the costs of other methods of treatment and disposal.

(4) *Type and cost of pretreatment of cannery waste.* In nearly all cases screening of the cannery waste is necessary, in many cases, pH adjustment of the cannery waste is required before its discharge to the sewer.

(5) *Charges which the canner must pay.* The charges to the canner for the privilege of discharging his wastes to the municipal treatment system are usually based on one or more of the following considerations.

(a) *No charge.* In some municipal areas, authorities and citizens encourage industry because of the employment provided and the disbursement of money through salaries and purchases.

(b) *Initial payment.* An outright purchase of the privilege of waste disposal services may be based on the cost of new equipment required to treat the cannery wastes, with no further service charges thereafter.

(c) *Annual charge for waste disposal services.* The charge for service may be annual payment of a fixed sum, which is usually an estimate of the additional expense incurred by the sewage plant in treating cannery wastes.

(d) *Charges based on water consumption.* Water consumption is probably the most commonly used basis for charge. It may be assumed that the amount of water metered into the plant is the amount of water discharged. However, a considerable volume of water is lost through evaporation or addition to the finished product, so a compensating reduction should be allowed. The charge to the canner may be only that which he pays for the water. If a separate charge is made for disposal services, the canner may find it profitable to meter the wastewater. In some plants, clean waters discharged to the sewer, such as cooling and condenser waters, are measured and the volume excluded from disposal charges. Ordinarily, disposal charges are calculated on the basis of each 1000 gal discharged, or a rate schedule of diminishing charge for increasing volume may be used.

Disposal to Absorption Ponds and Storage Lagoons. Impounding cannery wastes in storage lagoons offers a means of disposal that eliminates stream pollution and may be less expensive than other methods of treatment. Storage of liquid wastes in earthen ponds allows partial or complete decomposition of the waste, after which the waters can be discharged by controlled flow to a watercourse or to a municipal plant for further treatment. Where soil conditions are favorable, complete absorption into the soil may be obtained.

The lagooning disposal method requires a land area large enough to hold the volume of waste and situated within a practical distance for pumping or piping the wastes. Drainage characteristics of the soil should be studied. Seepage of wastewaters should not contaminate underground sources of water supply. Also of importance is the proximity of residential areas. Untreated lagoons develop odors that may cause complaint from people living within a radius of a mile or, under certain conditions, even farther.

As an aid in prevention of offensive odors from lagooned wastes, the lagoon itself should be as large and shallow as the situation permits. Septic conditions quickly develop in deep lagoons. A waste depth of not more than 3 ft is preferred, and 5 ft is the maximum. Growth of weeds and grass should not be permitted in lagoons. Because they are of organic composition, their presence in the lagoon contributes to the odor problem.

In the presence of free oxygen, the starches and sugars of cannery wastes are changed by bacterial action into stable inoffensive compounds such as water, carbon dioxide, nitrates, and sulfates. When oxygen is exhausted from the wastes, anaerobic bacteria continue the decomposition with the production of foul-smelling gases such as hydrogen sulfide, ammonia, and mercaptans. This anaerobic condition in lagoons occurs quickly unless fresh waste is continuously added or available oxygen is supplied by other means.

The most satisfactory method for odor control in lagoons is the addition of sodium nitrate, which supplies the available oxygen required for inoffensive decomposition of the wastes. Sodium nitrate of fertilizer grade is added daily to the fresh waste going into a lagoon, in an amount necessary to satisfy 20% of the 5-day BOD.

Disposal by Spray Irrigation. In recent years, spray irrigation has been used increasingly as a means of cannery waste disposal. In many respects it is an improvement over other methods. Spray irrigation consists of spreading the liquid waste over the surface of the ground by means of a high-pressure sprinkler system. A rate of application is used which produces only minimum damage to vegetative growth and avoids surface runoff and erosion. The system usually requires the following items: a mechanically operated screening unit, a collecting tank for accumulation of screened waste, stationary screens to prevent clogging of the outlet from the tank, a pump to develop the required nozzle pressure, a main for transporting waste to the irrigation site, lateral lines for distribution from the main, self-activated revolving sprinklers, the land on which to spray, and an actively growing cover crop to aid in absorption and to prevent soil erosion. With the proper equipment and controlled application of the waste, spray irrigation completely prevents stream pollution, creates no odor problem, and is usually less expensive than other methods of waste disposal.

(1) *Selection of the irrigation site.* Of major importance in waste disposal by spray irrigation is selection of land for the irrigation site. Its location must be within practical pumping distance of the cannery. Consideration should be given to the economics of pumping long distances as compared with the costs of disposal by other means.

The topography of the land and characteristics of the soil are important factors to consider. Spray irrigation of land that is not fairly level may not be successful because of runoff and erosion. The possibility of stream pollution from runoff should be considered. Depressions in the surface of the land may cause ponding of the wastewater, with odor production resulting from its decomposition.

The amount of land required to dispose of a given volume of waste is determined by the absorption characteristics of the soil, which are, therefore, important to the success of spray irrigation. At present there is no reliable method of predetermining this property. Persons having a knowledge of local soil conditions should be consulted.

(2) *Importance of the cover crop.* When screened raw wastes are sprayed over land without a vegetative cover crop, the rate of application is governed by the rate at which the land can physically absorb the waste. Waste runoff and soil erosion are always serious problems. The importance of a cover crop on irrigated land is quickly apparent when the rates of waste application with and without a cover are compared. For land without a cover crop the amount of waste absorbed is only about 10–15% of the amount which could be disposed of with a cover crop on the land.

The type of vegetative cover may be determined by what the land is to be used for either during or after the canning season. At some installations cattle are grazed on the vegetative growth during spray operations. The cutting of hay from the land is also common practice. One cover crop mixture frequently used includes the following: Mammoth clover, 3 lb; Ladino-Alsac mixture, 4 lb; Alta fescue, 4 lb; redtop, 3 lb; and orchard grass, 2 lb. This mixture is sowed at the rate of 16 lb per acre. As dense a cover crop as possible should be provided at the time spraying is to start.

(3) *Other considerations.* Failure to screen cannery wastes properly is frequently the cause of difficulty in the operation of a spray irrigation system, because the presence of gross solids results in plugging of the spray nozzles. The screen cloth used should not be so fine as to cause flooding-over of unscreened waste. A thorough screening with a coarser cloth would be preferable. Finely divided solids can be sprayed without trouble.

If odors are to be avoided in spray irrigating, the cannery waste must be applied to the land while it is still fresh. This is a factor to consider in constructing the collecting tank or sump. A tank of capacity to provide a long detention time can be a disadvantage, because fermentation of the waste may occur. Odors may then be a problem, and the lower pH of the waste may cause unnecessary damage to the cover crop. Ordinarily the detention time should not be more than 3–4 hours.

Biological Methods of Treatment. Screened cannery waste is amenable to treatment by biological methods, and high degrees of reduction in the strength of the waste can be obtained. However, treatment depending on biological oxidation should be attempted only after investigation of other methods and after careful consideration of the problems involved.

Biological methods are most suitable for treating small volumes of cannery waste. Where a small volume of strong waste can be segregated from the total flow, its treatment by biological methods can give a great reduction in the strength of the composite flow. For example, in fruit canning, the peeling operation contributes only 2–5% of the total volume of waste, yet removal of the spent caustic reduces the strength of the total waste by 50–60%.

All types of food canning wastes support the growth of bacteria which utilize the sugars and other carbohydrates present. The fermentation of these compounds occurs quickly, and the end products of the fermentation are compounds of much lower pollutional strength.

Both anaerobic and aerobic digestion of cannery waste have been experimented with, and successful large scale operations have been carried out with each type of digestion. Anaerobic digestion requires more elaborate equipment and more careful attention. For these reasons it is feasible only for certain wastes.

Aerobic digestion of organic wastes is more easily carried out. Usually a 2-stage process is planned. In the first stage, screened fresh waste is admitted to a tank where air is continuously diffused into it. This supplies the free oxygen required by the aerobic bacteria in their biochemical action on the organic compounds. The wastes may be detained and aerated in a batch or continuous operation. An efficient process is dependent on building up, in the aeration digestion tank, a vigorous culture of suitable bacteria. Conditions in the tank must be controlled to prevent inhibition of bacterial growth. Good diffusion of air throughout the tank must be maintained continuously. The pH of the waste must be held within a suitable range for growth of the bacteria. Certain types of wastes may require the addition of small amounts of available nitrogen as a food supplement for the bacteria.

In the second stage of the process, the waste passes through sedimentation tanks where the flow is made as quiescent as possible in order to promote either flotation or settling of suspended solids.

It has been shown that fruit and vegetable canning wastes are amenable to treatment in trickling filter systems, either alone or in combination with domestic sewage. However, certain conditions must be fulfilled. Fruit and most vegetable wastes are deficient in the available nitrogen needed to support microbial growth on the filter surfaces. This must be supplied by addition of nitrogen-bearing chemicals.

Another common characteristic of canning waste is its acidic nature, caused by inclusion of acids from the raw foods being canned or as a result of bacterial fermentation of sugars and starches in the waste. Continuous adjustment of pH of the raw influent and recycle stream is usually necessary to prevent damage to microbial growth in the filter.

Chemical Treatment of Canning Wastes. Chemical treatment to precipitate solids from liquid wastes was once a relatively common technique. This form of treatment is now considered ineffective. Reductions in BOD obtained by addition of flocculants or coagulants are not, in most cases, sufficient to meet the requirements of present day regulatory standards. However, addition of chemical coagulants may be worthwhile as a form of pretreatment.

Chemical treatment usually involves the addition of lime, followed by either ferrous sulfate or alum. The operation may be carried out in fill-and-draw or continuous flow systems. To be successful, the coagulant must be rapidly mixed into the waste. The floc which forms takes down the suspended and colloidal solids as it settles to the bottom. The sludge is drawn off and is usually disposed of to drying beds.

In the most efficient operation, chemical treatment removes no more than 50% of the BOD from such wastes as pea and corn. Less than 20% BOD removal is obtained with fruit wastes.

INDUSTRY TRENDS AND RESEARCH NEEDS

Concepts in water quality and water pollution control are rapidly changing to meet the impact of population and industry growth. Public health and regulatory agencies, long concerned about bacterial contamination in water, have broadened their concepts to include any deterioration of its quality. Consideration is now given to such characteristics of a waste entering a stream as its temperature, organic content, salinity, turbidity, color, and odor. Currently much attention is given to the waste's content of detergent, pesticide, and radioactivity.

The over-all situation with respect to water supply and pollution control has serious implications for the food processing industries. Federal agencies consistently point to food processing as being one of six major industry groups responsible for pollution of the nation's streams. This can result from direct discharge of untreated wastes or from the discharge of sewage-food waste combinations that are inadequately treated because of overloads on municipal treatment plants.

It must be expected that water consumption by the food canning industry will increase. Today, raw foods must be thoroughly washed to remove toxic chemical residues as well as the natural contaminants on field-grown crops. To this increased consumption of water per case must be added an over-all water consumption increase due to economic factors that have decreased the margin of profit per unit package of food. To survive, the individual food processor must increase production. Handling larger tonnages of raw product requires the use of larger volumes of water.

The concern for more economical methods in food canning has brought about development and use of bulk handling methods in preparing foods. Within the cannery, bulk handling includes the use of hydraulic dumps for receiving raw foods and hydraulic systems for moving the foods to and from various preparation operations. One result of these trends and changes is an increase in the volume of liquid and solid wastes that must be disposed of, at higher and higher costs.

To add to the complexity of present and future problems in disposal of food canning waste, it must be recognized that land disposal methods for these wastes may now or soon be unusable in many areas of the country. Explosive population growth and urbanization of rural areas will surround once isolated food plants with homes and other industries. Lagooning and sprinkler irrigation disposal of liquid waste may not be possible because of the value of the land required for a nonproductive purpose and the nuisance problems that often result.

OBJECTIVES OF CURRENT RESEARCH

To meet the growing need for reliable information about treatment and disposal of food canning and related wastes, well organized, adequately supported research programs must be initiated. Currently, only programs of limited scope are under way. There must be widely expanded research to develop new and improve existing waste treatment methods and equipment. More investigators must become interested in research applicable to food waste treatment. More funds must be made available for this purpose.

To the extent possible under existing conditions, research laboratories connected with the canning industry are striving to develop urgently needed information. A limited amount of research is being done in universities. In some phases of the research efforts, government funds are helping to develop information applicable to problems affecting the public.

Industry-financed research programs are designed to achieve the following objectives:

1. Development and demonstration of in-plant water use practices which limit the volume of process water to that necessary to carry out a sanitary canning operation
2. Segregation, within the plant, of strong wastes from weak wastes for the purpose of separate handling and treatment
3. Selection and evaluation of high-rate treatment methods applicable to handling small volumes of strong wastes.

The use of water in food plants and disposal of the water after use create problems so varied in character and complexity that their solution will require the attention of engineers, chemists, microbiologists, and other workers in many fields. Among the problems that must receive attention are the following:

1. New designs in equipment for harvesting canning crops should give consideration to the sanitary condition of the harvested crop. Excessive amounts of soil, leaves, and stems necessitate the use of excessive volumes of water to clean the product.

2. New designs in food plant equipment using water should consider factors which increase the efficiency of water use. In addition, the equipment should be designed so that it is easily cleaned without excessive use of water. Included in this are raw product washers using less water to give cleaner products, can coolers using less water to accomplish cooling, and evaporative condensers requiring less water.

3. Methods for cooling water, prerequisite to its reuse, should be more efficient and less expensive. Many canners now without cooling systems feel that the conventional redwood towers are too expensive and inefficient.

4. Greatly needed is equipment which would make possible the screening or filtering of process waters to remove soil and organic debris, thus rendering the water reusable. Perhaps a liquid cyclone separator would do this.

5. Evaluation of food plant wastewaters for irrigation of field crops could have far-reaching consequences. Before irrigation of crops with wastewater would be widely accepted, basic questions must be answered:

   a. How do various types of organic wastewaters affect soil structure, groundwater levels, and groundwater quality?
   b. What are the soil-building potentialities of organic wastewaters?
   c. What crops would be best suited to irrigation with wastewaters?
   d. What are the economics of transporting wastewaters to suitable sites for irrigation disposal?

6. Of great value would be an investigation of the feasibility of disposal of food wastewaters by direct injection into confined aquifers. Injection by pumping into a water-bearing stratum would not be a health hazard, because wastewaters from fruit and vegetable canning contain no microorganisms of public health significance. Admittedly, many problems would have to be solved by experimentation, but artificial recharge of groundwater resources with wastewaters of this type would have considerable potential for the ultimate solution of water problems in some areas.

REFERENCES

1. Eckenfelder, W. W., Jr., Woodward, C., Lawler, J. P., and Spinna, R. J., "Study on Fruit and Vegetable Processing Waste Disposal Methods in the Eastern Region." Manhattan College, New York, 1958.
2. Monson, H. G., Canner 116, No. 24, 14–16; No. 25, 35–36 (June 15 and 29, 1953).
3. O'Connell, W. J., Sewage Ind. Wastes 29, 268–280 (1957).
4. U. S. Public Health Service Publ. No. 952, "An Industrial Waste Guide to the Fruit Processing Industry," 1962.

Chapter 7

STARCH AND STARCH PRODUCTS

by R. E. GREENFIELD

The production of starch and starch products from various raw materials to furnish purified starch for use in industry and food often presents disposal problems for the waste residual liquids containing dissolved and suspended organic materials. These problems vary with the source material, manufacturing methods used, and local conditions. Disposal of wastes from the manufacture of potato chips is also discussed in this chapter because the wastes are similar to those produced in the manufacture of starch.

The industrial use of starch in operations such as textile sizing and paper and leather production also produces starchy wastes, discussion of which is included in other chapters of this book.

THE STARCH INDUSTRY

Starch is produced from a variety of grains and tubers, and from the pith of certain palms. Corn is the predominant starch raw material in the United States, with white potatoes, sweet potatoes, wheat, and milo maize being of secondary importance. In other countries starch is also produced from tapioca or cassava, sago, and arrowroot.

STARCH FROM CORN AND MILO MAIZE

The production of essentially pure starch from corn is called the wet corn milling industry or the corn refining industry. There are 10 producing companies in the United States, with plants at 13 locations. Most of them are in the Midwest and from economic necessity are of large capacity. The capacity of the smallest of these plants is over 20,000 bushels per day and the largest is over 100,000. At least one plant is equipped to produce starch from either milo maize or corn, as the processes are essentially identical.

The industry ground over 175 million bushels in the year 1962. Sales of starch, modified starches, corn sirups, corn sugars, feed ingredients, corn oil, and specialty products produce an added value due to manufacturing in excess of 80% of the original cost of raw materials. The industry gives employment to over 13,000 people.

STARCH FROM POTATOES

The production of starch from white potatoes is on a much smaller scale than cornstarch production. The industry consists of a number of small plants located in potato producing areas, mostly in Maine and Idaho.

Operation of these plants is seasonal, and total production is highly dependent on the magnitude and quality of the crop. Culls or surplus potatoes are generally used, as it is ordinarily not economical to process potatoes that can be sold in the food trade. Production of from 80 to 100 million lb of starch per year, representing 300–400 thousand tons of potatoes, is average for the industry.

Sweet potato starch was at one time produced in at least two plants, in Mississippi and Florida. These two plants were closed in the middle 1950's and since then there has been little or no production of this starch in the United States. While the processes were different in certain respects, the waste problems of starch production from sweet potatoes were similar to those from white potatoes, and will not be further discussed in this chapter.

STARCH FROM WHEAT

Several processes for production of starch from wheat have been described in the literature, but since the end of World War II essentially all production has started with dry milled wheat or wheat flour. The wheat starch industry is not large; it consumes about 175 million lb of flour per year in 6 production plants.

OTHER STARCHES

Starch is also produced from other grains and tubers and sago starch is produced from the pith of a palm. In the United States, production from these other materials is relatively minor, if carried out at all. In other countries, considerable starch is produced from tapioca (cassava), and production from sago and arrowroot, though smaller, is substantial. Waste problems and needs for disposal are, in general, similar to the major starch industries listed above. In some foreign countries these problems are locally quite acute.

THE DRY MILLING INDUSTRY AND BAKERY PRODUCTS

The production of wheat flour, corn meal, grits, and flour from corn, and the utilization of these products in bakeries of all sorts, while not classified as part of the starch industry, comprise a large segment of industry working with starch-bearing materials. The same consideration can be extended to other grain processing and to animal feed industries. The literature contains very little discussion of the problems of waste production and disposal in these large industries. They are essentially dry processes, and present little or no liquid waste for disposal. Dust losses into the air can cause air pollution problems, and when the dust settles it may find its way into the sewers or streams. Plant cleanup sometimes produces waste but this can often be handled in a dry manner. Special processes, such as the washing of grain, undoubtedly do produce liquid wastes. The general distribution of these plants often allows use of local treatment facilities for their relatively minor disposal problems; where such facilities are not available, standard methods of handling organic wastes do not require large installations.

THE POTATO CHIP INDUSTRY

The large volume potato chip industry consists of many small plants widely distributed over the United States. Census reports for 1959 show consumption of over 1,000,000 tons of potatoes for this product.

Although the waste loss from any one plant is usually not large, the total national loss potential is perhaps larger than for any other industry considered in this chapter. Using average figures given later in this chapter, the total organic loss represents a population equivalent of 150–300 million, compared with a probable total of approximately 175 million per year for the corn milling industry.

CHARACTERISTICS OF STARCH WASTES

Although widely differing processing features are used in the manufacture of starch from grains, starch from tubers, and potato chips, the untreated wastes from all 3 classes of manufacture have many common characteristics. The wastes originally are very dilute suspensions of solids in water, plus a higher proportion of dissolved substances extracted from the starch raw material. Chief among the soluble materials are nitrogenous compounds, carbohydrates, organic acids, and minerals; in the suspended solids are found proteins, carbohydrates, fat, connective tissue, and minerals.

Starch wastes lend themselves readily to all putrefactive and fermentation reactions. When discharged to streams, oxygen is absorbed and algae and plant growth encouraged. If the stream is overloaded, its oxygen content is depleted, anaerobic putrefaction sets in, and higher forms of life are killed. The discharged solid waste may form sludge banks consisting of the solid wastes themselves and the organisms growing on the wastes.

Correspondingly, these wastes usually are responsive to almost any complete disposal method that can be used on domestic sewage. Due regard must of course be given to load factors and, at times to supplying additional nutritive supplements to balance the nutrients in the wastes. These wastes differ from domestic sewage in being free from pathogenic organisms.

At times starch plant wastes are produced at temperatures above that of ordinary sewage. This is often advantageous in winter operation of disposal plants, but sometimes introduces problems in sewer construction and maintenance.

Because the in-plant recovery of what otherwise would be waste is so dependent on changes in the process, and because special disposal methods used on certain waste fractions are so related to the particular steps involved, brief discussions of the manufacturing processes will be included under the heading of waste disposal.

WASTE RECOVERY AND DISPOSAL

CORNSTARCH AND RELATED PRODUCTS

The manufacture of starch from corn or milo maize is a complex process, worked out over many years to attain maximum yields and qualities of various products, and more recently to retain and recover the maximum production with minimum waste. A flow sheet designed to show all the steps in the waste recovery becomes bewilderingly complex. A simplified version is shown in Fig. 1, and only the most basic steps will be presented in this chapter.

Cornstarch Process, the Bottled-up Plant. Cleaned, shelled corn is steeped in warm sulfurous water and the steepwater containing corn solubles is drawn off and evaporated, the solubles becoming a feed ingredient. The corn, softened by the steeping, is put through a milling process involving grinding, screening, flotation, and centrifuging, designed to separate the kernel into germ, fiber, gluten, and starch. Oil is removed from the germs to produce corn oil and corn oil cake meal. The corn oil cake, the fiber, and the gluten, along with the evaporated steepwater are used in feedstuff manufacture.

The starch is further purified by washing to free it from solubles. The starch washwater is the only water input to this milling process, and the steepwater withdrawn from the steeps is the only liquid outlet. With the exception of entrainment and distillation of volatiles from the steepwater evaporators, there should be, with ideal conditions, no other liquid waste from this process. This is the so-called bottled-up process which was developed in the late 1920's following the work of several people, and was adopted generally only after considerable litigation over conflicting patent claims. This process reduced losses from 2% of the corn

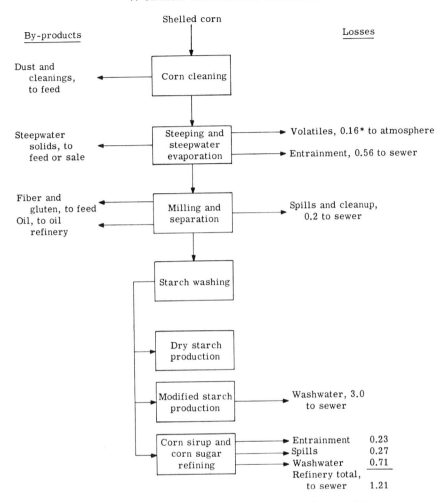

Fig. 1. Corn wet milling process showing by-products and losses.

* Figures are typical BOD population equivalents per bushel of original grind going to the individual department per day.

dry matter to less than ½% and BOD losses from more than 10 population equivalents per bushel ground per day to less than 1. Hatfield (3) and Greenfield et al. (2) give descriptions of this development.

Steepwater Evaporator Loss. Losses from the steepwater evaporators are caused by both entrainment of liquid and distillation of volatiles such as alcohols, volatile acids, and esters. Steepwater causes problems in vacuum evaporators in that it often forms scale on the heating surfaces, and is prone to foam and boil unevenly. This causes entrainment losses in the carrying over of foam and spray which contain dissolved solids. Such losses can be reduced to a minimum by use of well designed equipment, installation of proper entrainment catching devices, and by expert and vigilant operation on the part of the plant personnel.

Methods of prevention of loss of volatile distillation products to the sewer have been described by Pulfrey et al. (4). They describe a high temperature fermentation process for steepwater that promotes smooth boiling, and a steam stripping operation to remove volatiles from the steepwater prior to evaporation. It is thought that economical recovery of the alcohols by this process is possible; if recovery is not provided, the volatiles can be discharged to the atmosphere, thus removing them from the wastewater. The discharge of solubles into the air may add to an air pollution problem, which is further intensified by discharge of vapor and solids from starch and feed dryers. Greenfield et al. (2) describe an air stripping tower for removal of distilled volatiles from the warm condensate of the second and third effects of the steepwater evaporators, where most of the distilled volatiles are found. Discharge to the atmosphere is the accepted practice. In one plant, use of such a stripping tower lowered the organic load to the sewer by as much as 20,000 population equivalents per day.

Industry averages are not available, but a total evaporator organic loss of 0.72 population equivalent per bushel per day resulted from one typical operation; by stripping, 0.16 was diverted to the atmosphere and 0.56 went to the sewer.

Accidental Losses. Theoretically there should be no loss other than from the steepwater evaporators, but this is actually not the case. Unbalance of the complex water flows, equipment malfunction, errors in operation, leaks, spills, and necessary cleanup of floors and equipment, much of which cannot be returned to the process for esthetic or sanitary reasons, may produce large and sudden losses. Proper design and maintenance of equipment, expert operation, and eternal vigilance provide the only answer. If wastes are going to a treatment process, some provision must be made to smooth out sudden or shock losses in order to avoid upsetting the essential biological balances in the treatment plant. Accidental losses from a typical plant may be expected to amount to as much as 0.2 population equivalent per bushel per day.

Processing of Washed Starch. Washed, purified starch can be dried to produce the pearl and powdered starch of commerce. This should add nothing to the waste loss. A considerable portion, however, of the starch produced is further treated to make a large variety of modified starches, or converted to make corn sirup or corn sugar. Both of these uses of starch may result in additional losses.

(1) *Losses from modified starch production.* Modified starch is made by a variety of chemical agents, such as acids, oxidizing agents, and cross-linking agents. Many of the modifying agents produce little soluble starch, others may form soluble matter equivalent to 10% of the starch treated. The soluble is lost in the washing that precedes drying. Various methods of keeping this loss to a minimum are practiced, depending upon conditions. Some of the washwaters can be worked back into the bottled-up process. For modifications that produce a high concentration of solubles, direct evaporation and addition to the feed stream can be used. If the modifying agent is toxic, none of these methods of recovery can be used and some terminal disposal method must be found. Average figures for modified starch filtrate loss are meaningless because of wide variation between products and product mixes. On one typical product mix, the BOD loss amounted to 3 population equivalents per bushel of grind per day going to modified starch production.

(2) *Losses from corn sirup and sugar production.* Starch is converted with acid under steam pressure at high temperatures to produce corn sirup and corn sugar, and the resultant sirups are filtered to remove insolubles, containing protein and fat, for use as a feed ingredient. The sirup is evaporated and decolorized with a variety of agents such as bone char (now nearly obsolete), activated carbon, or ion exchange resins. Losses occur as entrainment from evaporators, as dilute waters from washing the spent decolorizing agents, and as leaks and spills.

Careful operation of well designed evaporators can keep the entrainment losses at a low level, as corn sirup and sugar sirups boil more smoothly than does steepwater.

Countercurrent methods of washing spent decolorizing material reduce the washwater losses but cannot completely eliminate them. Bedtype operations with bone char, ion exchange resins, or granular activated carbon produce more washwater losses than decolorizing with powdered activated carbon. The powdered material is added to the liquor in relatively small quantities and can be completely washed, with little production of washwater that is too dilute for recovery. At times, activated carbon has itself been allowed to flow into streams. This causes a visible black stain and is objectionable. Usually the carbon is disposed of by dry handling or by burning.

Total sewer losses from sirup and sugar refineries vary greatly with the type of decolorizing agent used. One plant considered typical had a

BOD loss over a period of time of 0.23 population equivalent from entrainment, 0.27 from spills, and 0.71 from washwater, for a total of 1.21 population equivalents per bushel per day of refinery grind allocated to the sirup and sugar refinery. Careful and perhaps fortunate operation often shows losses 30% less than this.

Oil Refinery Wastes. Corn oil is produced in the wet corn process. Some companies, but not all, operate oil refineries in conjunction with the corn processing plants. Because vegetable oil refineries also produce liquid wastes, this adds to the disposal problem. Oil refinery losses from the corn oil production approximate 0.03 BOD population equivalent per bushel of corn ground per day. In several of the refineries, purchased corn oil and other vegetable oils are also refined, which adds to the amount lost. Oily or fatlike wastes often make a valuable addition to the feedstuff product, and other organic materials can be disposed of with other such wastes from the plant.

Final Disposal of Wastes. Final disposal in several plants is by dilution in streams. Other companies send their final wastes to municipal plants for disposal as a mixture with domestic sewage. Often special use rates for this disposal are worked out to cover the extra costs to the municipality.

Treatment of starch wastes as a mixture with sanitary sewage is quite successful. Special attention must be given to loading, nutrient balance, avoidance of temporary overloads, and disposal or use of gas from digesters.

Special In-plant Disposal Methods. Where municipal plants or other available disposal methods are inadequate for the entire load, or where charges are high enough to make partial treatment before discharging to the sewers more economical, several in-plant treatment systems of interest have been developed.

One company operates what is essentially an activated sludge plant on a portion of the modified starch waste, with sufficient material from other process wastes to make a balanced nutrient for the biological growth. There is no admixture of domestic sewage or other human wastes. Because recovery of excess sludge for vitamin content or feeding value proved uneconomical, and because the company has an arrangement with the local municipal plant for disposal of residual wastes, the excess sludge is sewered along with the effluent. Even under these conditions a BOD reduction of 60–70% is attained. It is estimated that complete sludge removal and disposal would make 70–80% reduction possible.

Another plant has an extensive lagooning system to assist in a situation where the municipal system is inadequate to accept the entire load. A lagoon of approximately 10 acres giving 30 days retention time is receiving a loading of over 50,000 population equivalents per day. The lagoon is divided into two parts. One section with 25% of the area and 35% of the volume receives the entire load and operates anaerobically. The other section receives the effluent from the anaerobic section and, with the aid of mechanical aeration at its inlet, operates aerobically. Control of pH and maintenance of a temperature between 80° and 90°F in the anaerobic section are necessary. A floating blanket of 3-inch Styrofoam slabs covering a portion of this section helps maintain the temperature during the winter months. Addition of sodium nitrate to the anaerobic section helps control odors. This company has made changes in internal plant flow to produce as high a concentration of waste as possible and thus to gain a maximum of retention time. This treatment accomplishes over 90% reduction of BOD in the summer months and an average of 85% reduction for the year.

The use of cooling towers and cooling ponds on entrainment contaminated condenser water sometimes helps in reducing over-all sewer load.

As a general statement, cornstarch plants without extensive in-plant treatment methods but having a low proportion of modified starch, corn sirup, and corn sugar production can, by careful operation, keep their final sewer losses under 1.0 population equivalent per bushel of daily grind. With higher ratios of modified starch, corn sirup, and sugar, a final loss of 1–3 population equivalents per bushel per day may represent equally good operation. Special treatment methods can be designed which will greatly reduce these figures.

POTATO STARCH

Because potato starch factories are small and seasonably operated in the United States, not much work has been done on waste disposal. Economic consideration of this type of operation makes unattractive extensive disposal attempts. Most of the plants discharge their wastes directly into streams. In some locations this creates nuisance situations that cause local authorities to press for correction.

The essential steps in potato starch manufacture are: thorough washing of the potatoes to remove adhering soil, grinding or rasping of the whole potato, screening to remove pulp, removal of the protein or fruit water by centrifuging and washing, screening for removal of additional pulp, separation and washing of starch from the remaining pulp and protein by settling, tabling, centrifuging, or a combination of these methods. The washed starch is dried for commerce.

The first washing of the potatoes produces wastewater containing mostly earth from the fields. This has not been considered a serious polluting material and is disposed of without difficulty.

The most serious soluble wastes are the protein water washed from the ground potato and the washwater from the starch. Sometimes these waters are used in a countercurrent fashion to reduce the total volume and to increase the strength of the final waste. A lower volume simplifies final disposal and may lower the charges if municipal plants are used for final disposal.

The pulp and insoluble protein may be filtered and dried as cattle feed. In other plants these insoluble portions are discharged with the wastes.

Ambrose and Reiser (1) report that BOD losses average 348 population equivalents per ton of potatoes per day if the pulp and protein are not recovered as dried material, and 200 population equivalents if only the soluble waste is discharged. The amount of waste varies with the type of plant, the kind of potatoes, and the time of the year. Variation can be as much as 50% from the average.

If local municipal plants have sufficient capacity, and if arrangements can be made for them to accept these wastes, the disposal by admixture with domestic sewage and treatment by standard sewage processes is often the most attractive method. Laboratory experiments reported by Sproul (5) indicate that protein water can be treated successfully by the activated sludge process or by trickling filters without admixture with sewage or added nutrients.

Attempts at disposal at one plant by spraying in a wooded area and alternately by lagooning were only partially successful, primarily because the area used was too limited. The seasonal operation, providing a long winter and spring resting period, seems to hold out promise for these methods if the amount of land needed does not prove to be uneconomical.

There seemingly has been little work done on development of a bottled-up system in potato starch plants, although several authors have suggested that such work might prove productive.

WHEAT STARCH

The essential steps in the manufacture of wheat starch from wheat flour are: preparation of a dough, removal of starch by washing and kneading of the dough, screening of the starch slurry to remove coarse and fine fiber, and recovery of the starch by centrifuging, washing, and drying. The washed dough is dried and marketed as a high protein wheat gluten.

The soluble and insoluble wastes each amount to about 12% of the flour dry substance. Satisfactory disposal of these high-loss wastes has been possible primarily because the wheat starch plants are rather small. Undoubtedly in-plant recovery of a large portion of these wastes would be needed in larger plants, and may have been worked out in some of the existing plants. There is little published information on the waste problems of this industry.

POTATO CHIPS

Wastes in the potato chip industry result from peeling, trimming, and washing of the chips, all of which are carried out with the aid of water. Some wastes result from cleanup of the factory and equipment. This cleanup may contain oil and grease, making grease traps advisable; otherwise the wastes consist of starch and solubles washed from the potato itself and solids from the peeling and trimming. A U. S. Public Health Service report (6) indicates that losses, while varying with the kind and quality of potatoes, usually average 150 population equivalents of BOD per 1000 lb of potatoes used per day. Simple settling to remove starch and peel reduces this population equivalent by 50%. Some attempts at recovery of these solids as feedstuff have been made. More often they are disposed of by dry handling, digestion in the settling tank, or in separate sludge digesters. Discharge of these wastes, either after removal of the solids or with the solids, to the sanitary sewers and disposal through the regular municipal treatment plants is, where possible, a satisfactory and probably the commonest method of disposal.

Where disposal through sanitary sewers is not feasible, and especially where the plant is isolated and has space available around it, other methods have been successful. These include lagoons, irrigation of land, and spray irrigation of grass land or forests. Trickling filters probably can also be successfully used. Lagoons may produce odors that make their use in some locations inadvisable. If lagoons are of sufficient size to remain aerobic, as stabilization ponds, the odor trouble is avoided.

INDUSTRY TRENDS

The probable trends in waste recovery and disposal are fairly easy to foresee in parts of the starch industry, and quite difficult to foresee in others. The cornstarch industry has a history of over 50 years of rather strenuous efforts to resolve its gigantic waste prevention and disposal problem. The rapid and continuous increase in production has made more acute the necessity of continued effort. That this increase in total volume of production is still going on is illustrated by the fact that the industry grind increased in the 5-year period from 1958 to 1962 from 139 to over 175 million bushels per year. Various segments of the industry have been under constant pressure from local, State, and national authorities to abate their wastes or to work out treatments. Much has been accomplished and much remains to be done. The result is that all plants have active departments staffed with able men who are alert to the situation. Regulatory bodies, in their effort to abate excessive stream pollution from any source, are equally able and alert and continually exert pressure. It can be anticipated that advances and changes will be made continuously. Further efforts to contain wastes within the process will be made, and other means of in-plant treatments will be found. Some products will be dropped in favor of others, and further cooperation between corporations and local authorities for mutual working out of disposal problems will take place.

Although foreign practices are not of major concern in this chapter, there are several corn refining plants in operation abroad, especially in Europe and England. In these plants the state of knowledge and the general practices with respect to bottling up and final disposal of wastes are the same as in the United States. Because plants are smaller and often located on already heavily polluted waterways, the reduction of losses is not as completely carried out in these plants as it is here. Local pressures are building up, however, and will require greater effort on these problems in the future.

In the potato starch field the direction of future progress is not so clear. Pressures of local authorities may be the most important factor. This could well take either of two directions: the solution of waste abatement and disposal problems or the curtailment of operations to a point where the waste problem can be tolerated. Both approaches already have been used in different localities.

The potato chip industry is well distributed and tends to integrate itself within the general commerce of furnishing food to a more or less local population. Its problems have usually been worked out locally, within the framework of general municipal development.

REFERENCES

1. Ambrose, T. W., and Reiser, C. O., *Ind. Eng. Chem.* **46**, 1331–1334 (1954).
2. Greenfield, R. E., Cornell, G. N., and Hatfield, W. D., *Ind. Eng. Chem.* **39**, 583–588 (1947).
3. Hatfield, W. D., *in* "Industrial Wastes" (W. Rudolfs, ed.), pp. 132–40. Reinhold, New York, 1953.
4. Pulfrey, A. L., Kerr, R. W., and Reintjes, H. R., *Ind. Eng. Chem.* **32**, 1483–1487 (1940).
5. Sproul, O. J., "Biological Treatment of Protein Water from Manufacture of Potato Starch." Univ. Maine, 1963.
6. U. S. Public Health Service Publ. No. 756, "An Industrial Waste Guide to the Potato Chip Industry," 1960.

Chapter 8

SUGAR

by LLOYD T. JENSEN

Sugar is a pure carbohydrate and is one of the basic foods used in the human diet. The most common form of sugar is sucrose, $C_{12}H_{22}O_{11}$. This food commodity is consumed in the United States at an annual rate of nearly 10,000,000 tons or about 98 lb per capita.

Other than the sugar used in preparing meals, the principal uses are in soft drinks; bakery, cereal, and allied products; confectionery; canned and frozen foods; and ice cream and dairy products. Sugar is used for sweetening, flavor enhancing, and preserving. Refined sugar has a purity higher than a "chemically pure" chemical and this, together with its low cost compared with other chemicals, makes it a possible raw material in the chemical industry. There has already been a great deal of research undertaken to develop sucrose-base detergents. Molasses is used as a raw material for alcohol and chemical production by fermentation processes.

This chapter confines its discussion of industrial wastewater to that associated with the manufacture of sucrose sugar, softs drinks, and candy.

THE SUGAR INDUSTRY

Sugar is extracted from two principal raw material sources, sugar cane and sugar beets. Sugar cane is grown throughout the world in the warm climate areas generally existing between the latitudes of 30° north and south of the equator. Approximately two-thirds of the sugar consumed in the United States originates from sugar cane. However, only about 10% of this comes from cane grown in the continental United States, in Louisiana and Florida. About 13% is produced in Hawaii, a similar amount in Puerto Rico, and a smaller amount in the Virgin Islands—all of which is considered domestic sugar. Sugar, other than that produced from cane grown in the continental United States, comes into the country as raw sugar of about 96% purity. The Philippine Islands furnish about a million tons of sugar under the quota system prescribed by law, and the rest of the sugar requirements are obtained from a number of countries such as Mexico, the Dominican Republic, Peru, India, Brazil, Nationalist China, Nicaragua, and Colombia. Prior to the Castro regime in Cuba, the United States acquired by far the largest part of its needs from Cuba. In some years the Cuban imports exceeded 3,000,000 tons. It is the loss of this source that has brought about purchases from so many other countries. Raw sugar is refined in the United States in 22 plants located in the coastal areas. One large refinery is located on the west coast and the balance are on the east and Gulf coasts.

Sugar extracted from sugar beets is produced in 63 plants located in the areas where the beets are grown. California is the largest producer, followed by Colorado, Idaho, Minnesota, Nebraska, Montana, Washington, Michigan, Wyoming, Oregon, Utah, Ohio, South Dakota, and Iowa. Beet sugar satisfies about one-third of the total consumption in the United States. By far the greater proportion of the beets is grown in the western United States on irrigated land.

By-products are produced in both the cane and beet sugar industries. In the processing of cane, the insoluble residue of the cane is called "babasse" and is used either as fuel or as a raw material for building materials or paper products. The insoluble residue of the sugar beet, called "pulp," is recovered and used as livestock feed in either wet or dry form. Both industries produce molasses, which contains the extracted soluble nonsugars as well as various sugars including sucrose. Monosodium glutamate is produced from a raw material that was formerly a wastewater in certain beet sugar plants, using a special process called the "Steffen process."

The sugar industry operates on a quota system established by the Sugar Act of 1948, which was extended and amended in July 1962. The domestic area quotas, based on a consumption estimate of 9,700,000 short tons raw value, are as follows:

Beet area	2,650,000
Mainland cane area	895,000
Hawaii	1,110,000
Puerto Rico	1,140,000
Virgin Islands	15,000
Total	5,810,000

The Sugar Act provides the mainland cane and beet areas with 65% of the growth in consumption above the 9,700,000 tons. Deficits in quotas are allotted to the Philippine Islands and foreign quotas in the western hemisphere. A quota of 1,635,000 tons is set aside for Cuba to be available when that country is again in diplomatic relations with the United States. Until that time, Cuba's quota is treated as "global quota," to be filled by other foreign countries on a first come, first served basis. Approximately 1,200,000 tons are allocated in individual quotas to 22 foreign countries. The domestic sugar industry has an annual payroll in excess of $160,000,000.

The soft drink and candy industries are users of sugar as a major ingredient. From a waste disposal point of view, they are principally concerned with problems associated with accidental spills, cleanup waters, and disposal of unsatisfactory or rejected products.

WASTE CHARACTERISTICS

Both sugar cane and sugar beets have a common waste problem associated with the unwanted material that is brought into the processing plant, adhering to or included with the cane or the beets.

In the earlier days of the sugar industry, the cane and the beets were harvested with field labor. In the case of sugar cane, the field workers trimmed off the top and extraneous leaves which contain very little sucrose, and cut the cane from the root near the ground. The cane could then be loaded and shipped to the processing plant in relatively clean condition.

In the harvesting of sugar beets, the beet roots were loosened from the ground by a single lifting machine, then the field workers shook off most of the adhering soil and cut off the beet leaves at a point somewhat below the crown of the root; the leaves together with the top of the beet root (which contains very little sugar) were left in the field. In recent years in the United States, because of the high cost and lack of availability of agricultural labor, both sugar cane and sugar beets are mechanically harvested. Mechanical harvesting has added burdens to the receiving plants because there is much more soil adhering to and included with the sugar-producing raw material. Furthermore, the mechanical equipment does not remove all the unwanted leaves and trash as well as the field labor did.

Many devices have been installed in the plants to screen out and remove this foreign material before it is actually introduced into the extraction process. These preliminary cleaning systems do not usually incorporate water washing, so the waste products are fairly dry and can be handled in the same manner as ordinary refuse. There are many areas where it is necessary to incorporate rather elaborate rock handling equipment to remove rocks gathered by the mechanical harvesters. The sugar industry is attempting to improve the equipment used for mechanical harvesting to the end that this extraneous material can be left in the field in which the crop is grown. This is desirable because much of the adhering soil is fertile top soil, and the green, leafy material can provide organic fertilizer that is used in successive crops. In the beet sugar industry the leafy material, along with the crown part of the beet, is most often recovered and used as livestock feed. Agricultural experiment stations are also attempting to develop cane and beet varieties that will not only produce a greater yield of sugar per acre, but will also be of a form or shape that can be more easily harvested by mechanical means.

CANE SUGAR

Sugar cane ordinarily averages about 15% by weight of fiber and about 85% by weight of water and soluble solids. The cane is a type of giant grass that is a perennial. Cane received at the plant is usually processed within 24 hours after harvest because of possible deterioration of the sucrose content, which can occur in cane damaged from handling. Since the advent of mechanical harvesting, nearly all cane processing plants use water washing equipment to clean the cane before sugar extraction. Water utilized for this washing operation is usually water that has previously been used for condensing vapors in the barometric condensers. The amount of water used for this washing operation varies widely, depending on the cleanliness of the cane, the availability of the water, and the means to dispose of the wasted washwater. For purposes of identification, this water is called "cane wastewater."

The sugar juice is extracted from the cane by cutting up the cane and passing it through a series of rollers where it is subjected to a crushing and grinding operation to remove as much sugar as possible. Maceration water is added to remove the sugar further by solution. The fibrous residue, bagasse, is normally sent to the boiler plant where it is used as a fuel to produce steam required for the process operations. In some plants the bagasse may be used as a raw material for fiberboard or paper products. There is no liquid waste problem associated with the disposal of this insoluble material. The sugar juice pressed from the cane is screened to remove fine fibers that are then added to the bagasse. The next step in the process is a clarification operation wherein lime is added to the juice, and the mixture heated, to combine with and agglomerate impurities, forming an insoluble sludge that is removed in a sedimentation unit. An additional yield of sugar liquor is separated from this sludge or mud by means of rotary vacuum filters, and in the same filtration operation the mud is further desugared by washing. Filter cake must be disposed of as a waste product, and is hauled away for disposal or slurried and pumped to detention basins. Following the clarification step, the sugar liquors are concentrated in multiple effect evaporators and then crystallized in vacuum pans through successive crystallizations until recovery is no longer feasible and the sirup is discarded as "blackstrap" molasses. The crystalline sugar product recovered is raw sugar, with a purity somewhat over 96%.

Another source of waste in cane processing is that associated with floor washings and boiler blowdown, in which the pollutional effects are largely caused by sugar. Barometric condenser water has a pollutional effect because of organic material carried in the vapors from evaporators and vacuum pans into the condensers. Another source of waste is created by the soda and acid residues resulting from descaling the heating surfaces in the evaporators and vacuum pans. There are also occasions when a considerable quantity of sugar may be carried into the condensate of the multiple effect evaporators, either from an excessive foaming condition or from lack of control of evaporator levels. In this event, the condensates become unsuitable for boiler feed water and must be wasted. The BOD values of these infrequent discharges of condensate may be high because of the high loadings of organic material in the water. Table I gives typical data on the volume and character of wastes from a plant producing raw sugar from cane in Louisiana.

TABLE I

REPRESENTATIVE CHARACTER AND VOLUME OF RAW SUGAR MANUFACTURING WASTES
(2,400 TONS OF CANE DAILY CAPACITY)

Kind of Waste	Average flow rate, gpm	5-day BOD average, mg/liter	Total daily BOD load, lb
Cane wash water	1000	680	8,157
Floor washings and boiler blowdown	100	378	453
Soda and acid wastes[a]	10	—	—
Excess condensate	50	10	6
Condenser water[b]	5000	69	4,138
Totals	6160	—	12,754
Average, per ton of daily capacity	—	—	5.31

Taken from reference (6).
[a] Principally NaOH, NaCl, and HCl.
[b] Assumes once-through operation.

As indicated in Table I, refined cane sugar is produced in two steps: first, the manufacture of raw sugar, and second, steps carried out in a refinery wherein the raw sugar is converted into the various sugar products for market. Plants producing raw sugar operate on a seasonal basis during the period when the cane is mature and weather conditions are suitable for harvest. Cane must be processed immediately after being harvested, but the raw sugar produced can be stored almost indefinitely and the refineries, collecting raw sugar from many sources, can operate around the year.

The pollutional wastewaters produced in a refinery are associated with the operation of evaporators and vacuum crystallizers utilizing barometric condensers, and with sugar entrainment losses in condensates. Other sources are floor washings, boiler blowdown, and soda and acid wastes. The process in a refinery consists of washing the raw sugar crystals to remove surface impurities, then "melting" or dissolving the sugar in order to further purify it by a defecation or clarification process. This is followed by ash and color removal by means of boneblack or bone char. The traditional crystallization steps are employed, with the end products being sugar and molasses. The clarification step produces a solid waste and the bone char operation is a pollution hazard because the dilute washwaters that are disposed of contain trace quantities of sugar.

BEET SUGAR

Sugar beets, when received at the processing plant in either trucks or railroad cars, are transported into the plant by means of water flowing in flumes. This water, as in the cane sugar industry, is mostly comprised of the outfall of the barometric condensers used on the evaporators and vacuum pans. The flume method of conveying beets also provides initial cleaning. When the beets are transported into the plant proper, equipment is provided to remove rocks, leafy material, and weeds. Then the beets are thoroughly washed in a beet washer. The product of this flume water and washwater is a wastewater, normally classified as "flume wastewater."

The sugar beets are cut into thin slices and sugar is extracted from them in a diffusion apparatus. In most sugar beet plants today the insoluble pulp is pressed to remove as much water and sugar as possible, and is then dried in direct-fired rotary drums to produce a livestock feed. Two wastes are produced: water that is drained from the wet pulp before it is pressed, called "pulp screen water," and water that is squeezed out in the pulp presses, called "pulp press water." There are still a few plants where pulp from the diffuser is merely screened and discharged into silos that are provided with channels to remove "pulp silo drainage water." This wet pulp ferments in the silos, and produces a desirable type of wet livestock feed. In producing this product, there are two possible sources of wastewater: pulp screen water and pulp silo drainage water.

The raw sugar juice extracted in the diffuser after heating is purified by adding lime. The lime is then precipitated in two steps by CO_2, and the insoluble precipitate containing organic and inorganic impurities is filtered out of the sugar liquor and washed to produce a waste product called "lime cake." This is normally slurried and pumped to detention ponds. As in the cane sugar industry, barometric condenser water may not all be used for fluming and washing, and can become another waste-water.

Sucrose can be recovered from molasses by the Steffen process. This is carried on in conjunction with the main sugar extraction process and is used in some, but not all, of the beet sugar plants. Finely ground calcium oxide is added under low temperature conditions to a dilute molasses solution to precipitate a calcium saccharate. This insoluble saccharate is filtered out and introduced into the raw sugar liquor at the main purification step of the normal extraction process. The filtrate separated from the calcium saccharate precipitation is classified as "Steffen waste."

TABLE II

REPRESENTATIVE CHARACTER AND VOLUME OF BEET SUGAR MANUFACTURING WASTES

Waste	Flow, gal per ton of beets	5-day BOD, mg/liter	Suspended solids, mg/liter	5-day BOD, lb per ton of beets sliced
Flume water	2600	210	800–4300	4.5
Pulp screen water				
Side-dump celltype diffuser	1420	500	620	5.9
Continuous diffuser[a]	400	910	1,020	3.0
Pulp press water	180	1,710	420	2.6
Pulp silo drainage	210	7,000	270	12.3
Lime cake slurry	90	8,600	120,000	6.5
Lime cake lagoon effluent	75	1,420	450	0.89
Barometric condenser water	2000	40	—	0.67
	Flow, gal per ton of molasses[b] processed			5-day BOD, lb per ton of molasses[b] processed
Steffen waste	2640	10,500	100–700	231

Taken from Reference (5).

[a] Water-transported pulp in lieu of mechanical conveyor.

[b] Converted to 50% sucrose (sugar) basis.

Table II gives typical values of the volume and character of wastes from a beet sugar manufacturing plant. This is a seasonal industry, so the values are those that occur during the 3–4 months of operation and are not averages for the year. The figures for Steffen waste are based on tons of molasses processed.

WASTE DISPOSAL

The emphasis placed, both legally and morally, on stream pollution abatement has made it necessary for all industry to look first at in-plant practices for possible elimination or reduction of harmful wastes at the source. The sugar industry is no exception, and remarkable reductions have been made by this method. The manufacture of sugar requires extensive use of multiple effect evaporators and vacuum crystallizers. Sugar liquors are inclined to foam and, without the use of effective vapor entrainment separators, substantial quantities of sugar can be lost into the condenser waters which may become a part of the wastewater. Vacuum batch crystallizers, because of human frailties, can be overfilled to the degree that effervescence of the boiling liquor carries large quantities of sugar over into the barometric condensers. These two conditions can create significant shock loadings of BOD in the wastewater and cause a real economic loss. Both beet and cane sugar manufacturers must carefully and frequently analyze the condensates and the condenser waters for sugar in order to evaluate this problem. If better entrainment separators or mist eliminators can be acquired, efforts must be made to effect these additions. The use of level controllers in some equipment is justified to eliminate the human errors. Administrative instructions must be devised and enforced. An advantage of in-plant analysis of waste sources is that it often provides some economic return in addition to helping solve the problem of pollution control. Two raw cane sugar plants have realized savings of around $2500 per day each, together with BOD reductions from several thousand to 20 or 30 mg/liter (3). This loss of sugar in wastewater is a problem common to the cane raw sugar producer, the cane sugar refiner, and the beet sugar producer.

In that part of the cane sugar industry engaged in the production of raw sugar, disposal difficulties largely revolve around the handling of cane washwater. The other wastes, except soda and acid wastes, are low in BOD; good in-plant control, coupled with an adequate stream flow, can provide a system for assimilating these wastes. Filter cake should be returned to the fields as a fertilizer. Cane washwater can be brought to lower volumes by recycling, but the BOD values increase in proportion, so this does not provide much relief from waste treatment.

Some attempts have been made to discover a suitable system for waste treatment, but nearly all systems now in use employ lagooning. The cane washwater can be treated adequately by microorganisms in a properly designed multibasin arrangement. Soda and acid wastes can be added to the washwater for treatment, but it is preferable to employ a separate lagoon for this material. It has been reported that a lagoon system, using aeration in the first basin, reduced the BOD from 1000 to several hundred milligrams per liter (3). Another report substantiated these results, with final BOD in the 100 mg/liter level.

The beet sugar industry has been able to reduce effectively the pollution caused by its wastewater, principally through the system of recirculation and reuse. Development of a successful type of continuous diffuser for the extraction of sugar has prompted the industry to install this equipment as rapidly as possible. For the past several years it has been the practice, where these continuous diffusers are installed, to incorporate additional equipment in order to include pulp screen water and pulp press water from the pulp drying operation as a part of the diffuser supply water. This completely eliminates the discharge of two wastes that previously contributed a substantial percentage of the total pollutional load. It is now also common practice for the industry to pump lime cake slurry into retention ponds to prevent its entrance into the streams. There are no difficulties associated with this other than the ultimate problem that will be generated by large accumulations of this material on the plant properties. In some areas of the United States lime cake can be returned to the farms to correct an acid soil condition. In a few installations the lime cake is reburned in special equipment so it can be reused in the purification step of the process or in the Steffen process.

At the few plants where pulp is not dried but is placed in silos for use as wet livestock feed, screening equipment is being installed to fine-screen the silo drainage water to remove suspended material. Barometric condenser water can usually be assimilated into the receiving streams in the quantity that is in excess of the requirements for flume water and other services. Where water supplies for the plant are not adequate, cooling towers or spray ponds are used to permit recycling.

The Steffen waste, which was harmful to receiving streams because of its high BOD, suspended solids, and alkalinity, has now been almost completely eliminated from the wastewaters that reach the streams. The discovery that this waste contained a basic chemical needed for the production of monosodium glutamate prompted the construction of two plants to use Steffen waste as raw material. The Steffen waste, which is in reality a filtrate, has only about 2 or 3% solids. To prepare this filtrate for use as a raw material for production of monosodium glutamate, it is necessary first to reduce the pH to precipitate the CaO. The material must then be concentrated to a dry substance of 40–60%. During the course of this process, or immediately following, the basic ingredient must be hydrolyzed to glutamic acid. The plants producing monosodium glutamate from this source first precipitate the inorganic salts, largely potash, then dry the material which is sold for fertilizer. After the glutamic acid is precipitated and separated from the feed material, the end product is a liquor of about 65% dry substance with a high protein content, usable as livestock feed either directly or after ammoniation. It appears that, within a short time, the Steffen waste that is not used as raw material for monosodium glutamate production will be concentrated and added to the dried pulp to provide a higher content of protein for feedstuff use. It can be seen that nearly all wastes that have a deleterious effect on streams, except flume water, will soon be eliminated. Each year the industry builds several pulp drying plants, and it should be only a relatively short time before pulp silo drainage also will be nonexistent.

Previous to the more recent developments that incorporate reuse and recycling, many attempts were made to treat the various wastes either separately or jointly. Attempts were made to treat the pulp screen water and pulp press water with lime or chlorine or with flocculating agents, with the hope that the BOD could be reduced substantially. Reuse of these waters as process water, after sterilization to control the microorganisms, has been a successful means of eliminating this waste. Additional extra equipment is required, and there are corrosion problems, but reuse is now almost a standard practice.

A joint study was carried on by the U. S. Public Health Service, the Nebraska and Wyoming State Departments of Health, and the Great Western Sugar Company to evaluate the broad field disposal of sugar beet wastes (2). This system, which was fed by the combined wastes, was found to be a satisfactory method of treating beet sugar wastes, but the plant studied is only moderate in size and the land requirements exceeded 160 acres, which makes the cost depend largely on land value and availability.

A study of the disposal of beet sugar wastes by the lagoon method was made by the Minnesota Department of Health in collaboration with the U. S. Public Health Service and member states of the Missouri River Basin Sanitation Agreement (4). This report was responsible for development of the lagoon method, which retains beet sugar wastes through a 6- or 7-month period to effect as much reduction of BOD as possible by natural means before discharging the wastes into a stream at a controlled rate during periods of high water.

As in the raw cane sugar industry, the lagoon system using single or multiple basins has been the common method of treating beet sugar wastes. The efficiency of this system depends to a large degree on the climatic conditions and on the ability to maintain uniform flows through the basins. Lagoon systems are effective in removing all the floating and suspended solids. Although the BOD reduction on a percentage basis is good, the final effluent BOD is often higher than it should be for the flow rate in the receiving streams. Effluents of low BOD can be attained only by maintaining long retention periods which require large land areas. The water in the lagoons must be kept shallow and flowing in order to avoid the generation of H_2S with its attendant nuisance odor.

At least one beet sugar factory has a completely closed system, from which no wastewater of any kind is discharged during the operating season. This is accomplished by recycling the condenser water and re-using all pulp screen and pulp press water for process water. The lime cake is pumped to retention ponds and the effluent from these ponds is contained in a holding lagoon. The flume water is fine-screened and then passed through large thickeners. The overflow is returned to the flume water system and the heavy mud or underflow is pumped to another retention pond. The new makeup water, which must be used for the final cleaning of the beets and for some process water, is limited to about 300 gal per minute. All of the excess waters that are accumulated during the operating period are contained in a large lagoon where they remain 4 or 5 months after the season is completed. At the end of this period, the BOD is low enough for the water to be discharged into the municipal sewage system for treatment in the conventional manner. The capital costs of this system are high in relation to the value of the plant and the maintenance costs also represent a significant per cent of the total operating cost. There are other installations somewhat similar to this one where the capital costs are less, but they are in areas where inexpensive land can be utilized for lagoons and settling basins.

The soft drink and candy industry is composed of many manufacturing units ranging from the small proprietor-owned and operated to the large manufacturing plants in the major cities of the United States. There has never been a comprehensive report prepared covering the various methods of waste disposal employed in these industries, but in nearly every case these plants are so located that wastes are discharged into municipal systems. In any event, the amount of wastewater discharged is small and is most suitable for treatment in a municipal treatment plant.

SUGAR INDUSTRY TRENDS

Recent developments in the sugar supply and demand situation in the world indicate there will necessarily be expansion of the domestic sugar industry. This expansion will undoubtedly take place in both the cane and beet sugar producing areas. Most of the installations that have been made to reduce stream pollution in the industry have been in plants that are old and that were built at a time when little consideration was given to waste disposal problems. This has, in some instances, made capital costs higher than would otherwise have been the case. New plants being constructed, however, will be designed at the outset to incorporate all of the water conservation practices together with the known ultimate in reuse of wastes and their utilization for other products. By far the larger part of the beet sugar industry is located in the western United States, and wastewater discharged from the plants is nearly always beneficially used for irrigation. There are more and more installations where this water is stored behind dams and becomes valuable for recreational use.

The increase in population in the United States, plus the greater demand made on water supplies, will make it necessary for the sugar industry to become more concerned with water quality. Improvement in the design and arrangement of new equipment for the industry should help prevent unintended losses of organic materials into the wastewaters. Expanded use of automation will also assist in maintaining better plant control and reducing shock waste loads. There will continue to be improvements in the mechanical harvesting equipment of both cane and beets, to the end that the crops will be received at the plants in cleaner condition. Improvements are also being made, almost routinely, in the equipment used for dry separation of the unwanted material from the sugar-bearing material. The basic process used for extraction of sugar has remained essentially unchanged over the years. Research is now being carried on with the hope that a satisfactory ion exchange resin will be found to better separate sucrose from the nonsugars. If successful, this might change some of the wastewater characteristics.

Although the lagoon system is now commonly used for treatment of sugar wastes, there is much interest in trying to develop systems that require less land area and are not so variable in efficiency because of climatic conditions. Both the cane and the beet industries need more effective treatment systems for the cane washwater and the flume water, respectively. Research is badly needed in this area and with the research will have to come pilot plant studies. Many conventional treatment systems that might be applicable are not suitable to the sugar industry because of the seasonal nature of its operations. If such systems are to be utilized, wastewater would have to be stored in large ponds in order to keep the operation on essentially a year-round basis. The capital costs of installations to handle sugar wastes, which usually involve rather large quantities of water, are relatively high compared with the value of the products manufactured over the short operating periods. Although much has been accomplished, it is evident that advanced waste treatment systems of one kind or another will ultimately have to be used. The industry is quite aware of the solution to the problems of eliminating or reducing pollutional effects of most of the components of the total wastewater discharges. However, a satisfactory method for all wastes has not yet been developed. Steps have been taken to carry on research on a cooperative basis which should hasten attainment of the sought-after goals. The industry has reduced the pollutional load of its wastes by better control of in-plant practices, by reuse of some wastes as process water, by recirculation for reuse of other types of wastewaters, by screening, by settling, by treatment with chemicals such as chlorine and lime, and by treatment in oxidation ponds. The present trend is to reduce the volume of wastes to make the treatment more effective. In the beet sugar industry there were plants where wastewaters contained nearly 40 lb of BOD per ton of beets processed; now many of these same plants have reduced this waste to less than 7.

Most of the difficult situations occur in the "arid" West, where water is at a premium and stream flows are normally small compared with the watersheds they serve. It is obvious the final answer to stream water quality, as far as the sugar industry is concerned, will come from the results of more research.

REFERENCES

1. Guzmán, R. M., *J. Water Pollution Control Federation* **34**, 1213–1218 (1962).
2. Hopkins, G. J., Neel, J. K., and Nelson, F. L., *Sewage Ind. Wastes* **28**, 1466–1474 (1956).
3. Keller, A. G., and Huckaby, H. K., *J. Water Pollution Control Federation* **32**, 755–760 (1960).
4. Minnesota State Dept. of Health, "Progress Report on Study of the Disposal of Beet Sugar Wastes by the Lagoon Method: Sept. 1950 to March 1951."
5. U. S. Public Health Service, "An Industrial Waste Guide to the Beet Sugar Industry," 1950.
6. U. S. Public Health Service, "An Industrial Waste Guide to the Cane Sugar Industry," 1959.

Chapter 9

FERMENTATION PRODUCTS

by Russell K. Blaine

Fermentation is a natural process around which several industries have been built. Traditional uses of the process have expanded over the past quarter-century, and many new uses for microbiological processes have developed, mostly in the pharmaceutical industry. In the same period, the competitive technique of chemical synthesis has replaced fermentation as the preferred production method for certain compounds.

Manufacturing operations related to fermentation are discussed in the chapters on Dairy Products, Starch and Starch Products, Sugar, Organic Chemicals, and Pulp and Paper. The interlocking of these industries is significant. One view of fermentation shows the process as a link in the stepwise degradation of biologically decomposable agricultural materials. The interdependent economy of raw materials, processing needs, and products allows surplus by-product material of some of these industries to be fermented for profit, rather than to be disposed of directly as waste material. For example, corn steepwater is currently used as a major component of industrial microbial media. Also, corn processors now prepare and market "ready-mix" liquid brewers' adjuncts; this sequence leaves the industrial wastes from adjunct preparation as a problem of the corn processor rather than the brewer.

Shifts of economic advantages of competing processes have caused industrial or nonbeverage alcohol prepared from molasses to fall below 9% (25,000,000 gal) of the total estimated 1964 production in the United States. Until 1949, molasses fermentation provided more than 50% of the product. Alternate animal feed markets for molasses, with its residual sugar intact, are being expanded. As these markets shift, applications of the fermentation process also shift, and the responsibility for disposal of the industrial wastes associated with these industries moves from one industry to another.

Many of the processes used in cheese making, meat curing, and other food manufacturing operations may correctly be called fermentation processes; these topics are covered in the chapters dealing with such products. Use of the fermentation process to produce ethanol from sulfite pulp waste has been investigated as to economics and technology by the paper industry, primarily as a means of pollution control, and is mentioned in the chapter on Pulp and Paper.

147

INDUSTRIAL FERMENTATIONS

Apparently, fermentation processes were operating as a part of the world's ecology long before man began to modify nature's processes to serve his needs. The fermentation of wines and other beverages was a commercial pursuit for many centuries before the Christian Era. Legal controls were applied, even in early times, to maintain quality and to draw taxes from these products. In more recent times, there has been a period when laws of the United States prohibited the sale of alcoholic beverages produced by fermentation. This prohibition has been relaxed, but has been replaced by taxation well beyond the manufacturing cost of the product.

About the time of World War II, the biosynthesis of penicillin gave the medical profession the first of a series of antibiotics produced by microorganisms. The use of industrially practical microbial processes has expanded to such an extent that review of the meaning of the word "fermentation" has become necessary. Indeed, the meaning is undergoing change or expansion beyond the concepts of the older schools of microbiologists. The Latin word itself, *fermentare*, to boil, would appear to cover any bubbling reaction. Pasteur's description of the "life without air" of certain microbes limits the definition of fermentation to anaerobic microbiology, with yeast conversion of carbohydrate to alcohol as the process in mind. Expansion of the concept includes the production by *Clostridium* of acetone and butanol from molasses carbohydrate, usually considered a typical fermentation process. More lenient usage includes the commercial production of lactic acid and propionic acid, the conversion of wine to vinegar, and the processes for producing citric acid and antibiotics.

A recent book by Rainbow and Rose (3) uses 14 chapter headings to group the products obtained from microorganisms. Among the headings are baker's yeast, microbial food, vitamins, organic acids, amino acids, gibberellins, alkaloids, antibiotics, fermentation processes, and sewage treatment. Rainbow and Rose and their associated authors, however, quite definitely define the "fermentation process" as one of the series, not the entire series, of industrially important microbial processes.

Wastes versus By-products

Descriptions of waste composition are of little value if based on the averages of composite wastes from several microbial process industries. If the descriptions are limited to the fermentation industries under the strictest definition of the word, or even if they are limited to the distilling or brewing industry alone, they must still be qualified and applied carefully. This logic is based on the fact that microbial processes are merely unit processes: they are supported by other processes which must vary, not only with the product desired, but also with the raw materials available under the interlocked economy of these industries. Therefore, the type and sequence of supporting processes used in industries employing the fermentation process form an important part of the study of fermentation wastes.

The economic downgrading or degradation of agricultural products has been stated in the sequence: Food, Feed, Fertilizer, Fuel. Any of the last three of these, economically significant though it may be, might have been discharged as a waste material from any category of higher rank. The manufacturer's decision on when to omit steps in this value sequence, such as to go directly to conventional waste treatment with the production of methane and sludge, is based on the economy relating recovery and marketing at the step where the material is produced. The material remaining after the desired products of a fermentation have been obtained is usually of the value level of animal feedstuff, with the cost of recovery as feed near the market value. Final wastes from these plants then include the wastes from by-product processing, but the potential waste of the fermentation residues is reduced to the extent permitted by efficiency of the recovery operation and market for the feed.

The practice of in-plant waste control has been so successful in some large units of the fermentation industry that final effluent can be discharged directly to the river or combined with city sewage. Thus, the unit processes used to accomplish most of the waste abatement in these industries are not of the conventional waste treatment type but, insofar as practical, are at the feedstuff or perhaps the fertilizer level. Because of the fermentation industry's reliance on nonconventional in-plant abatement of pollution, the materials that might be wastes become by-products instead. Improvement of the manufacturing processes and perfection of means for patrolling the improvements have been the procedures preferred by these industries in attaining waste abatement and pollution control.

THE PROCESS

Applied research on the fermentation process has been pursued since ancient times. Pasteur's work advanced this endeavor tremendously, and was a beginning of basic research. Knowledge is presently increasing concerning the intermediate reactions that occur between the glucose and ethanol stages, and between other substrates and the desired compounds of microbial processes. Application of the research on biochemical pathways may lead to additional improvement of fermentation yields. However, the knowledge will probably prove more valuable in raising the efficiency of the newer uses of microorganisms rather than in improving alcohol fermentations, for which satisfactory efficiencies have been achieved. Research using chromatography and other sensitive analytical techniques is finding answers to questions on the specific compounds that make up whiskey, wines, beer, and antibiotic structures. Improvement of the flavor qualities of alcoholic beverages will become possible when this information can be combined with the new knowledge of biochemical reaction routes. More intelligent control may then be exercised over the biosynthesis of important flavor compounds, which are produced as side reactions during the fermentation.

Several tools for control of fermentations are available and used. The nature of the substrate material, whether a grain, a fruit, or a cane product, is especially significant. The fermentation may or may not be conducted in the presence of the protein, pectin, and pentosan portions of the raw material; these substances are converted during fermentation to compounds affecting color, flavor, and other properties of the product. The pH, temperature, and dilution of the medium in which the yeast must work, and the time allowed for fermentation are further controls on the process. The efficiency and the timing of supplementary enzymes supplied to the yeast also control reaction sequences. Research on the fermentation process is aimed at more precise control of the synthesis route and the end products, as well as the quantitative efficiency of the fermentation.

For some industrial microbial reactions, the efficiency with which the desired product is produced may not be directly related to the degree to which the biochemical oxygen demanding substances of the substrate are consumed. Although alcohol is produced by the substantially complete metabolic activities of yeast operating anaerobically, other desired products of microorganisms may be accumulated by intermediate blocking or side-tracking of a metabolic or cell-structuring reaction. Cell material itself is not a desired product of the microbial processes, except in the production of yeast or the experimental production of foods by microorganisms. The disposal of mycelia, production of which is incidental to an antibiotic process, is one of the troublesome waste problems in this industry.

Raw Materials

To put fermentation to efficient and precise use requires attention to preparation of the substrate and to product and by-product recovery as well as to establishment of proper conditions for the biological process.

The type and quantity of the products and wastes produced by fermentation, from a given amount of raw material, are functions of the efficiency attained in the supporting operations as well as of the inherent efficiency of the yeast or other biological system.

Fermentations for beverage products require raw materials such as grain, malted barley, fruit, and molasses. For the entire range of commercial microbiological processes, it is estimated that over 200 strains of organisms are under controlled culture. The satisfying of so many diets requires supplements such as corn steepwater, meat and fish by-products, and surplus animal fat. Protein and carbohydrate raw material supplied in these several forms obviously includes unwanted fibers and other materials that are rejected by the fermenting organisms and that remain for reclamation as another by-product or for disposal as wastewater. These are predetermined or premeditated waste materials, and are not a function of process efficiency in the manner that loss of desired fermentable material would be.

The wastes incidental to substrate preparation and product recovery, as well as the amount and type of the predetermined waste, can be controlled to a significant extent by careful selection of the raw materials. The cheapest material containing the necessary substrate nutrients is not always the material of lowest over-all cost when fermentation product value, by-product value, recovery cost, and pollution control cost are all considered. The amount of substrate preparation carried out at the fermentation plant varies from one plant to another, and has a major effect on the waste potential. If the preparation is done elsewhere, the discarded portions of the material are wastes belonging to someone else. As may be concluded from the interlocking nature of the economy surrounding the fermentation industry, a considerable amount of shopping for raw materials is possible and proper. In the past, this privilege has been neglected to a surprising extent by the older fermentation industries.

Cleaning, tempering, sprouting, and drying of barley are usually accomplished off the premises of the main brewery or distillery. Malt sprouts, a low-value feed ingredient, remain with the maltster. In addition to ground malt, the brewing recipe may include corn grits, brewer's rice in ready-milled form, or one of the new liquid adjuncts prepared to the brewer's specifications by the corn refining industry. The preparation of brewing wort is completed by extraction with hot water at atmospheric or slightly elevated pressure. Distillery mash is cooked at higher pressures. Winery fermentations are of several types, some conducted in a lightly pressed juice, some in juice containing grape skin components, and others with the skins as part of the substrate.

AUXILIARY OPERATIONS

Methods of obtaining the desired primary products from the fermented material are varied. A brewery ferments a cleanly filtered wort; after the fermentation is halted, the product needs little more than adjustment of clarity and carbonation before packaging for sale. Grain distilleries in the United States ferment a whole-grain slurry, then distill to yield whiskey distillates containing about 60% alcohol or spirit distillates of up to 95% alcohol. Wineries are concerned with the direct products of fermentations, in the form of wine, and also with distilled brandies. The desired products of some pharmaceutical fermentations are commonly produced by the microorganisms in concentrations of a few milligrams per liter, and processes of adsorption, solvent extraction, ion exchange, and filtration are required to recover the marketable product from the broth.

The final packaging of the products of the fermentation industries is the subject of research and quality control effort. Advancement of design and maintenance of package quality is important in the competitive beverage market. With pharmaceuticals, fine packaging is necessary to protect the expensive products. Wastes from packaging at breweries, mainly from washings and spillage, may form a significant portion of the waste load. The packaging wastes of distilleries are almost zero because at this stage these products are at full tax-paid value. Distillery containers are not reused, so there is no washing loss.

MARKETING OF BY-PRODUCTS

The marketability and cost of reclamation of by-products left in the fermentation residues are among the most strategic points in determining the degree of waste control to be sought. Under favorable market conditions, the profit on feed by-products from a completely integrated distillery may almost pay the cost of the grain. To accomplish this requires not only production efficiency but also competent research to substantiate the values of the by-product and to develop its market. Some microbial processes yield residues that are difficult or impossible to market. In these processes, much can be gained by selecting low residue raw materials, such as refined sugars or other pure compounds, as sources of soluble nutrient.

Commonly used recovery operations include screening, filtering, centrifuging, evaporation, and drying of the substrate residue. By these steps, breweries reclaim yeast and enzyme products as well as animal feed; distilleries have found the animal feed market most profitable.

BEVERAGE ALCOHOL

The oldest and largest segment of the fermentation industry is the manufacture of products containing ethyl alcohol, for beverage use. The major subdivisions are distilleries, breweries, and wineries, each of which is discussed later in this chapter.

The processes and the wastes that result from the manufacture of industrial fermentation products may be studied in the light of experience and standards of practice developed in the grain distilling industry. Waste surveys spanning several years have been conducted and published for this branch of the industry. The author conducted such a continuing distillery survey for several years (1). Identification of the wastes from several of the unit processes of the grain distilling industry, and description of the survey methods illustrate typical fermentation industry wastes and pollution control practices.

By limiting the presentation of quantitative waste survey data to the well-established procedures of the distilling industry, the nature of the wastes and the techniques of abatement can be illustrated more specifically than if necessarily wide ranges of data are used to show the quantities of waste expected from all commercial applications of the fermentation process. This procedure also avoids estimating the closely held production data of the pharmaceutical industry, and avoids fermentations for which waste abatement standards are being determined. A study of winery processes would similarly provide a good illustration of fermentation industry wastes; certainly the wine industry is one of the oldest applications of fermentation, but modern winery procedures and wastes are not as neatly standardized. This is not a fault but a characteristic of the industry, because the market demands many types of wine and brandy, necessitating varied fermentation and recovery techniques. So wide a field would not make a concise illustration.

The survey referred to is a summary of waste inventories for a distillery using full stillage recovery processes. Inventories were adjusted to the nominal production rate for this plant of 100,000 bushels per week, and were arranged to reflect the complete weekly cycle of normal operation. Since the original publication of these studies, further improvements in waste rates have been accomplished by continuing use of the waste inventories. Water throughput for this installation totals somewhat over 100 million gal per week. This is an unusually high volume, not typical of the distilling industry in general. The plant is arranged for once-through cooling water flow and for making maximum use of river water for cooling in order to conserve well water supplies.

Among the survey techniques found important in these studies was the conversion of all quantitative waste data to a common denominator, based on the production rate of the plant. Distillery production is based on the 56–lb "as received" bushel of grain, carrying a moisture content of about 13%, and ash of about 2%. For example, the total waste values shown in Table I—0.51 lb BOD per bushel and a population equivalent of 3.0 per bushel—are derived by dividing total waste discharge by the production rate. Similar data, in the same units of waste divided by raw material, may be obtained for each process or operation. This permits the addition of similar figures to compute the total waste rate in similar units, and makes possible immediate comparison with plant yield data.

TABLE I

WASTE DISTRIBUTION IN A GRAIN DISTILLERY

Total effluent: Pounds of BOD per bushel	0.51
Population equivalents per bushel	3.0

Operation	Per cent of total BOD
Cooking and fermenting	12.3
Distilling	1.8
Power plant	2.5
Feed recovery	83.4

Adapted from Blaine and Van Lanen (1).

In this way, waste survey figures are ready for the production manager, and are stated in terms to which he is accustomed, with little need for additional interpretation. Statement of waste inventories in terms related to production rate, after the manner of process efficiency ratings, is not new, but application of the procedure in the grain distilling and brewing industries has met with notable success. Industrial waste literature contains many references to microbial process wastes in terms of milligrams per liter or pounds or BOD, with no reference to a unit of production or size of the principal operation. Such data do not fully serve the needs of in-plant waste abatement procedures.

Rigid application of the standard terms to the collection of survey data makes it unnecessary to survey all waste entry points simultaneously. The effects of process changes and equipment breakdowns are minimized. Each process unit must be sampled and resampled until its content of solids, BOD, and other waste constitutents is known at each production rate under which the unit may operate. A data card may be prepared for each process unit and a log kept of operating and waste data for valid runs of the unit, along with the production rate for each run. Much of the survey can be scheduled as a daily operation, thus providing for sampling and analysis of many daily and weekly runs of the equipment. This type of survey schedule has been found better, in distilleries and breweries, than attempting to select a day of typical operation for a full-time study of the entire plant. Of course, under such scheduling, extra care must be taken to keep survey goals in sight and to maintain the flow of data on standardized and fully comparable terms.

Wastes from a fermentation plant have a high potential biochemical oxygen demand per ton of raw material or per unit of product, caused by residual oxidizable organic material normally remaining in the spent fermentation medium and in unwanted material screened or filtered out when preparing the medium. Also, both the prepared medium and the product characteristically have high BOD values and, if small amounts are wasted through accident or inefficient processing, a heavy load is added to the effluent. For these wastes, BOD remains the most practical and useful parameter. However, residue on evaporation, its fixed and volatile fractions, and chemical oxygen demand furnish useful support to the BOD analysis, especially in the evaluation of test runs or attempts to improve operating efficiency of a single process. Useful correlation of COD and BOD analyses is possible if comparison of the two analyses is limited to wastes from an individual unit process. Final summaries of the wastes may rightly consider only BOD, frequently expressed as the corresponding population equivalent. The BOD is, after all, the nature of the pollution that may be sustained from these wastes.

DISTILLERIES

The Process. Typical primary products of a grain alcohol distillery include the beverages: whiskey, gin, and vodka. Cooked slurries of ground whole grains, called "mash," are fermented, without prior filtration, using a yeast that operates rapidly at about 95°F. Ratios of the various grains are varied within specified limits, and malted barley furnishes saccharifying enzymes. Complete conversion of the grain starch to alcohol is sought in a fermentation time of 2–3 days. The alcohol content of a finished fermentation is about 7%. Small quantities of amyl alcohol (fusel oil), lactic acid, and glycerol are formed during fermentation. The slurry is sent to the stills without separation of the solid material. Extraction of botanicals and redistillation complete the gin process. Whiskey attains its color and significant parts of its flavor from oak wood while aging in charred barrels. By-product feed recovery includes the use of screens, centrifuges, vacuum evaporators, and rotary and drum dryers.

Wastes. Typical wastes from a beverage grain alcohol distillery are shown in Table I, based on BOD data. The total population equivalent per bushel of incoming grain is about 3.0. Good correlation exists between in-plant survey totals and periodic effluent surveys, and between these surveys and production efficiency accounts. The portions of waste originating from 4 groups of unit processes are shown in the table. Each waste entry includes startup, normal operating, and cleanup activities. Substrate preparation (cooking) and fermenting operations contribute 12.3% of the plant's BOD. Distillation of the fermented slurry adds 1.8%, and powerhouse losses account for 2.5%. Losses from maturing, blending, and packaging the final products of a grain distillery, in contrast to brewery practice, are so small as to warrant omission from this summary. Wastes amounting to 83.4% of the total come from operations performed on residues from the stills after the desired primary products are obtained. This sizable portion of the waste continues to present a challenge for further waste abatement measures in modern grain distilleries.

A major purpose of a summary such as Table I is to indicate the best possibilities for further improvement. For example, the subtotals that make up the figure of 12.3% for substrate preparation and fermenting wastes, though not shown in Table I, are useful. The 12.3% breaks down as less than 2% resulting from routine operations of cooking and fermenting, over 7% from entrainment from flash cooling the mash, and about 3% from equipment cleanups. Improvements made recently have included lowering the operating and cleanup losses by a system of improved spray washers, so that prepared fermentables may go with greater efficiency to fermentors rather than to cleanup wastes. Other possible improvements would be better reclamation of weekend scourings, and design and operating changes to reduce flash cooler losses. The cost of equipment changes and the possibility of loss of cooling efficiency by changing vacuum cooler cycles enter the picture. The value of additional by-products recovered from better retention of scouring would not be great enough to control the decision, and the final question would relate more to the cost of waste abatement than to additional by-product profit. To date, abatement by the means discussed here has been judged cheaper than an equivalent amount of waste treatment.

In another example based on Table I, an improvement that helps maintain distilling wastes at 1.8% of the total came about by finding a buyer for a mixed fusel oil fraction. Cost of reclamation and storage until a salable quantity accumulates exceeds the selling price; this is an example of waste abatement by accepting a small loss on a by-product.

Although powerhouse wastes do not form a significant portion of grain distilling wastes, the nature of many power plant effluents is such as to cause possible errors in waste analysis. Powdered coal and fly ash washings, resulting from air pollution abatement equipment, have a much greater COD than BOD. Useful correlations on composite waste streams are possible only if power plant washings are excluded.

By-product Recovery. Further improvement in stillage recovery may be possible within the narrowing limits of low profit or nonprofit expenditures. Subtotals within the 83.4% of total BOD shown in Table I include about 50% from stillage evaporator condensate, 32% from dry entrainment from feed dryers and coolers, and 1% from cleanup. Pilot tests have indicated that changes in control of the steam and vacuum may reduce evaporator losses. However, all abatement measures pointed out by in-plant surveys have not been developed so simply.

By-product reclamation in order to lessen industrial waste is not novel, but it is noteworthy that reclamation procedures, in an industry previously identified with heavy organic wastes, now permit operation of large installations with minimum emphasis on waste treatment. The major potential waste of the grain distilling industry is the stillage, or residual portion of substrate not used by the fermentation process. Grain distilleries produce this stillage at the rate of 40 gal per bushel of incoming grain. BOD analyses indicate a population equivalent of about 53 for the 40 gal quantity of stillage. It carries about 7% residue on evaporation, of which one-half is suspended matter and one-half dissolved matter. Before the Prohibition Era, stillage was fed directly to livestock or was discharged to a river, hence this industry's reputation for waste nuisance. After Prohibition, United States distillers independently and competitively developed reclamation processes for stillage and markets for the by-products. Equipment and processes currently in use vary because of the independent methods of development. All are aimed at salable product quality and steam economy as well as waste abatement. The products enter the feed market where purchasing decisions are based on nutrient content and price, and where they must compete with other agricultural residues as the markets change.

At first, only the suspended solids trapped by screening were reclaimed. This product, known as distillers' dried grains, decreased the population equivalent of the waste from 53 to 43. Heavy BOD still remains in the soluble matter which passes through the screens. Concentration of the screened effluent in vacuum evaporators has proved successful. Centrifuging or filtering prior to evaporation, to remove residual suspended matter, permits evaporation to 50% solids concentration. This placed two more products on the market. Distillers' dried solubles is prepared by drum or spray drying of the evaporated concentrate. If the concentrate is mixed with the distillers' grains for drying, the resulting mixed grains and solubles product is called distillers' dark grains.

A portion of the screened effluent has also been used as the base or medium for a secondary microbial process which synthesizes riboflavin. On drying, this yields a feed rich in riboflavin. Current markets list distillers' dark grains in the best profit category of these distillery by-products. Between 17 and 18 lb of this product is reclaimed from the 40 gal of stillage from each bushel of incoming grain. It sells for about $60 per ton. Distilling industry feed sales annually total about $20,000,000. Certainly, these are better markets than the value of methane and fertilizer from treatment plants. Thus, as a result of standard operating practices, the potential population equivalent of 53 in the 40 gal of stillage from one bushel of grain has decreased to a population equivalent of 2.5, as indicated in Table I (83.7% of 3.0). The addition of wastes from other operations in the grain distillery brings the total BOD load to a population equivalent of only 3.0 per bushel of grain.

BREWERIES

In-plant methods of waste abatement have been applied successfully in the brewing industry, using about the same techniques as in the grain distilling industry. The ratio of waste to production used in the brewery, however, is based on the traditional 31-gal barrel of beer as a unit of production, rather than the bushel of grain used by distillers. Comparison with the distilling industry is not simple because, in most published surveys, spills and cleanup wastes form a single account, whereas distillery practice assigns cleanups at each unit process. Processes required for the primary products of the brewery have yielded by-products different from distilleries, but the waste reduction accomplished has been a factor in the trend to large economical brewing plants. At the same time, brewing production in the United States has expanded from sales of 84 million barrels in 1959 to approximately 97 million in 1964.

In making beer, a water extract is made from the malt, adjunct materials, and hops. This wort is filtered, and inoculated with a yeast that works slowly in a cool environment. After fermenting and blending over a period of a few weeks, the product is clarified, the carbonation is adjusted, and the beer is bottled or canned. Selection of raw materials and control of fermentation is such that certain residual carbohydrates and protein flavor components remain in the product.

Several surveys of breweries have shown normal operating waste totals ranging in population equivalent from 12 to 19 per barrel. This is a wide range for a description of normal operations, but peak wastes are known to be even higher. Variations in the amount of substrate preparation done on the premises, cleanup routines, and the amount of spillage of beer are the most significant variables. Some surveys have reported up to 75% of brewery BOD losses originating from spillage and washing operations. Wastage of product is due in part to lack of interest in the loss. Tax allowances on spillage are more lenient than for distilled spirits, so the untaxed beer may not be judged valuable enough to require elaborate precautions against loss. However, the ratio of all costs and the waste rate per barrel would decrease if more of the product were saved.

Depending on the brewing recipes, about 12 lb of brewers' dried grains can be reclaimed as animal feed for each barrel of beer produced. A small and diminishing portion of extracted grain is squeezed and marketed as wet grains. At least 0.5 pound of yeast may be recovered, for which human food markets are available. Brewers' dried grains sells for about $42 per ton. Nutrient values are different from distillers' feeds because the brewing process does not take the grains through the fermentation.

WINERIES

The wine industry presents some of the most difficult or complicated waste control problems in the fermentation industries. The problems stem from the traditional production patterns of the industry, many of which are based on European and South African wine industry practice. To meet the current market, many types of wine are needed, each requiring a different process. The wine industry is currently working to meet its waste, production, and marketing problems; hence, firm standards of practice for waste control in the wine industry cannot yet be established.

Three different types of waste are recognized at wineries. These are not necessarily produced at the same plant; indeed, trends to relocate and consolidate parts of the wine production are steps in the abatement of waste. Some disposal possibilities involve supplying the wastes of one group to another, but most of these possibilities would still be available if the operations were at separate locations.

The first waste results from the pressing of fermentable juice from the grapes, leaving a canning industry type of waste called "pomace." Of course, wastage of fermentable juice at these installations is also a potential source of BOD. Pomace corresponds to the intentional wastes from substrate preparation noted in discussing other fermentations.

A second type of waste comes from the fermenting, racking (decanting), blending, and bottling of the wines. This group of wastes may be likened to brewery wastes in that yeast residues and the spillage of fermentables and final product are included.

A third waste comes from the brandy plant and may be compared with the de-alcoholized stillage of grain or molasses alcohol distilling plants. Separate study of these 3 types of waste is necessary in contemplating either reclamation or treatment. As standards of practice develop, along with more firmly set pollution limits, 3 different criteria will be necessary for these 3 groups of unit operations.

As dumped from the presses, pomace contains 30–40% water, and on this wet basis amounts to about 12% of the original grape weight. High fiber content lowers its potential value for animal feed and fertilizer. Residual fermentables vary with the thoroughness of the pressing. Hard pressings yield a heavier wine or a raw material for brandy, and enter a different market than first-press juice. Other types of wine call for fermentation "on the skins," which brings a pomace residue problem to the fermenting section of the industry. Pomace, because of its residual sugar content, may be handled by fermenting and subsequent extraction in a pomace brandy still. A promising sequence for waste control calls for as complete as possible a pressing, then extraction of the residues with several recyclings of hot water. The extract would be available for various types of fermentation. Fiber content can be reduced by removal of seeds and extraction of the seed oil, if economic boundaries permit. Dried pomace with seeds contains about 35% fiber; the seeds contain over 50% fiber. The California wine crush of about 1.25 million tons annually uses about 60% seedtype grapes, which implies a potential of 1500 tons of oil per year. At present, some of the seed oil enters food markets; seed oil from "seeded" raisins is used to coat the raisins and thereby improve their quality.

The lees (residues from fermentation) resulting from winemaking are available for distillation to brandy, and can be readily transported from winery to brandy plant if these are at different locations. Spillage losses in the fermentation division are housekeeping and operating problems. Tartrate (cream of tartar) is a marketable by-product of winery operation, and has been obtained from each of the 3 classes of wine waste, including stillage, when the market demanded it. The best quality of tartrate, reclaimed with the least effort, crystallizes in wine maturing vessels as a white deposit called "argol." Tartrate from this source enters the domestic market profitably, although tartrate from other wine wastes now meets difficult competition from imports from other wine producing countries. Removal of tartrate reduces the BOD of winery wastewaters directly.

In evaluating brandy stillage, the source must be considered. Brandy can be made from wine, which forms a low solids substrate; from lees, with a medium amount of residue sustained; or from pomace, which gives a ratio of BOD to alcohol produced similar to grain stillage. Mixtures of these substrates may also be used for brandy production.

OTHER INDUSTRIES

The manufacture of alcohol, rum, or other microbial products from molasses is, in reality, a waste control operation of the sugar refining industry. Molasses is a seasonally supplied and priced material, and may at times be available at no cost or for the cost of transportation alone. It is important to distinguish black strap molasses from high test molasses; the former is a by-product of sugar refining, the latter is a whole molasses, containing the sugar, made available in times of sugar surplus.

INDUSTRIAL ALCOHOL

The competition of industrial alcohol derived from petroleum has reduced fermentation production to only 9% of the industrial alcohol market in the United States. In the preparation of molasses for industrial alcohol production, most of the noncarbohydrate material is separated and left at the sugar mill, near the cane or beet fields. A variable degree of further removal of protein and pectin material is accomplished by heat precipitation and lime treatment. After adjustment of pH and balancing of auxiliary nutrients, a suitable yeast accomplishes practically complete conversion of fermentable carbohydrate to alcohol. Molasses is used as a substrate for microbial production of several other commercially important compounds. Stillage from other fermentations may be handled in a similar manner. One gal of 190 proof alcohol and 10 gal of stillage are produced from about 2.5 gal of black strap molasses. The stillage carries about 8% solids and a BOD of approximately 25,000 mg/liter. When evaporated and dried, in much the same manner described for grain distilling operations, the resulting product contains approximately 30% ash, 10% sugars which are mostly nonfermentable but available for BOD, 8% protein, and lesser amounts of glycerine and organic acids. The high ash content is not encountered with grain stillage, and must be taken into account in feed formulation. Secondary fermentations to produce a feed ingredient with high riboflavin content have survived feed market fluctuations somewhat better than similar products from the grain distilling industry. A sirup of 50% solids, from the evaporation of molasses stillage, has found a good market as a feed ingredient. It is not subject to spoilage at this concentration, it is acceptable to feed blenders, and its production reduces molasses distillery operating waste by eliminating wastes incidental to the drying process. A few rum and alcohol production plants located on cane growing islands or at tidewater locations on the mainland may practice disposal of stillage directly to the ocean.

ANTIBIOTICS

Microbial processes have been widely adopted by the pharmaceutical industry for the production of a spectrum of antibiotic agents. The first commercially significant item was penicillin, developed during World War II.

The ratios of waste to production, which are of considerable value in the fermentation industries described earlier, are more difficult to apply to the manufacture of antibiotics. A major reason, of course, is the high potency and the small yield, on a weight basis, of the active product. In other words, the ratio of waste to raw material is nearly 100%, unless primary wastes can be converted to useful by-products. The ratios can be used, however, in reporting reclamation costs or waste reduction accomplishments. Modifications in the fermentation process, which may be of little significance in relation to product yield, may be important with respect to material recovery and pollution control.

Antibiotic concentrates have entered the feed market for their feed value as well as their antibiotic content. Determination of recovery costs for borderline profit items is important when exploiting new markets.

Heavy mycelia from streptomycin filtration is difficult to treat for any value greater than that of fertilizer; sometimes burial in garbage dumps is the simplest means of disposal. The relative advantages or disadvantages of various dewatering units could be shown by unit cost accounting, and perhaps good accounting of the costs of mycelia production might promote new research on the primary process, to improve antibiotic production and decrease cell production in the fermentation.

Chemical solvents used in certain antibiotic extractions must be of high purity to gain the efficiencies required. For recovery and reuse, stripping of the solvent in waste reclaiming operations must be highly efficient if the effort is to prove more economical than the purchase of new solvent accompanied by conventional waste treatment for the old. The potency of solvent waste is readily calculated from BOD values of the pure compounds. Isolation and selection of waste streams for simultaneous application of different types of conventional treatment, solvent recovery, feed reclamation, or composting may provide a practical choice of processes if accurate waste accounting points the way.

TREATMENT OF NONRECOVERABLE WASTES

Knowledge of the types of waste expected from industrial fermentation processes permits setting general guides for conventional waste treatment, when this is necessary. The wastes remaining after application of in-plant abatement procedures are of about the same chemical type as were the heavy loads from these plants in the days before good in-plant control. They exhibit a strong demand for oxygen. The main difference lies in the dilution factor. Among the troubles encountered are too much dilution, deficiencies of certain components needed to nourish a healthy sewage flora, and frequently more organic acid than is desirable.

Fermentation wastes are amenable to treatment by most of the modern conventional biological treatment processes. The Water Pollution Control Federation's annual review of waste literature* usually reports a variety of treatments of wastes from microbial processes. The summary published in 1964 mentions lagooning, irrigation, underground disposal, composting, and several modifications of conventional anaerobic and aerobic treatment.

The combined treatment of industrial fermentation wastes and domestice sewage has been described by Kraus (2), who reported that molasses stillage was for several years treated anaerobically as a separate waste at the Peoria Sanitary District plant, while in the same district a brewery sent its wastewaters to the municipal sewer after in-plant reclamation processes, and a distillery relied completely on in-plant abatement.

In reviewing the rather voluminous literature indexed under the general topic "fermentation wastes," it should be noted that this topic includes all dilutions and that the older articles, in particular, refer to operations without in-plant waste reduction. The value of one company's treatment experience to another company is also limited by differences in the residual portion of waste for which treatment is intended. The wastes may be similar in type but, depending on the in-plant measures applied, the concentration and BOD may vary widely.

In-plant measures may still be valuable when treatment is added as an auxiliary process. The plant surveys provide definitions of the wastes for which treatment is contemplated. Knowledge of the amounts of waste emanating from various parts of the plant is needed in order to select portions of the waste for treatment, and to select different portions for different treatments. The size and cost of the treatment facility depend

* Published annually in *Journal of the Water Pollution Control Federation.*

to a considerable degree on these final applications of the in-plant approach.

The fermentation industry is fortunate in another aspect of waste treatment planning, in that the technologies required by the fermentation itself and by the waste treatment are similar. Both rely on biological processes and employ techniques of bioengineering. Advances in aeration techniques, for example, have been applied both to activated sludge and to microbial processing. If exploited, the common knowledge can eliminate any remaining barriers between fermentation plant and treatment plant, and the entire-plant approach can really be applied.

Summarizing waste abatement planning, it should be possible to define the concentration and the total quantity of that portion of the waste for which treatment is contemplated, then to decide which portion to treat and to consider all applicable types of treatment in order to select the most economical, not forgetting combined treatment with municipal sewage to balance the nutrients. In-plant abatement measures of borderline economic advantage may then be reevaluated, after treatment costs have been estimated.

POLICIES

When planning the location of a new installation of the fermentation industry, modern waste abatement practice of the industry should be the criterion, rather than the historical data covering discharge of the entire fermentation residue. Proximity to a raw material processor or a feed market assumes importance, along with the waste-accepting capacity of the stream.

In any existing plant in the fermentation industry, two questions must be answered. What are the next steps in further reducing the fermentation wastewater? Who should have the responsibility for progress in this area?

Progress to date has included specific identification of wastes from the several unit processes. Methods of extensive in-plant waste control have been adopted, and conventional biological treatment has been found satisfactory for residual or nonrecoverable wastes. Substantial reduction in pollution potential at the large installations of these industries has been accomplished. Another measure of progress is the extent to which satisfactory standards of waste control have been developed for several fermentation industries through routine practice of the control measures. Additional uses for fermentation, the competitive nature of these industries, and public interest in pollution control inevitably will require the continuing development of adequate and efficient wastewater control.

An evident next step will be to maintain and further improve the efficiency and economy of waste control in those branches of the fermentation industries for which waste control standards have been developed. Another endeavor will be development of concepts of satisfactory waste control for branches of the industry that have not yet settled such points. By stating present or practically attainable waste limitations, in terms of production units or total plant discharge, reference points are developed against which progress or maintenance of accomplishment can be shown. Alternatively, additional improvement may be reported from time to time, although each added increment is apt to be more expensive. The concept of maintenance of a satisfactory level of waste control is not established by the latter method.

It is particularly difficult to obtain and allocate credit for in-plant waste abatement, regardless of how practical or economically sound the system may be. A well-established statement of the waste control to be sought is helpful to the men who must build the public relations image or prove compliance with regulations. The development of standards of waste control requires more than reduction of wastes; the progress must be measured and reported. As a dividend, insofar as an industry leads pollution control progress, it has a voice in guiding the direction of the progress.

Who should have the responsibility for progress in wastewater control? Can waste control problems in the fermentation industries be turned over to a waste engineer alone? In an industry emphasizing in-plant control, should his job be assigned and his salary charged to the laboratory, engineering, or the production department? To whom does he turn for policy decisions and authority when a waste problem exceeds the limits of interdepartment liaison? Who might authorize changes in substrate recipes to gain a better by-product quality or recovery rate? Who would accept the summons or responsibility if government pollution control authorities must act? Who will see to it that the company's waste abatement program is recognized where recognition is desirable? These questions are seldom stated. They are waste control problems, but those working with the problems in the industry are reluctant to ask the questions; others do not understand them. The answers are pertinent to development and use of in-plant methods for waste abatement. Single answers will not apply to all the industries involved; but many questions can be resolved if responsibility for waste control is accepted by one or a few qualified members of a high echelon management team. Experience suggests the level of operating vice-president. The responsibility should include assignment of the tasks, such as sampling, analytical work, trial of processing improvements, and the public relations activities concerned. It should include the acceptance and study of reports of the completed tasks and, finally, the decisions and implementation of the action necessary to accomplish progressive measures.

REFERENCES

1. Blaine, R. K., and Van Lanen, J. M., *Biotech. Bioeng.* 4, 129–138 (1962).
2. Kraus, L. S., *Sewage Ind. Wastes* 30, 199–207 (1958).
3. Rainbow, C., and Rose, A. H., eds., "Biochemistry of Industrial Microorganisms." Academic Press, New York, 1963.

Mining

Chapter 10

COAL MINING

by ERNST P. HALL

The water pollution problems of coal mining have received great attention in the popular press. Most of these water pollution problems are not completely unique to the coal industry. The mining of metals such as iron, lead, zinc, and copper sometimes has acid drainage problems similar to those of coal. Gold mining, phosphate mining, sand and gravel washing, and other mineral dressing operations have the problem of suspended solids in their effluents. These suspended solids differ from coal's problem principally in the color of their effluent. This chapter will not discuss the sister problems of other industries but will cover acid mine drainage from coal mining and suspended solids from coal preparation. Water pollution problems of industries using coal as a fuel or a raw material, such as coke and power, are discussed in their respective chapters.

THE COAL MINING INDUSTRY

Wherever thermal energy is required in large quantities, coal is one fuel which is always considered and most frequently used to produce this energy. In terms of total dollar value produced, coal is the most valuable mineral mined; and coal mining is the largest segment of the mining industry. In 1962, the bituminous coal mining industry of the United States employed 143,822 people, with an annual payroll of $857 million, and produced $1890 million in coal sales. During 1962, coal was mined in 27 of the 50 states, and 442 million tons of coal was produced. This production included 422 million tons of bituminous, 17 million tons of anthracite, and 3 million tons of lignite coals. As bituminous coal is the principal type mined in the United States, this chapter will be devoted primarily to water pollution control from the mining and processing of bituminous coal.

Geologically, coal is an organic rock having a structure of layers that vary greatly in thickness, luster, and texture. This structure is most obvious in bituminous coal, but is present in all ranks of coal. Coal occurs in seams or beds, each made up of many layers and interspersed with other geological strata. There may be one or several seams of coal at any point beneath the earth's surface in coal regions, as shown in Fig. 1.

Coal is removed from the earth by either of two mining procedures.

The historical method is underground mining, in which coal is removed from the earth by tunneling procedures without removing the rock and other strata above the coal seam. Approximately 70% of the coal pro-

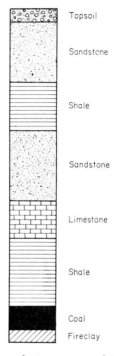

FIG. 1. Typical geologic strata overlying a coal seam.

duced in the United States is obtained by underground mining. When the coal is relatively near the surface of the earth (approximately 100 ft or less), it may be removed by surface or strip mining procedures. In surface mining, the rock and other strata overlying the coal are excavated and removed to expose the top of the coal seam; the coal is then lifted and removed from the mine.

After coal has been taken from the earth, it frequently must be processed to make it suitable for use. Processing generally consists of removing rock and other mineral impurities, and of sizing or screening the coal. Many processes are available for removing the extraneous mineral matter, and most of these operations use water as the cleaning medium.

During mining operations, void spaces are created in the earth's surface, and water percolating through the earth finds its way into these voids. When the water is removed so that mining can continue, or when it leaves the mine by natural drainage, it sometimes has become acid in character. This acid mine drainage causes the coal industry its greatest water pollution problem. Pollution may occur also during cleaning and preparation operations, where finely divided mineral particles become suspended in the water. These must be removed to prevent pollution when the water is discharged to a natural stream. These two forms of water pollution—acid mine drainage and suspended solids—are the principal water pollution problems of the coal industry.

CHARACTER OF WASTE DISCHARGES

The water discharged from bituminous coal mines cannot be readily characterized. It is improper to call this water an industrial waste as it has not been used in the mining process. In fact, it is an unwanted and costly intruder to the mining operation, and in an operating mine it must necessarily be handled and disposed of so that mining can continue. Mine drainage also issues from many abandoned mines, exceeding in quantity and pollutional effect the drainage from active mines. Because water pollution from acid mine drainage is the largest pollution problem of the coal mining industry, it is proper to consider it here even though it is not an industrial waste in the usual sense.

Groundwater draining from coal-bearing strata is a product of nature, and the equivalent of acid mine drainage existed long before Columbus discovered America. Early explorers investigating the then virgin Allegheny Mountains deduced the presence of large deposits of coal from the runs of "sulphurous waters." The drainages from bituminous coal mines today may vary from highly acid waters to water of drinking quality; and good quality drainages are known even in normally acid regions. Acid mine drainage must be understood rather than characterized, and usually prevented rather than treated. To understand acid mine drainage, a working knowledge of the geology, hydrology, chemistry, and bacteriology involved is necessary.

The acid constituents of almost all acid mine drainages originate from oxidative destruction of iron disulfide. Iron disulfide in the crystalline form of pyrite is frequently found in the thin layers or partings between layers of coal in a coal bed. Additionally, pyrite may be found in the coal substance itself, both in the form of small nodules dispersed throughout the coal and in large masses or lens-shaped concretions occurring at random in certain coal seams. Pyrite is often found in layers of slate, sandstone, and other rock overlying the coal.

The pyrite in and near coal seams may appear as bright, sparkling, yellow crystals characteristic of fool's gold, or as a gray-black, hard, pyritic mass. Early investigators, on the basis of appearance and oxidation rate, hypothesized that the iron sulfides in coal consisted of pyrite, marcasite, and pyrrhotite. However, pyrrhotite is iron monosulfide, FeS, and chemical analyses quickly demonstrated that the mineral was a disulfide compound. The pyrite crystal is isometric while marcastite is orthorhombic. X-ray diffraction patterns of these two crystals are easily distinguished, and studies of the iron disulfide in several coal seams have readily identified the presence of pyrite, whereas marcasite has not been found. It is concluded that the iron disulfide mineral associated with and near coal seams is pyrite rather than marcasite. The high rate of oxidation of this material is presumed to result from the small particle size and the intimate association with carbonaceous materials.

Pyrite reacts with dry atmospheric oxygen to form ferrous sulfate and sulfur dioxide in accordance with Eq. (1). In the presence of moisture the reaction proceeds more rapidly, and ferrous sulfate and sulfuric acid are formed in accordance with Eq. (2). When the pyritic material is exposed to atmospheric oxygen under wet conditions, bacterial action also may take place. The bacterial action may somewhat accelerate the rate of oxidation of pyrite; however, the degree of acceleration is a subject of controversy among the various researchers who have investigated it.

Ferrobacillus ferrooxidans and *Ferrobacillus thiooxidans* are two of the organisms credited with the capacity to accelerate the natural oxidation of pyrite. It has been shown that these organisms thrive in a very limited pH range (approximately pH 3.5) and that their activity becomes quite limited when the pH of the medium is appreciably above or below this point. Because of this limitation, it is probable that the total effect of iron- or sulfur-oxidizing bacteria is relatively small in comparison with the chemical oxidation reaction.

During the process of mining, most of the coal is removed from the mine, and the pyrite associated with the coal is also removed. However, the pyrite in some portions of the coal and in the adjacent strata is left behind. The overlying strata, which often contain appreciable quantities of pyrite, are broken and exposed to atmospheric oxygen both during and after the mining operation. As the earth settles, overlying strata are broken and crushed, filling the voids left by removal of the coal. When the pyrite oxidizes, the oxidation products remain in place in the earth unless they are dissolved and transported by flowing water. Groundwater percolates and flows through various soil strata and eventually finds its way into almost all void spaces of the earth. When it flows into an active mine it must necessarily be removed so that mining can continue. When water flows into an abandoned mine it may fill the cavity with stagnant water or it may drain on through and out of the mine. Water flowing through and out of the mine, which has passed over or through acid-forming materials, dissolves the oxidation products of these materials and transports them to the stream.

The initial reaction forming ferrous sulfate and sulfuric acid is usually followed by a series of secondary reactions in which these materials are further oxidized and sometimes neutralized by other minerals dissolved in the water. When the water discharging from a mine has had little exposure to additional oxygen and alkaline materials, it frequently has a pH of approximately 5.6 (the buffering point for ferrous sulfate) and may have the appearance of good water. On further exposure to atmospheric conditions, the ferrous sulfate is oxidized and forms a precipitate of basic ferric sulfate. Additionally, the reaction between ferrous sulfate and naturally occurring alkalies causes the precipitation of yellow ferric hydroxides.

Some of the chemical reactions occurring in the formation and further reactions of mine drainage are:

$$FeS_2 + 3O_2 \rightarrow FeSO_4 + SO_2 \tag{1}$$

$$2FeS_2 + 7O_2 + 2H_2O \rightarrow 2FeSO_4 + 2H_2SO_4 \tag{2}$$

$$4FeSO_4 + 2H_2SO_4 + O_2 \rightarrow 2Fe_2(SO_4)_3 \downarrow + 2H_2O \tag{3}$$

$$4FeSO_4 + O_2 + 2H_2O \rightarrow 4Fe(OH)SO_4 \downarrow \tag{4}$$

$$Fe_2(SO_4)_3 + 2H_2O \rightarrow 2Fe(OH)SO_4 \downarrow + H_2SO_4 \tag{5}$$

$$Ca(HCO_3)_2 + FeSO_4 \rightarrow CaSO_4 + Fe(HCO_3)_2 \tag{6}$$

$$4Fe(HCO_3)_2 + O_2 + 2H_2O \rightarrow 4Fe(OH)_3 \downarrow + 8CO_2 \uparrow \tag{7}$$

$$Ca(HCO_3)_2 + Fe_2(SO_4)_3 + 4H_2O \rightarrow CaSO_4 + 2Fe(OH)_3 \downarrow + 2CO_2 \uparrow + 2H_2SO_4 \tag{8}$$

$$Ca(HCO_3)_2 + H_2SO_4 \rightarrow CaSO_4 + 2CO_2 \uparrow + 2H_2O \tag{9}$$

Many of these reactions may occur concurrently or sequentially, and the composition of acid mine drainage is neither constant nor consistent.

Precipitated iron hydroxide causes the water to appear yellow or yellow-orange. As it is deposited on the bottom and sides of creeks or streams, it causes them to develop a characteristic "yellow boy" color associated with most acid mine drainage.

The yellow color of drainages from bituminous coal mines is erroneously considered by some to indicate that these discharges are acid. In some areas, because of the local geology, water discharging from bituminous coal mines is alkaline and contains large amounts of ferrous bicarbonate. Other groundwaters in these areas also usually contain ferrous bicarbonate. This material oxidizes in the presence of atmospheric oxygen [Eq. (7)] to precipitate the iron as ferric hydroxide. The precipitated ferric hydroxide gives a yellow-orange appearance similar to acid mine drainage.

The acidity of mine drainage is a function of the degree of contact between flowing water and oxidized acid-producing materials and the amount of alkaline material which the water may contact and dissolve either before or after its contact with acid-producing materials. The pH of mine drainage cannot be correlated with the acidity of this drainage, and hence is not a suitable yardstick for determining the effect which a given mine drainage might have when discharged into a particular stream. The lack of correlation between pH and acidity is often confusing and has led many people, both mine operators and water pollution control officials, to erroneous conclusions about the quality of mine drainage water. The lack of correlation between pH and acidity, however, can be understood if we remember that mine drainage is a mixture of unstable chemical compounds that are continuously changing under ambient conditions. Some of these unstable compounds include unreacted alkali materials, ferrous sulfate, ferric sulfate, a variety of ferric hydroxide sulfate complexes, and sulfuric acid that may be occluded and mechanically held in the precipitates.

Most acid mine drainages contain large amounts of sulfate, calcium, magnesium, and iron, and may also contain aluminum, manganese, and other heavy metals. The actual amount of each component and the ratio between components vary over extremely wide ranges, depending upon the peculiarities of each specific location. An average acid mine discharge (if in fact such exists) would contain perhaps 500–1000 mg/liter acidity as $CaCO_3$, 100–300 mg/liter iron, approximately 2000 mg/liter sulfate, and total dissolved solids of approximately 3000 mg/liter. The pH might vary from about 6.0 down to 2.8. Acid mine drainages rarely contain a high concentration of chloride and almost never contain oxidizable organic materials.

Water discharged from the preparation of coal is not greatly dissimilar to the water discharged from sand and gravel washing or other mineral preparation operations. The principal water pollutant in these wastewaters is suspended solids. Additionally, the water may contain an increased but not usually troublesome amount of dissolved inorganic solids such as calcium or magnesium sulfates and iron. Wastewater from coal preparation plants is sometimes acid in character, but usually it is deliberately kept alkaline to minimize corrosion of the processing equipment. This water has a negligible content of oxidizable organic materials. Historically, chlorides were at one time dissolved in the water of certain preparation processes to give the solution a high specific gravity and to assist in the separation of extraneous mineral matter from coal. These processes have largely disappeared and chlorides are rarely a problem in wastewaters from coal preparation plants.

WASTE DISPOSAL AND POLLUTION PREVENTION

The process through which acid mine drainage is formed and discharged to cause water pollution may be illustrated as a 6-link chain. Figure 2 graphically shows this chain and the part each link plays in the formation and discharge of acid mine drainage. Any treatment or abatement procedure intended to lessen the pollutional effect from acid mine drainage must necessarily break this chain at one or more of its links.

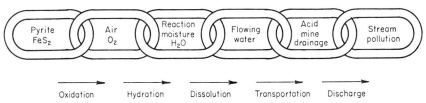

FIG. 2. The chain of the formation and water pollution of acid mine drainage.

Pyrite. The sulfide mineral pyrite is present not only in the coal seam but frequently in geologic strata overlying the coal. In underground mining it is virtually impossible to remove and eliminate from the mine all the pyrite that may be present. Some of this material is removed with the coal as it is mined. Unfortunately, the amount removed with the coal is only a small percentage of the total pyrite near the coal substance. In strip mining, all the strata overlying the coal and all the coal substance are removed. Even in this method of mining it is impossible to remove all the pyrite from the mine, and even if it were removed there would be little economic use for it. However, surface mining does sometimes offer the opportunity of placing acid-forming materials where the chain of formation can be broken at another link.

Oxygen. Oxygen in its gaseous form is one of the more ubiquitous elements. It constitutes approximately 23% by weight of the earth's atmosphere and permeates the earth's surface to a much greater degree than is commonly supposed. Every cave or void in the earth not otherwise occupied is filled with air. This air, while it may become too stagnant to support human life, is not completely stagnant as changes in atmospheric pressure and air temperature cause the earth to "breathe," and some air is periodically expelled from and returned to the void.

The mining process itself establishes almost ideal conditions for air to permeate into an abandoned mine. As the earth settles to fill an underground void the various strata are crushed and broken, making the cover above the mine quite permeable.

Early attempts at breaking the chain of acid formation entailed the construction of siphon-trap seal closures at all the openings of mines. These closures, while they prevented the flow of air in and out of the mine at those points, were ineffective in stopping the formation of acid in most cases because of the mine's ability to breathe through hidden openings and permeable cover. It has since been documented through scientific study that siphon-trap seals are ineffective in preventing the formation and discharge of acid mine drainage from shallow cover above drainage mines.

Proposals have been made to prevent oxidation by inhibiting the reaction of iron disulfide and oxygen. Antioxidants are known which will prevent or greatly reduce the rate at which oxygen reacts with other materials. To be effective, these antioxidants must be applied directly to the interface between the material and oxygen. While some antioxidants appeared to be of value in laboratory studies, no method has been devised by which they can be applied effectively to mining situations. Experimental application of antioxidants has been made through gaseous transfer, aqueous transfer, and direct spraying or application. None of these has been effective in preventing the oxidation of iron disulfide. Even if they had been effective in the situations in which they were applied, their total value is questionable because of the difficulty of applying them to actual mining situations and to the economic considerations involved.

Some underground mines lie below the drainage level, so that it is feasible to prevent oxygen from reaching the pyritic materials by flooding them with water. The procedure of permanent inundation has been successfully applied to some underground mines where it was practicable, and to the disposal of coal refuse materials from preparation plants. (These refuse materials frequently contain high percentages of pyrite). Unfortunately, this procedure is not applicable in most coal mining situations because water cannot be retained in most above-drainage-level mines and cannot be tolerated underground where it jeopardizes active or operating mines.

Sometimes it is possible to place acid-forming materials so that they are thoroughly covered by a compact layer of other earth materials during surface mining. If the degree of compaction of the acid-forming materials and the earth cover over them is great enough, the flow of oxygen may be reduced to the point that these materials remain virtually unoxidized. This is one of the more effective methods for handling earth strata containing large percentages of pyrite, and is being used effectively in many surface mining operations.

Moisture. It has been shown, in Eqs. (2) and (4), that moisture is a necessary part of the chemical reaction in forming acid mine drainage. Although pyrite will oxidize in a dry atmosphere, the oxidation rate is greatly accelerated by the presence of moisture. The amount of moisture required for the reaction is small and atmospheric moisture is sufficient. It is almost impossible to eliminate moisture vapor from underground atmospheres, and hence sufficient reaction moisture is almost always available for accelerated oxidation.

Transport Water. The acid oxidation products of pyrite must be dissolved and transported to the streams before they can cause water pollution. If these products are not dissolved and carried away by flowing water, they remain in the mine and cause no pollution. Control of water flow, in both underground and surface mining operations, is probably the most effective method available to minimize the amount of acid discharged from a mine. The principle, as stated for application to mining situations, is that the contact (both time and quantity) between water and acid-producing materials shall be minimized.

In surface mining, the contact between water and acid-producing materials can be minimized by diverting the flow of surface runoff and flowing stream waters around and away from the mining operation. This may take the form of highwall diversion ditches, drains, and conduits to carry flowing water through or around the mining operation, and rechanneling or diverting of streams away from the mine. Contact between water which does gain entry to the mine and acid-forming materials can be minimized by removing this water from the mine as quickly as possible after it accumulates.

In underground mining, contact between flowing water and acid-producing materials can be minimized by sealing off the surface of the earth above the mine to close cracks, fissures, sink holes, and other openings when they can be detected, by picking up water as close as possible to its points of entry in the mine, and by conducting it through and out of the mine either in closed conduits or in ditches or sewers that prevent further contact of the water with acid-producing materials.

Acid Mine Drainage. Acid mine drainage as it discharges from a mine is a complex solution of ferrous and ferric iron salts, calcium, magnesium, sometimes manganese, and other sulfate salts. The flow of mine drainage may vary from only a few gallons per hour to millions of gallons per day, depending on the specific drainage point being considered.

In some of the drier areas of the country, where annual evaporation equals or exceeds annual rainfall, it is possible to impound low flows of acid drainage and hold them permanently in a pond so they do not flow into any stream. Particularly in surface mines this may be accomplished by proper handling of the overburden. No cases are known where this has proved practicable for underground mining.

Where extremely low flows of acid drainage are encountered, they can sometimes be neutralized through the use of lime or related alkalies. Because of the costs and other factors involved, neutralization is usually uneconomical and completely impractical. In those situations where it can be used, it is a difficult operation, especially on continuous flows. Special equipment is required, which will compel intimate contact between the individual particles of alkali and the acid water. As acid mine water containing dissolved iron is neutralized, the iron precipitates and tends to coat individual particles of alkali, rendering unavailable and useless the remaining alkaline material in the particle.

Under some conditions it may be practicable to neutralize small standing pools of acid mine drainage before these pools are discharged to the streams. Such neutralization can be accomplished by the proper application of lime to the acid water. However, neutralization again is difficult because of the coating effect of the precipitating iron hydroxide.

The suspended ferric hydroxide carried with acid mine drainage can sometimes be reduced by permitting the water to stand in a lagoon for many hours or days before releasing it to the stream. Additionally, lagooning of acid mine drainages that contain large amounts of ferrous sulfate may permit the sulfate to oxidize and deposit some of its iron content. When these procedures are applicable, and where space and property availability permit, they are considered and used. The precipitated and settled iron hydroxide progressively fills lagoons of this type, and the sludge must be removed or a new pond constructed after prolonged use.

Stream Pollution. Stream pollution by coal mine drainage occurs only after the natural alkalinity of the receiving water has been used up and the concentration of undesirable elements has reached such a point that it renders the receiving waters unsuitable for their proposed downstream uses. The ultimate downstream effect of mine drainage frequently can be minimized by discharging these waters as uniformly as possible from the mine. This may be accomplished through an elaborate system of pumping controls to hold the water level in the mine at a particular point and to discharge water from the mine in direct relationship to rate of inflow. Additionally, surface impoundments can be built and controlled so that water pumped intermittently from a mine is released as uniformly as practicable to the receiving streams. Under these conditions the effect on the receiving stream is relatively uniform and the downstream effects are minimized.

Control of the discharge of black solids from a coal cleaning operation is quite similar to the control of suspended solids from any other mineral preparation operation. The black solid material is finely divided clay, black shale, and other minerals, along with coal. Normally the first step in clarification of coal washery wastewaters is to concentrate the solid material through the use of hydraulic cyclones or thickeners. From these operations the clarified water is returned to the coal washing circuit while the high-solids water is further concentrated. The underflow from the final clarification stage, usually a thickener, may be passed through filtration equipment such as a drumtype continuous filter or, more normally, may be pumped to a settling pond where the solids are permitted to settle. The clarified water from the settling pond may be either returned to the preparation circuit or discharged into a receiving stream. As new preparation plants are designed and built, more and more effort is being expended to make these plants closed-circuit units so there is normally no process water discharge into the streams.

Most coal preparation plants have suspended solids removal equipment installed and operating; however, there are frequent complaints from water pollution control officials that this equipment does not perform satisfactorily. Probably the most common problem other than normal maintenance is overloading of the clarification system so it cannot function properly. This condition could be overcome by designing and installing larger equipment, and clarification systems are often unwisely designed at absolute minimum safety factors. A more immediate and economic solution usually can be attained by properly balancing the water circuits in the coal washing operations so the minimum amount of water necessary for proper coal preparation is used and discharged to the clarification system. Proper and constant attention to this detail may forestall the requirement of installing larger clarification equipment and may at the same time yield better water pollution control.

There have been specific instances where the fine coals recovered from washery water clarification have had economic value; in a few cases their value has been great enough to defray a considerable portion of the expense of water clarification. Normally, however, the solids recovered from water clarification operations are of no economic value and must be disposed of by permanent impoundment, by disposal with other solid refuse where it will be permanently stored, or by disposal in specially constructed pits, so it does not again become waterborne and pollute the streams.

INDUSTRY TRENDS

For a number of reasons the water pollution problem of the coal industry may be decreasing even though the pressure for water pollution abatement is increasing tremendously. Much of the available coal located near the surface of the earth and in above-drainage locations has already been mined or is presently being exhausted. As new, larger mines are opened they are frequently in deeper seams of coal where less water is encountered below ground and where the mine will flood naturally and prevent the formation and discharge of acid mine drainage at the termination of mining. Changes in mining methods in the coal industry have been great over the past 30 years. The present-day methods of full-seam mining used in many parts of the bituminous coal industry are less likely to cause acid mine drainage than the older, hand mining techniques. First, as more of the coal is removed and the roof is deliberately collapsed, subsidence takes place quickly and more thoroughly, leaving less void space underground, causing less breakage of the acid-forming materials, and generally compacting the earth above the mine, so there is less tendency for the mine to form acid drainage. Second, as mining methods have shifted from hand to machine operations, the loose acid-forming materials which formerly were thrown back and left underground are now brought to the surface with the product coal. These materials, when separated from the coal in the cleaning process and properly disposed of in coal refuse piles, produce relatively little stream pollution.

There is a tremendous and ever increasing public pressure in the coal regions for clean streams. In the older coal mining regions much of the mine drainage stream pollution comes from abandoned coal mines. It has been estimated that drainage from abandoned mines constitutes 50–90% of the problem. Unfortunately, within the limits of our present knowledge, there is little that can be done to reduce the amount of acid discharged from an existing abandoned mine. This points out one of the major areas in which research is needed.

The problem of the prevention and control of acid mine drainage from coal mining needs much painstaking research. The problem is difficult by its physical nature and is aggravated by the fact that the chemical reactions involved are slow and long-term in their nature. We normally think of an inorganic reaction as being almost instantaneous and primarily limited by the speed of mixing. The inorganic reactions concerned with the formation and discharge of acid mine drainage have time constants which are a matter of days or even years. With such long-time constants, research in this area is extremely difficult, time consuming, and costly.

Research needs include the development of a more complete under-standing of the oxidative process which converts pyrite to various acid salts; possible methods for the recovery of sulfur, iron, and other mate-rials from mine drainage; effective ways of preventing the formation of acid materials in active mines; and effective treatments which can be economically applied to control the formation and discharge of acid from abandoned mines.

Research on the various problems of acid mine drainage has been conducted by the coal industry and by a variety of governmental agen-cies over the last 50 years. Among the organizations taking an active part in this research are the Coal Industry Advisory Committee to the Ohio River Valley Water Sanitation Commission (ORSANCO), Bitumi-nous Coal Research, Inc., Mellon Institute, West Virgina University, the U. S. Bureau of Mines, and Ohio State University. Additionally, ORSANCO and other governmental agencies are greatly interested in the problem from the standpoint of developing water pollution control regulations, and ORSANCO in January 1960 adopted the first water pol-lution control regulation aimed at reducing the amount of pollution from acid mine drainage.

The discharge of substantial concentrations of suspended solids by coal preparation plants is prohibited in almost all states in which coal is mined. There are few uncontrolled discharges and the number is be-coming smaller with each passing year. The problems in this phase of water pollution control in the coal industry are largely those of space and economics, rather than basic technology. Methods which can be used to remove suspended solids from water are currently available, and almost all coal preparation plant effluents can be controlled using one or more of the available clarification techniques. Where older coal preparation plants are concerned, water clarification is made doubly difficult because of space limitations and economics. Often the clarification equipment for an older preparation plant has a present cost considerably in excess of the total value of the existing installations. Additionally, in the hilly and mountainous areas where coal is often mined, the necessary space for proper settling pond lagoons is virtually unattainable, making the prob-lem even more difficult. Despite the economic and other problems, great progress is being made in this area, and complete control of the dis-charge of suspended solids from coal preparation plants is entirely feasi-ble.

Chapter 11

METAL MINING

by C. J. LEWIS

This chapter covers industrial wastewaters resulting from the removal of ores from the ground and from their subsequent treatment to produce an ore concentrate. The reduction of ores to metal, and the processing of nonmetallics such as potash ore, fluorspar, and kaolin clay are discussed in other chapters. Emphasis in this chapter is on those metallic ores that are mined in substantial amount in the continental United States. These include iron, copper, zinc, lead, molybdenum, and uranium. Of less significance are metal mining operations involving aluminum, tungsten, vanadium, gold, manganese, magnesium, mercury, and lithium. A single operation accounts for 70% of the molybdenum concentrate produced in the United States. Practically all manganese and chromium ores are imported and, although one state yields 90% of the domestic bauxite production, most bauxite for the aluminum industry is imported. Vanadium concentrate is chiefly obtained as a by-product from uranium ore milling operations, and may eventually be recovered in substantial quantity from wastes of the phosphorus industry. Considerations such as these preclude many mining operations from this discussion of industrial wastewater control in the metal mining industry.

The metal mining industry is not unique with respect to control of industrial wastewaters. There is similarity between the mining procedures and subsequent ore upgrading steps in coal mining, metal mining, and nonmetal mining. The metal mining industry produces substantial mine drainage, as does the coal mining industry, and contends with a paucity of water in arid areas, as do many nonmetal mining industries. The magnitude of domestic metal mining operations for the major tonnage ores is shown in Table I.

INDUSTRY OPERATIONS

Ore removal operations are carried out in both open pits and underground mines. Ore may be subjected to a primary crushing operation in the mine or at the pit before it is moved to the mill for further processing. Only when the raw ore is of high value, as is uranium ore, do economics justify its transportation for any considerable distance. At the mill, the ore is usually further reduced in size and is then subjected to

TABLE I

CRUDE ORE MINED IN THE UNITED STATES

Ore	1958	1962
Bauxite, crude	1,468,000	1,533,000
Copper ore (includes old tailings smelted or re-treated)	114,824,000	150,217,000
Copper, lead, zinc, gold, and silver ores	134,516,000	—[a]
Iron ore	75,834,000	80,448,500
Lead ore (recoverable content)	267,377	236,956
Crude lead and zinc ores	16,534,000	4,497,158
Manganese ores	1,484,600	1,144,400
Molybdenum crude ore	6,363,000	8,185,000
Titanium (ilmenite ore)	565,164	809,000
Uranium ore	5,178,315	7,052,870
Zinc ore (recoverable content)	412,005	505,491

Adapted from 1962 Minerals Yearbook, Vol. I, U.S. Bureau of Mines, and 1958 Census of Mineral Industries, Vol. I, Summary and Industry Statistics, Table 7.

Values expressed as short tons.

[a] Data not available.

physical upgrading processes, such as simple water scrubbing to remove slimes and clays, heavy media or flotation operations to effect mineral concentration, and caustic or acid dissolving procedures to yield pregnant solutions of the desired metals from which precipitate concentrates can be obtained.

Most ore processing steps, as shown in Table II, require water. Many of them produce wastewaters. Although some metal mining operations bring in water to alleviate dust, it is usual that water is drained or pumped from the mine or pit in order to avoid flooding. Often this results in an acid discharge from the operation. Water is, of course, necessary in ore washing operations, in wet grinding, jigging, tabling, aqueous classification, and chemical processing. (It is axiomatic that water is also used for power generation, cooling, and for sanitary purposes.) Table III has been prepared from statistics pertaining to such uses, as given in the 1954 United States Census of Mineral Industries. Using water intake and gross water use data from the Census compilation, water reuse has been calculated and is presented in column 3 of Table III. Further analysis, by regions, surprisingly indicates more reuse in those states having relatively high rainfall than in those states normally considered to be arid or semiarid.

Although the metal mining industry requires much water, it also produces much water by virtue of its operations penetrating the water table. Moreover, the relative geographic isolation of the industry and the geologic circumstances which seem to concentrate its effort in water-scarce areas have combined to render the industry sensitive to its water problems. Because of such factors, the industry is knowledgeable with respect to wastewater control, water recovery, and water reuse, and has been able to maintain its water resources ample for growth. Simultaneously, pollutional aspects of its waterborne wastes have been thoughtfully controlled.

TABLE II

ORE PROCESSING OPERATIONS

Operation	Frequency[a]
Mining	87
Crushing and grinding	69
Froth flotation	55
Filtration	34
Gravity concentration	32
Sizing and screening	28
Classification	19
Magnetic separation	11
Leaching	10
Roasting and smelting	9
Precipitation	8
Drying	7
Ion exchange	7
Thickening	7
Pelletizing	3
Amalgamation	2
Cyanidation	2

[a] Based on 100 responses to a recent questionnaire.

INDUSTRY WASTES

The principal characterization of metal mining wastewaters is their settleable solids. In various forms, as mud and slimes washed from the ore during processing, as gangue from wet gravity separation operations or froth flotation systems, and as undissolved residues from chemical leaching procedures, these suspended solids represent the industry's major waterborne waste. This is not surprising when it is borne in mind that most domestic ores contain from 1% to 10% of the desired concentrate, hence the bulk of the ore fed to the mill must be discarded. Another waste, acid drainage from both active and abandoned metal mines, may, as a tonnage flow, dwarf the production of waterborne waste solids. However, such mine flows are relatively dilute and their dissolved min-

TABLE III

Water Use in the Mineral Industries in the United States, 1954

Industry group	Water intake including mine water, millions of gal	Gross water use including recirculation, millions of gal	Indicated % water reuse $\left(\dfrac{\text{use} - \text{intake}}{\text{intake}} = \text{reuse}\right)$
Metal mining, total	137,781	240,669	75
Iron ores	26,855	59,666	122
Copper ores	59,112	82,547	39
Lead and zinc ores			
Valued chiefly for lead	11,015	18,212	65
Valued chiefly for zinc	11,134	19,411	74
Gold and silver ores			
Lode gold	4,277	7,049	65
Placer gold	10,752	16,034	49
Silver ores	2,291	2,299	< 1
Bauxite	179	179	0
Ferroalloy ores, except vanadium			
Manganese ores	2,834	3,858	36
Tungsten ores	3,380	4,913	46
Molybdenum ores and ferroalloy ores (except vanadium)[a]	1,447	4,788	231
Metal mining contract services	99	100	1
Miscellaneous metal ores			
Mercury ores	12	12	0
Uranium-radium-vanadium ores	1,601	1,601	0
Titanium ores and metallic ores[a]	2,793	20,000	616

Taken from 1954 Census of Mineral Industries, Vol. I, Summary and Industry Statistics, Table 5.

[a] Not elsewhere classified.

eral content, converted to potential solids, is minor compared with the waterborne undissolved solids in the wastewater of the industry. Another source of wastes is the wide variety of reagents used in froth flotation processes. Most of these reagents appear in the effluent from the mill. Some, such as slime depressors, adhere to the waterborne gangue; others remain entrained or dissolved in the process waters. Table IV lists some of the reagents used in milling operations and their principal functions,

TABLE IV

TYPICAL REAGENTS USED IN MILLING OPERATIONS

Reagent	Use	Composition
Separan 2610	Settling and filtering agent	
Jaguar	Settling and filtering agent	Galactomannan
Guartec	Settling and filtering agent	Galactomannan
Pine oil	Flotation frother	
MIBC	Flotation frother	Methyl isobutyl carbinol
R-404	Flotation collector	Mercaptobenzothiazole
Xanthate	Flotation collector	Dithiocarbonate ($RO–\overset{\text{S}}{\underset{\shortparallel}{C}}–SX$)
Lime	pH modifier	$Ca(OH)_2$
Oleic acid	Flotation collector	$C_8H_{17}CH:CH(CH_2)_7COOH$
Aerofloat 31	Flotation collector	P_2S_5 in cresylic acid
Alamine 26	Flotation collector	Tallow amine
Alamac 26	Flotation collector	Tallow amine acetate
Sodium cyanide	Pyrite and sphalerite flotation depressant	NaCN
Sodium silicate	Flotation gangue flotation depressant	Na_2SiO_3
Syntex	Flotation collector	Sulfated monoglyceride
Zinc sulfate	Pyrite and sphalerite flotation depressant	$ZnSO_4$

although the table is by no means complete. Finally, the metal mining industry utilizes some, though relatively few, leaching operations, usually employing soda ash, caustic soda, or acids, chiefly sulfuric. These reagents, or water-soluble products thereof, further add to the wastewater streams of the industry. Table II lists the principal metal mining operations which give rise to wastewaters.

WATER POLLUTION POTENTIAL

The pollutional potential of wastewaters from the metal mining industry is relatively low. There have been and are exceptions to this, such as waterborne wastes from cyanide leaching circuits or waterborne radioactivity from uranium milling operations. However, cyanide leaching circuits in the United States are so few and so isolated as to preclude their further consideration. Waterborne radioactive waste discharges presented some problems in uranium milling districts until prompt and decisive action on the part of all concerned corrected the situation. Except for the relatively negligible input of sanitary wastes (where sanitary sewers enter mine and mill waste streams), wastes from the metal mining industry have no significant biochemical oxygen demand. Moreover, these wastes, on the average, have practically no toxicity. This is because the processing steps in the industry consist essentially of water washing, gravity separations in a water medium, flotation using small dosages of nontoxic reagents, and leaching involving either sodium alkalies or sulfuric acid; and because the potentially toxic metal ions are efficiently scavenged from wastes as part of the milling operation.

CONTROL OF INDUSTRY WASTES

The principal control of waste effluents by the metal mining industry is usually accomplished by a settling pond or ponds. Few operating mills may be found anywhere in the United States without their nearby tailings ponds, settling ponds, impounding dams, lagooning areas, or similar devices.

Sometimes these structures take advantage of the local topography, but more often they must be constructed by damming, excavating, diking, or a combination of the three. In most metal mining localities, substantial land area is available, and the use of much land area for waste disposal is fortunately both technically and economically feasible. The common tailings pond serves many purposes. It is a primary settler for the gangue, a clarifier for the water, a treatment tank for pH adjustment or chemical precipitation as desired, a water storage area, a surge tank for controlling discharge into public waters, and an investment storage because, in many instances, the mill tailings contain secondary values which it is anticipated can be reclaimed at a future time. It is of particular significance that the reservoir of water in the pond (the pond being necessary *per se* to settle out solids) is, by virtue of its relatively low burden of dissolved process chemicals, at least a tempting and usually a vital source of water for reuse.

Depending upon the ratio of atmospheric evaporation to precipitation and the ground and effluent characteristics affecting seepage, many tailings ponds never overflow their confines and some may go nearly dry during certain periods of the year. This is especially true in the arid and semiarid areas of the country. On the other hand, this situation may be reversed in normal and heavy rainfall areas. In either situation, tailings ponds at least retain substantially all, if not all, of the waste solids from the metal mining operation.

In addition to tailings pond techniques, the industry utilizes many innovations for industrial wastewater control primarily dictated by local circumstances. If the effluent to the tailings pond is alkaline, acid mine drainage may also be run into the tailings pond to effect a neutralization and a better grade of water for reuse. Conversely, when the mill effluent is acid, and particularly when acid mine drainage is also entering the tailings pond, pulverized limestone or lime is frequently added to the effluent ahead of its discharge to the tailings pond to effect pH control of the clarified effluent in the settling area. In some instances, acid effluent from copper mills containing dissolved copper, or copper-pregnant acid drainage from the mines, is first passed over scrap iron to precipitate the copper, while simultaneously dissolving iron. The value of the recovered "cement" copper is considerably greater than the cost of lime subsequently used for pH control and iron precipitation in the settling pond. Where flotation reagents, untreated sanitary sewage, or other chemicals that might adversely affect the reuse of tailings pond waters are present, activated carbon may be added to the pond influent for the purpose of adsorbing undesired organic matter into the common precipitate. Of course, rupture of a tailings pond dike can have serious downstream consequences, and occurrences of this nature have resulted in assessments for damage, particularly fish killings. The impounding of radioactive wastes has produced a problem as to legal responsibility when operations are abandoned and ownership of the property changes hands. Sometimes tailings pond waters are suitable for livestock watering, irrigation, and sanitary facilities. Possibly no other industrial waste control device produces so much reusable water as the tailings pond, and at a price that the industry can afford. Conversely, probably no industry is better situated than the metal mining industry, in terms of geographic and technological considerations, to utilize tailings ponds to their fullest advantage.

SPECIFIC INDUSTRY CONTROLS

The disposal of liquid effluents at the Reduction Department of the Anaconda Company in Deer Lodge County, Montana, may be used as an illustration involving copper mining wastes (1). This operation handles 3000–5000 gpm of copper-bearing acid mine drainage. A few miles downstream the mill provides a tailings pond area enclosing 4200 acres and of sufficient depth to store 400 million tons of tailings solids. Classifi-

cation of sands and slimes at the mill sets the stage for better classification of sands and slimes in the tailings pond, so the overflow from the
pond is of satisfactory quality for discharge into the local creek. However, the acid mine drainage upstream is first passed over tin cans to
remove dissolved copper. Subsequently, acid waters from the copper removal step are mixed with the decant water from the downstream tailings pond in such a manner that, with pH control by lime addition, all
iron is precipitated and an approximately neutral pH is reached. In-
terestingly enough, still further downstream, the creek enters a 400 acre
settling basin near Warm Springs, Montana, where the precipitating
iron carries down with it any other solids, to yield a clear overflow into
the Clark Fork River. The vital role of the tailings pond (settling basin)
in this massive waste control complex is obvious.

Another example of the use of the tailings pond is the resin-in-pulp
uranium extraction process of the Mines Development Company, Edge-
mont, South Dakota (4, 5). In 1962, this mill received uranium ore,
which was crushed, ground, and leached with sulfuric acid to dissolve the
uranium. Coarse sands were then separated and discharged to waste, and
the remaining slurry, commonly referred to as "pulp," was fed to the
conventional resin-in-pulp process. Subsequently the uranium was
stripped from the resin, precipitated, and processed to the desired end
product. The now uranium-barren pulp slurry was neutralized with lime
and discharged to the slimes pond. This mill participated in a survey
conducted by the United States Public Health Service for the purpose of
analyzing mill processes and characterizing the resulting liquid wastes.
As a result of this survey, it was concluded that about 17% of the gross
alpha activity of the ore processed at this mill was due to radium, and
that 99.8% of this radium remained in undissolved form through the
process and was effectively retained in the sands and slimes tailings
ponds. Here, again, the significance of the tailings pond is evident. It can
also be noted that, where there is possibility of discharging waterborne
radioactivity, the addition of finely divided barite ($BaSO_4$) to the tailings pond water or in the plant waste stream absorbs radioactivity which
then remains with the settled barite solids. It is a common practice to
sink monitoring wells around mill ponds containing radioactivity so that
possible underground movement of the radioactivity can be detected.

As has been pointed out, the metal mining industry practices substantial water reuse. A recent survey (unpublished) indicated that about half
the metal mining and milling companies employed reuse, presumably to
the extent that technology and economics dictate. The fact that such a
large percentage of the industry is reusing water shows that an industry
pattern has been established, and that companies which may find it nec-

essary to practice water reuse in the future have the guidance of prior experience and current practice.

Copper and uranium are the most significant of the metal mining industries in which pollution potential could be serious, as a result of dissolved substances, if control measures were not being practiced. Iron, zinc, lead, complex ore operations, molybdenum, and other segments of the industry have no pollution problems as far as dissolved wastes are concerned and, of course, solid tailings are impounded by practically all industry units.

The iron industry, by the very nature of its operations, adds little to its process water other than hardness. It uses water primarily for washing its ores and avidly reuses water from its settling ponds. In some plants, where a heavy medium of finely divided ferrosilicon is involved, a slight solubility of iron in plant water may result. However, clarified waters from the iron mining industry can generally be discharged into public waters without detrimental effect. One mill discharging wastewater from iron ore upgrading involving milling, flotation, and agglomeration, reports its analysis of discharge into public waters, as follows:

	mg/liter
Hardness, as $CaCO_3$	287
Pb	0.014
P	0.002
As	0.005
Se	0.005
Cu	0.005
Fe	0.167
Mn	1.94
Mg	27.6
Zn	0.03
Cl	10.9
$SO_4^=$	227.0
Phenol	0.005
pH	7.0

In zinc production, the usual processing involves mining, crushing, grinding, flotation, thickening, and filtering. This industry produces considerable mine drainage, a typical composition of which is 1450 mg/liter Zn, 800 mg/liter Fe, and pH 2.3.

Waters from most of the abandoned mines flow at will and in the natural water courses and can be used for irrigation purposes. Water from the settling and impounding of zinc mill process tailings tends to be alkaline, so the combination of mine water and clarified tailings pond overflow results in nothing more than a hard water with a pH in the vicinity of 7.0. The zinc content of drainage from both active and abandoned mines presents a challenging problem with respect to development of an economic process for zinc recovery, but is not considered to be a pollution problem. Analytical data furnished by one major zinc milling operation with reference to waste effluent discharge appear in Table V.

Essentially, the foregoing statements on the zinc industry apply also to those industries processing lead-zinc, copper-zinc, and complex lead-zinc-silver-gold-copper ores. Mine drainage from these operations has a pH near 7.0, and clarified mill process water from the tailings ponds generally ranges from neutral to slightly alkaline because of the slightly alkaline nature of the mill concentration systems usually employed. It is not uncommon to find the wastewater from these operations in demand for irrigation and livestock watering, particularly in arid areas. There are a few abandoned mines in which aging processes have been undisturbed for a long period, and the sulfur bodies present have produced so much sulfuric acid that the drainage water has a pH as low as 2.5 or 3.0. However, it is general practice not to pump water of this acidity; and when such water does overflow the mine, it is usually diluted to a harmless acid strength by the freshet producing the overflow.

Scant attention can be given here to the mining and milling of other metals. It is not to be inferred that these metals are unimportant in terms of their economic worth or magnitude of the operation involved, but rather that their mining, however huge on a local scale, is confined to one or a few operations throughout the United States. A barium concentrate is produced from the mineral barite by steps involving mining, crushing, jigging, grinding, flotation, filtering, and drying. Copious quantities of water are used, and solid gangue tailings are impounded. Although some flotation reagents occur in the clarified water from the tailings pond, and although in at least one plant a chemical flocculant is added to the tailings pond water to remove fine solids, discharge to the stream, when all clarified pond water is not being returned to the process, is reported to cause no pollution. The mining of beryllium in the United States is relatively minor, as dependence is placed on imported beryl mineral. This is true also of chromium, the concentrate of which is practically all imported into the United States.

The mining of gold, involving cyanide leaching, could beget a water pollution problem, were it not for the fact that gold operations are so limited and their locales so isolated. In one gold operation, using a cyanidation process, wastewater overflows the settling pond at a pH of approximately 9.0 and is almost immediately lost into the ground of the isolated area. In another plant, mill tailings are impounded in a dry mountain canyon, apparently capable of serving this purpose for some generations ahead. At another gold operation where only concentrate re-

TABLE V

ZINC MILL WASTE CHARACTERISTICS AND EFFECTS ON RECEIVING STREAM

Waste component	Stream analysis above mill	Stream analysis below mill	Discharge from mine pumps	Discharge from flotation tailings pond	Discharge from limestone sand plant	Discharge from mill thickeners
Total solids, %	—	—	0.0	15.00	4.3	0.036
Dissolved solids, mg/liter	180	205	243	410	208.8	434
Silica, mg/liter	4.5	4.9	9.8	4.1	5.9	5.4
Iron, mg/liter	1.8	1.6	3.1	2.2	1.8	1.8
Calcium, mg/liter	45	47.7	44	45	42	43.2
Magnesium, mg/liter	9.0	10.2	20.9	21.1	12.3	144
Bicarbonate, mg/liter	93	107	171	99	93	94.5
Sulfate, mg/liter	29	36.0	25.2	32.4	29.2	45
Chlorine, mg/liter	6.3	10	9.5	36	24.3	18
Pine oil, mg/liter	None	None	None	Trace	None	None
Copper, mg/liter	None	None	None	None	None	None
Dry solids, tons/hour	—	—	0.0	7.377	3.0	0.0018
Water, gal/minute	—	—	900	147.6	296	135

covery is practiced (no leaching), there are no pollutants other than flotation reagents and their potential BOD. The tailings pond overflow is being discharged into public waters with no apparent effect. Another gold mine reports a mine drainage of pH 8.3 with calcium and magnesium sulfates, and a tailings thickener overflow with a pH of 8.4. Both the mine drainage and the thickener overflow are reused, and apparently any cyanide values escaping from the tailings pond are permissibly discharged into public waters which are classified as primarily for industrial use.

Raw material for the metal magnesium is primarily sea water and brines, but it may be noted that the process of producing magnesite (natural magnesium carbonate) by a heavy medium separation and froth flotation finally yields a clarified overflow from settling ponds, which returns to the lake supplying the mill waters. Trout fishing in this lake is known to be excellent.

Lithium ore operations may make use of desliming and flotation. Clarified effluents from the settling ponds contain ions of ferric iron, sulfate, fluoride, and sodium, but the pond overflow is reusable.

Manganese ore processing operations may produce some mine drainage. The milling operation itself produces nothing important by way of waterborne waste other than the gangue solids which, of course, are removed by the tailings pond. Mercury operations, consisting primarily of mining, crushing, and roasting, are of little significance in stream pollution; this is true also of nickel, titanium, rare earths, vanadium, and silver. Although a considerable quantity of silver is produced in the United States, silver is primarily a by-product of lead-zinc-copper operations. Vanadium concentrate is also chiefly a by-product of other ore processing operations, hence vanadium concentrate production adds little, if anything, to the volume of industrial waste effluents of the metal mining industry.

Titanium operations involve the mining of around 1 million tons annually of ilmenite ores. These ilmenite operations for producing a titanium concentrate are essentially physical and, although large quantities of water are used, the tailings pond adequately clarifies the effluent. This is approximately neutral, and the pond overflow can enter natural drainage or be recycled.

Tungsten may be mentioned as, like copper and uranium, some chemical processing is involved in the production of the concentrate. Processing may involve mining, crushing, concentrate flotation, and chemical processing of the concentrate at the mill. The usual tailings pond is, of course, employed. Because of the alkaline nature of the chemical processing, clarified effluent from the tailings pond has a pH in the neighborhood of 8.0 and is apparently suitable for discharge into public waters without injurious effect.

Summarizing the foregoing observations, it may be concluded that the mining industry enjoys relatively high standards of industrial wastewater control. This is largely the result of the inherent technology of the industry and the practical necessity of water reuse, but it is no less a tribute to the awareness of the industry of the value of protecting and respecting natural water resources.

INDUSTRY TRENDS

An assessment of the long range aspects of industrial wastewater control in the metal mining industry must be based on the premises that the industry already has the situation well in hand, it is not an expanding industry as a whole, it is essentially wed to its ore reserves, and metal mining industry processes (statistics notwithstanding) may well consume less rather than more water even though production of some metal concentrates does increase.

Considering these premises individually, the first should be readily apparent: public domain activities on the part of regulatory agencies confirm the relatively inoffensive nature of mining industry effluents, assuming, of course, the impounding of waste solids. In Colorado, for example, the only metal mining operations treating tailings water before release are two uranium mills which add chemicals to reduce the radioactive content of the overflow. All other milling operations in Colorado impound their tailings and decant clear water which, even though impregnated with chemicals used in the milling processes, is actually beneficial to the receiving streams. This is because most mill tailings water carries a high pH and has a tendency to neutralize any acid that might be released into the stream from mine water.

As for expansion of the industry as a whole, it is difficult to expound an optimistic forecast in view of the continuing impact of imported ores, concentrates, refined ore, and semirefined metals; for example, Mexican lead, Canadian nickel, South American beryl, Japanese iron, African manganese, and Korean tungsten. On the other hand, copper production is increasing on known reserves and the steel industry is vigorously exploring for additional iron ore reserves, particularly in the western states. Also, research to develop economic processes for presently known marginal or submarginal ore reserves is being actively pursued; any successful developments along this line could augment the growth of the industry.

However, it is interesting to note that process development is considerably oriented toward dry rather than wet processing. While mine drainage would surely increase as the result of the opening of new ore bodies, wastewaters from processing would not necessarily follow suit. As one example, nonaqueous leaching procedures use volatile solvents that could result in a relatively dry gangue residue, to be used subsequently as land fill. Another developing technology relates to improved smelting techniques that may permit direct smelting of low grade ores, and result in slag dump wastes rather than tailings pond impounded wet solids and potential effluents. Finally, chlorination techniques are being developed to volatilize metal values directly from concentrates; any commercialization along this line could reduce industrial wastewater resulting from wet processing. Other examples could be cited, and, while it is not intended to imply that the newer processes would not produce any industrial waste effluents, it is fairly safe to assume that these will minimize the discharge of effluents.

Finally, the metal mining industry must, for the most part, remain near its ore reserves and these, as a whole, are well established. Years of geologic exploration have uncovered most of the major accessible ore bodies in the continental United States. As ore bodies of quality and magnitude sufficient to justify mining operations may be proved in such neighboring areas as Canada and Mexico, or in Alaska and Hawaii, operations at such locations will competitively decrease industrial wastewaters from mining in the continental United States drainage basins. It is the author's opinion, therefore, that mining industry growth within the United States during the next generation will not, *per se,* significantly increase the production of industrial wastewaters from the industry.

If its industrial wastewater situation does become a problem to the mining industry, this is likely to be the result of population explosion and the birth of new towns and cities in the present relatively isolated major mining industry areas. This is a definite possibility and should be carefully weighed by all planners concerned with the preservation and improvement of natural resources. Rather than increasing present water sources and reserves, the mining industry may be hard pressed to keep what it already has. If population growth produces a demand for domestic water in excess of the region's ability to supply, it is in this area that research at all pertinent levels is needed—research to achieve even greater reuse of the industry's industrial waste effluents; research designed to minimize the industry's present water requirements; research to make better use of the terrain for impounding water reserves and for preventing their loss due to seepage and evaporation; research to extract more usable water from the industry's wet tailings solids; and research on the reclamation of presently unusable water as well as on the pipeline transportation of water and water slurries to enable mills to operate economically even farther from the ore bodies involved. Based on summation of all experiences thus far, there is little doubt that the metal mining industry of the United States will be equal to the challenges that may be imposed upon its industrial wastewater control by an expanding population.

REFERENCES

1. Day, F. H., *Mining Congr. J.* 47, No. 11, 52–56 (November, 1961).
2. Gilkey, M. M., and Beckman, R. T., "Water Requirements and Uses in Arizona Mineral Industries" U. S. Bur. Mines Info. Circ. 8162, 1963.
3. Mussey, O. D., "Water Requirements of the Copper Industry," U. S. Geol. Surv. Water-Supply Paper 1330-E, 1961.
4. Tsivoglou, E. C., and O'Connell, R. L., "Waste Guide for the Uranium Milling Industry," U. S. Public Health Service Tech. Rept. W62–12, 1962.
5. Tsivoglou, E. C., Kalda, D. C., and Dearwater, J. R., "Resin-in-pulp Uranium Extraction Process," U. S. Public Health Service Tech. Rept. W62–17, 1–18, 1962.

Chapter 12

INDUSTRIAL MINERAL MINING

by RICHARD J. LUND

The production of industrial minerals is well differentiated from the mining of coal and metallic ores, which were discussed in the two previous chapters. This chapter covers the mining and beneficiation of minerals and rocks that are used for purposes other than fuel or the extraction of metals. Included in this discussion of wastewater practices and problems are both mining operations and such mineral dressing processes, at or near the mine or quarry, as washing, crushing and grinding, separation from other materials, sizing, and dewatering—in brief, those operations needed to produce marketable products.

THE INDUSTRIAL MINERAL INDUSTRIES

The nonmetal mining industry is, by all yardsticks, a major factor in United States economy. Including the manufactured products cement and lime, as is done by the U. S. Bureau of Mines in its statistical reports, total output in 1962 was valued at just over $4 billion—more than double the $1.9 billion value of metal output. Three commodities—the bulk construction materials of cement, stone, and sand and gravel—accounted for three-fourths of the total value in 1961. Of the total value of nonmetallics (except fuels), 97% is accounted for by these three plus lime, clays, salt, phosphate rock, sulfur, potash, and boron minerals.

For several decades, nonmetallic minerals have been termed "industrial minerals" in the trade. A complete listing, even with some grouping, includes 56 items, as discussed in an authoritative reference on this group of materials (1). By and large, they comprise the basic raw materials for our huge construction and chemical industries, plus many industries of smaller size such as refractories, whitewares, and abrasives.

Quantity and value of nonmetals (except fuels) produced in 1961, by major minerals or groups, are shown in Table I. Total value for that year was $3.85 billion. In 1958, the latest year for which detailed Bureau of the Census data are available, nonmetallic mineral mining, not including fuels or the manufacture of cement and lime, involved 7236 companies, operating 8872 establishments, employing 143,137 persons, paying wages of $633.3 million, making capital expenditures of $191.5 million, and using the equivalent of 48.9 billion kwh of energy.

TABLE I

Nonmetals (Except Fuels) Produced in the United States, 1961

Mineral	Quantity, short tons	Value, thousands of dollars
Abrasive stone	2,495	238
Aplite	109,161	651
Asbestos	52,814	4,347
Barite	798,785	9,315
Boron minerals	602,613	46,936
Bromine	90,399	44,517
Cement	61,935,000	1,105,537
Clays	47,389,000	156,829
Emery	6,180	106
Feldspar	556,425	5,120
Fluorspar	205,083	9,275
Garnet	12,057	1,036
Gem stones	—	1,309
Gypsum	9,500,000	34,950
Lime	15,192,000	210,127
Magnesite	603,656	3,129
Magnesium compounds from sea water and brine (as MgO)	356,384	25,545
Mica: scrap	99,044	2,417
Mica: sheet	240	3,308
Perlite	310,338	2,664
Phosphate rock	20,786,000	130,535
Potassium salts (as K_2O)	2,732,000	104,464
Pumice	2,463,000	6,799
Pyrites	1,107,000	7,418
Salt	25,707,000	160,223
Sand and gravel	751,784,000	751,301
Sodium carbonate (natural)	805,828	20,444
Sodium sulfate (natural)	465,814	9,296
Stone	615,388,000	950,560
Sulfur: Frasch process	5,692,000	117,884
Sulfur: other mines	198,855	1,694
Talc, soapstone, and pyrophyllite	761,318	5,267
Tripoli	54,641	225
Vermiculite	206,000	3,350
Other items	—	44,743
Total	—	3,846,000

Adapted from U. S. Bureau of Mines Minerals Yearbook, 1961.

Because of the large variety of products of nonmetal mining, discussion on water usage and wastewater practices and problems will be confined largely to seven major industries that are important water users:

sand and gravel; crushed limestone; kaolin and ball clay; potash, soda, and borate minerals; phosphate rock; salt; and sulfur.

GEOGRAPHY

Covering as many minerals as it does, and including such commonly occurring materials as sand, gravel, and crushed stone, the nonmetal mining industry has an exceedingly widespread distribution throughout the United States.

Sand and Gravel. Sand and gravel output accounts for the biggest tonnage among the various nonmetallics, and this production is also the most widely distributed. Each of the 50 states recorded output in 1961, with only two (Delaware and Hawaii) amounting to less than 1 million tons. With 110 million tons, California was far out in front, followed by Michigan with 55 million and Wisconsin with 40 million tons. Construction uses—largely building and paving—account for 97% of the total. The trend toward more exacting specifications is forcing increasing amounts of sand and gravel to be washed, screened, or otherwise processed; in 1961 over 90% of the commercial output was so treated.

Crushed Limestone. Production of crushed limestone and dolomite comprises the next largest tonnage of nonmetallics, and is widely distributed. Illinois and Pennsylvania each produced 36 million tons; 16 additional states had productions of more than 10 million tons each in 1961; and 14 states produced between 1 and 10 million tons. As with sand and gravel, the production pattern follows that of construction (buildings and highways) throughout the country, although the resource is not as widely distributed.

Kaolin and Ball Clay. Georgia accounts for the preponderance of kaolin produced in the United States, and Tennessee and Kentucky for most of the ball clay.

Potash, Soda, and Borate Minerals. About 92% of the domestic potash came from southeastern New Mexico (Carlsbad area) in 1961, with the remainder from California and Utah.

Natural sodium carbonate is produced from brines in California and from bedded deposits in Wyoming. Natural sodium sulfate comes from deposits (mainly brines) in California, Wyoming, and Texas.

Borate minerals are produced solely from bedded deposits and brines in the Mojave Desert area of southern California.

Phosphate Rock. Florida accounts for about 90%, of the phosphate rock produced in the United States, and the remainder comes about equally from Tennessee and the western states of Idaho, Montana, Utah, and Wyoming.

Salt. Louisiana, Texas, New York, Michigan, and Ohio were the chief producers of salt (NaCl) in 1961, accounting for 82% of total United States output. Of total salt production, salt in brines (pumped from wells and sold or used as such) accounted for 58%, rock salt (mined in solid condition) for 25%, and evaporated salt for 17%.

Sulfur. Consideration is given in this discussion only to native sulfur from Frasch-process mines, which in 1961 accounted for 75% of total sulfur produced in the United States. Deposits in salt domes along the coastal areas of Texas and Louisiana (in about equal amounts from the two states) account for all the Frasch-process sulfur output.

NATURE OF OPERATIONS

The great preponderance of nonmetal mines, both in numbers of operations and in tons of output, produce by the surface mining methods of dredging, open pit mining, or quarrying. Of the seven major products previously cited, underground mining methods, including wells, are characteristic of potash, salt (except for a few sea water evaporation plants), and sulfur production. There are perhaps a hundred underground operations for limestone and a relatively few for phosphate, all of the latter being in the western states. Borate minerals are produced from underground mines, from wells (brines), and since 1957 from a large open pit operation.

Preparation of the mined material to produce a salable product varies extremely in the nonmetallic minerals industry—from none at all (sale of pit-run sand or gravel) or simple dry screening, through various stages of separation of unwanted material (often with prior crushing and grinding) by washing or other gravity methods, flotation, magnetic, electrostatic, or complex chemical treatment processes, or a combination of these. Summaries for most of the industrial minerals, with numerous case examples detailed, are given by Gillson (*1*), and in numerous publications of the U. S. Bureau of Mines.

WATER USAGE

Quantities. Quantities of water used by sectors of nonmetal mining and for total nonmetallics (excluding lime and cement manufacture) in 1954, together with other pertinent data concerning water usage, are shown in Table II. These comprise the only available detailed data on water usage by separate sectors of the nonmetal mining industry, and are

TABLE II
WATER USE IN SELECTED SECTORS OF NONMETAL MINING, 1954

Mineral	Water intake, millions of gal				Water discharge, millions of gal, except mine water	Gross water use including recirculation, millions of gal	Per cent of total water intake (except mine water) by principal source				Number of mines and pits	Number of preparation plants
	Except mine water		Including mine water				Public water systems	Company surface systems	Company ground systems	Combinations ground and not specified		
	Total	Per production worker	Total	Per production worker								
Construction sand and gravel	122,617	4.31	179,035	6.29	118,206	247,721	3	54	24	19	3766	3156
Crushed limestone	34,821	1.40	53,610	2.15	33,913	57,639	3	53	21	23	1437	1356
Kaolin and ball clay	3,788	1.34	3,890	1.38	3,732	4,481	–	35	65	–	61	38
Potash, soda, and borate minerals	10,561[a]	2.23[a]	10,561	2.23	6,455	26,332	–	23	74	3	20	16
Phosphate rock	39,720	8.67	62,618	13.68	40,891[b]	138,399	–	21	69	10	73	54
Rock salt[c]	2,968[a]	1.79[a]	2,968	1.79	2,689	3,086	–	2	75	23	15	13
Sulfur	15,969	5.19	15,969	5.19	15,414	16,735	22	20	30	28	16	5
Total nonmetallic minerals (except fuels)	264,732	2.73	369,092	3.80	253,848	586,865	4	43	34	19	9273	6415

Adapted from 1954 Census of Mineral Industries, U. S. Bureau of the Census.

[a] Mine water used is included.

[b] Exceeds water intake, in part due to accumulation of rain water in storage facilities.

[c] Includes only operations mining rock salt as such; excludes operations recovering salt by evaporation and from pumped underground brines and solution mining.

taken from a census report. There is some question concerning the completeness of the data, but no other figures exist. Data on water used by the metals and nonmetals branches of mining were collected, for 1958, in connection with investigations of the Select Committee on National Water Resources of the United States Senate, but were published only as totals for each branch, with a geographic breakdown (5). Compared with 265 billion gal total water intake, excepting mine water, for nonmetallic mining, given in the 1954 Census of Mineral Industries, the Senate Select Committee (Kerr) report showed a much lower 1958 water use by nonmetals of 207 billion gal. To add to the confusion, the 1958 Census of Manufactures reported an estimated water intake for all purposes in nonmetallic mineral mining of 938 billion gal. Recognizing these serious discrepancies, the 1954 data are most useful as they show details for industry sectors under nonmetal mining. The U. S. Bureau of Mines canvassed mineral producers in 1963 to obtain a more reliable picture on water usage.

Compared with total water intake of 265 billion gal in 1954, water discharged amounted to 254 billion gal (both figures excluding mine water); gross water usage, including recirculation, totaled 587 billion gal. Most of the water for nonmetal mining was obtained from company systems, with surface waters accounting for substantially more than underground water.

In terms of total quantities of water used, the sand and gravel industry leads all others by far, having accounted in 1954 for about 123 billion gal, excluding mine water, or almost half the nonmetallic minerals' total water usage. Phosphate rock with about 40 billion gal and crushed limestone with 35 billion gal were next. In terms of annual water (except mine water) intake per production worker, phosphate rock led in 1954 with 8.7 million gal followed by sulfur with 5.2 million gal and sand and gravel with 4.3 million gal; the industry total was 2.7 million gal per production worker.

Water usage in nonmetal mining and beneficiation has risen substantially since 1954. Total value of output of nonmetallics (omitting fuels) has risen from $2.62 billion in 1954 to $4 billion in 1962, or 53%. Average unit mine value in that period for nonmetallics rose only a little over 8%, so physical volume of output increased by about 40%. Conservation practices in water use may well have advanced, but certainly not enough for that much increase in physical output of these materials.

In terms of water usage per ton of product produced, this varies in nonmetal mining from zero in dry process operations to probably a top average of around 50 tons of water per ton of product produced, as is characteristic of the extensive pebble phosphate rock operations of Florida. In the sand and gravel operations where washing is employed, total water use varies over a wide range from 1 to 2 tons of water per ton of product up to 20 or more tons in small dredging operations. A government survey of waterborne wastes from mineral operations in the northeastern United States showed that nine producers of washed sand and gravel averaged about 460 gal or almost 2 tons per ton of product produced.

Geographic Distribution. Water usage shows extreme variations geographically, being much higher, naturally, where water is abundant and cheap, and very low (with heavy recirculation or reuse) where supplies are scarce and expensive. Population centers or markets are also major factors in determining heavy water usage. Regionally, the pattern of water intake for normal mining shows fairly uniform distribution (5); but with concentrations in the eastern half of the United States and along the Pacific coast. In terms of ratios of gross water use, including recirculation or reuse, to water intake (excluding mine water), regional patterns varied in 1954 from a low of about 1.2 in the lower Missouri Basin and the Great Basin region (surprisingly), to highs of 3.9 for the Rio Grande and Pecos River basins and about 3.0 for the upper Missouri River and Ohio River basin. Virtually all the nonmetallic mineral processing operations in the San Juan and Rio Grande basins of New Mexico use dry methods, requiring no water except for cooling and domestic purposes.

So-called mine water is an important source of water to supply operating needs, as shown by differences between columns 1 and 3 of Table II, although some industry sectors show no distinction. Mine water usage can vary from small quantities (or none) encountered in underground operations to abundant waters met in dredging or drag-lining open pit deposits at or below groundwater levels near streams or lakes. Even in underground operations, water may be encountered in such heavy flows as to comprise a major obstacle—witness the severity of this problem met in sinking a 3300-ft shaft to mine potash at Esterhazy, Saskatchewan.

Nature of Usage. Water performs a large number of functions in nonmetal mining and beneficiation. In mining, water may be used in large quantities to perform major functions that include floating a dredge, hydraulicking, dissolving underground material in solution mining of salt and potash, or melting underground material as in the Frasch method of sulfur production. Water may be used in smaller amounts in rock drilling; in allaying dust after blasting; and in cooling engines and other machinery used in mining, loading, and transporting ore.

In beneficiation, water finds its greatest use. Although dry preparation methods are common in beneficiation of nonmetallic minerals, as in crushing stone, dry grinding of cement, feldspar, talc, and pyrophyllite, and screening of sand and gravel, most beneficiation processes utilize water to meet product specifications for markets or for further processing. The major function performed by water is to provide a medium that allows for separation of products into grades of purity by various types of gravity methods (simple sprays for washing, spiral cones, screws, log washers, jigs, various types of classifiers, scrubbers, cones, etc.), flotation methods, wet magnetic methods, and many other processes. Water also provides the medium for chemical processing of some nonmetallics—as in purifying and separating saline brines and in solution and selective crystallization purification of potash. In all wet preparation methods, moreover, water serves a vital function in transporting the product through the equipment, by means of pipes and launders, with flow maintained by gravity or pumps.

Including wet preparation methods applied to all types of metallic and nonmetallic ores, gravity treatment uses 10–20 tons of water per ton of ore treated, and flotation methods use 3–5 tons.

Another important function of water in preparation plants is dust suppression. Although methods are available for controlling dust in dry processing, water is a most effective means of minimizing this troublesome problem. It is most useful in handling dusts high in free silica, where dangers of employees' contracting silicosis are encountered.

Finally, water serves such conventional uses in treatment plants as coolant in processing operations and for engines powering various equipment, steam generation, fire prevention, and domestic needs of the community of workers and families.

WASTE CHARACTERISTICS

TYPES AND SOURCES

Contaminants in water that is used in or results from mining and beneficiating nonmetallic minerals vary over tremendous ranges—both in type and in quantity. Considering the entire industry, it can be said that the types of contaminants that are most commonly encountered and are most abundant are suspended particles of fine sand, silt, and clay, and lesser amounts of fine particles of limestone and dolomite. These result from the washing of sand and gravel, and crushed limestone—the two most widely distributed and largest water users in nonmetal mining. Fines or slimes also result from the crushing and grinding of rock to produce grades and sizes of product that meet market specifications. Quantities of solids in the water as it leaves the washing or preparation plant may vary from a few per cent up to perhaps 10 or 20%. In sand and gravel dredging operations, waste returned to the stream may amount to as much as two-thirds of the product recovered, as indicated by a survey of 47 dredge operations in the lower Missouri River basin. A total of 6 million tons of waste was returned to rivers or streams in producing 9.5 million tons of sand and gravel.

Contaminants also occur naturally as dissolved mineral matter in waters from mining other products (not very frequent in nonmetal mining), or they may actually comprise the mineral being sought, such as chlorides, sulfates, borates, and carbonates of sodium, potassium, calcium, magnesium, and lithium, in production of saline minerals from brines from drilled wells, from underground solution mining of salt, or from saline lakes or the ocean. In Frasch sulfur operations, contaminants are derived from the original underground waters that must be tapped through bleeder wells to relieve hydraulic pressure that would otherwise build up from the injection of huge quantities of hot waters. Such sulfur well bleedwater is a saline liquid that contains the same constituents found in sea water, plus sulfides as H_2S normally ranging from 270 to 1200 mg/ liter. Sulfide is the major culprit that has necessitated extensive and costly treatment in those Gulf coast areas where sulfur is produced.

In Florida phosphate operations, a huge wastewater problem arises from the sliming character of the land pebble phosphate material. This results in part from fines occurring in the ore itself, and in part from the milling and flotation processing to which the phosphate is subjected. The colloidal properties of these slimes prevent dewatering by settling or other simple methods beyond 30% of solids.

Reagents used in the flotation separation of various nonmetallics, especially phosphate rock, are other sources of wastewater contamination. Reagents vary, but frequently include fatty acids, soaps, amines, caustic soda, sulfuric acid, kerosene, and fuel oil. Separation of potash from halite in New Mexico potash operations involves use of such reagents as cresol, causticized starch, lead chloride, amines, pine oil, and petroleum oil. Normally, reagents for flotation of any of the nonmetallics are added in very small amounts, of the order of ¼–4 lb of reagent per ton of solids processed. Several different reagents may be used in a single flotation process.

Heat is another type of wastewater contaminant that may be troublesome. Hot wastes are not at all common in nonmetal mining and beneficiation, except for minor amounts of water used in cooling machinery used in mining and milling operations. If the operations require process steam (unusual for these operations except for sulfur), or if the operation generates its own power, as in isolated areas such as open ocean mining of sulfur, much water will be used for cooling, and the waste will carry sizable amounts of heat as a contaminant.

EFFECTS OF WASTES

Consideration of effects of wastes from nonmetal mining and beneficiation must necessarily be confined to a few highlights. These will be aimed especially at wastes that are somewhat unique to nonmetal mining operations.

As pointed out in the previous section, the great preponderance of pollution in nonmetal mining wastewater is physical in character, comprising fine particulate matter such as sand, silt, clay, and limestone. If this escapes to the air from dry-process preparation plants, there is cause for complaints from the public. If wastewater containing such particulate matter is discharged directly to streams, without effective treatment, turbidity of the stream is raised. This can impair use of the stream as a source of water for municipal or industrial purposes because of excessive settling or filtration required, and can seriously impair recreational uses of the stream, such as swimming and fishing, and other esthetic qualities. By continued deposition over many years, the stream may become thoroughly choked up and its flow impaired. If discharge is into a pool or reservoir behind a dam, it accelerates silting and shortens the pool's useful life.

Closely related to the physical pollutants in wastewater is the unique problem of wastes from plants that wash and concentrate phosphate rock in Florida. In these waters the slimes are of such fine size (typically 65% less than 0.5 micron) that settling occurs at a very slow rate. However, a comprehensive 2-year study of the effects of such wastes, made in the late 1940's, concluded that clear effluents from the settling areas used in the operations were not toxic to fish or animal life in field tests or in controlled experiments.

In the unique wastewater problem in Frasch sulfur operations, along the Gulf coast areas of Louisiana and Texas, the hydrogen sulfide content of bleedwater is the objectionable pollutant. The saline characteristics are similar to sea water and are no problem because, in the great majority of wells, the bleedwater is discharged to brackish streams, tidal lagoons, or the open ocean. The H_2S content at the lower end of the range is stated to be not toxic or dangerous (presumably to humans), but is apt to produce odors and paint blackening (3). These concentrations, however, may be highly toxic to aquatic life, especially if discharged to fresh water streams or lakes.

Saline wastes from salt mining operations obviously are harmful in polluting waters if discharged to fresh water streams and lakes or to non-saline underground aquifers. Such pollution would impair or prevent usage of such fresh waters for municipal or industrial purposes, and might well endanger or kill aquatic life. However, such saline wastes are not objectionable if pumped through wells into underground saline aquifers or discharged to the ocean or to enclosed basins of saline waters in desert regions. Even in isolated regions, disposal of highly saline wastes is being more and more closely controlled because of dangers of downward percolation into fresh water aquifers that may thus be severely polluted.

WASTE DISPOSAL

The principal problems of waste disposal from nonmetal mining, like other industries, include water reuse, effective treatment processes, recovery of marketable materials, and methods of ultimate disposition of effluent and sludges.

WATER REUSE

Generally speaking, a high degree of reuse of water is practiced where water is relatively scarce and expensive, and little or no reuse where it is abundant and cheap.

An example of high reuse is the extensive potash operation of southeastern New Mexico, where potash is dry-mined and wet-concentrated. Wet concentration involves recirculation of saturated brines, with resultant losses in recovery through solution of the KCl. Efforts were aimed for some time at developing a dry process for separation, with special attention to electrostatics. More recently, the State has imposed limits on the quantity of water that can be pumped from fresh water aquifers for industrial use. Efforts are now aimed at developing beneficiation processes that can use available saline groundwaters, with the ultimate goal of reducing fresh water usage to chemical processing, boiler makeup, and other essential needs.

In Florida phosphate rock operations, about 75% of the large quantity of water used is reclaimed from waste disposal ponds; in other words, gross use amounts to 4 times new water intake.

Another example of high water reuse is sand and gravel washing in states that prohibit direct discharge of turbid effluent to streams or lakes. Such regulations are imposed in Ohio, Pennsylvania, and many other states. Use of one or more settling ponds in series is found most effective in preparing wastewater for ultimate discharge, and water from such ponds can be continuously recycled through the washing plants. New water must be added to make up for losses incurred in the plant and by drainage of wet material from stockpiles. The latter, of course, percolates into the ground and ultimately returns to the stream or underground aquifer.

An example of low reuse of water is the washing operation on sand and gravel dredges, where reuse is virtually zero as all the water is discharged directly to the stream or lake from which the material is being dredged.

Considering the total nonmetallic minerals industry, a rough indication of over-all average water reuse can be obtained from the 1954 water data given in Table II. Total gross water use, including recirculation, was 587 billion gal compared with water intake of 265 billion gal—a ratio of about 2.2 to 1.

TREATMENT PROCESSES, PRODUCT RECOVERIES, AND EFFLUENT DISPOSAL

The most universally used method of treatment of wastewater in nonmetal mining before final discharge is settling ponds or (for sulfur) aeration reservoirs. These are typical of the large water-using segments of the industry—sand and gravel, crushed stone, phosphate rock, sulfur, and saline minerals. A great variety of conventional methods of treating and dewatering pulps is used in the processing circuit—to separate desired products by grade or quality or size, to dewater the product for ultimate sale, and to recover water more immediately for reuse. Types of processes thus utilized, together with the multitudinous types of equipment employed, are discussed more appropriately in texts or handbooks on mineral dressing. Certain types of equipment, such as thickening tanks, scalping tanks, classifiers, and hydrocyclones, are being applied more and more by sand and gravel operations before discharging wastewater to settling ponds. One objective of such treatment, in addition to recovering salable fine sands, is to minimize siltation of the settling ponds and thus to prolong their useful life.

Discussion of wastewater treatment methods and their effectiveness, product recovery, and effluent disposal can best be handled by brief descriptions of practices characteristic of separate segments of the nonmetal mining industry.

Sand and Gravel. Descriptions of sand and gravel operations generally omit detail oncerning wastewater treatment and recovery practices. It is common, however, to find settling ponds either already in use or in the planning stage to answer any tightening of water disposal regulations that may be encountered in the future. A settling pond operation in Washington involves a series of basins, in which alum is used to speed the settling process. At this plant, filling of the large basin is visualized ultimately to result in a building site. Other operators eventually recover settled fines from pits for use as land fill. Settling ponds, however common, are not entirely satisfactory in that:

(a) A certain amount of fine granular material, commercially valuable, is lost with the undesired slimes, silts, and clays.
(b) In order to allow for settling of the solids—for ultimate drainage and relative drying for reclamation, or merely impoundment without reclamation—the cost of the land immobilized may be a severe problem or even prohibitive.
(c) The solids-water separation to the point where water is reusable entails losses of water by percolation into the ground and by evaporation. Furthermore, large quantities of water are immobilized for long periods prior to reuse, which involves additional investment.

Many references point to the use of hydrocyclones before discharging wastewater to settling ponds. These serve the dual purposes of recovering sizable tonnages of fine sand (minus 50, 100, or 200 mesh) that can be mixed with coarser sands to meet product specifications, and of reducing the amount of fill in settling ponds, prolonging their usefulness. Cyclones use centrifugal force to accelerate settling of solids from water (clays, silts, and fine sands) at 60–70% of solids, with the overflow carrying only slimes below 10–15 microns in size. Some of this overflow can be reused in screen spray-bars and scrubbers; but to prevent buildup of slimes in the circuit, a certain amount of this reusable water—usually 20–40%—is bled to settling ponds and is replaced by fresh water or by water from the pond after complete solids-water separation. Other equipment used for this general purpose includes thickening or classifier tanks, scalping tanks, rake classifiers, and screws.

Water left in the dewatered product (shipped or stockpiled) varies according to the process and equipment used, as well as with the coarseness of the product. Coarse and medium aggregates carry 4–6% of moisture (by weight), equivalent to 0.04–0.06 ton of water per ton of product, while sand will average about 20% of moisture (less with coarser sands, more with finer sands). This is equivalent to 0.2 ton of water per ton of product.

Crushed Limestone. For many years the trend in preparation of crushed stone has been toward use of more water. Although many crushed stone plants operate dry, modern specifications call for washing of coarse and medium concrete aggregates. This can be included in wet processing (grinding, screening, and classification) or in a final wash of the product prior to loading or stocking; the quantity used generally runs between 0.75 and 2.25 tons of water per ton of crushed product. Wet processing naturally produces a cleaner product, and also serves to prevent a dust problem that might cause complaints from the public, especially if the plant is near urban residential areas.

Methods of treatment are generally similar to those used for sand and gravel. Dewatering is accomplished by various means, such as classifiers and thickening tanks, prior to discharge of wastewater into settling ponds. Frequently, abandoned quarries are used as settling basins, and the clear water is recirculated; in other operations, ponds are constructed by dikes built of stripped material. In one sizable operation, solids in the wastewater average 50% minus 200 mesh. The coarser material settles out closest to the point of discharge into the pond, and is sometimes marketed for fill material. As with sand and gravel, regulations prohibit discharge of turbid wastewater to streams and lakes in many states; even where laws are absent, many operators employ recycling practices for water conservation or to prevent complaints from the public concerning stream pollution.

Phosphate Rock. As mentioned earlier, wastewater treatment from pebble phosphate rock operations in Florida comprises one of the major problems encountered by the nonmetal mining industry. Because of the abundance of extremely fine particles of phosphate rock and accompanying clay and silica in the material as mined, plus the additional fines produced by grinding prior to concentration by flotation, the losses in slimes may be as high as 40%. This occurs in spite of extensive and costly settling ponds. The problem has been well summarized in a Bureau of Mines report (2):

> The slimes discharged from the washer plants containing 4–6 per cent solids in the Florida pebble field contain approximately one-third of the P_2O_5 present in the original phosphate ore and in the Tennessee brown-rock field contain nearly one-half of the P_2O_5 present in the original phosphate ore. These slimes represent large losses of potential phosphate values and impose a disposal problem that is becoming progressively more serious. Huge areas must be provided for settling these slimes and for returning the water in which they are suspended to the washer plants for reuse. Even after settling for two or more years these slimes contain 75 per cent of water, and no economic method of utilizing them has yet proved economically feasible.

In a more recent government report on methods for recovering the phosphate rock in these slimes, it is estimated that slimes stored through 1960 total about 324 million tons and represent a potential resource of 45.4 million tons of P_2O_5. It is also pointed out that water recovery from such slimes, while not urgent now, may become of increasing importance as availability of fresh water in the area becomes a more serious problem in the future. The report describes several methods of dewatering and beneficiating the slimes, but concludes that none of them is economic.

Detailed descriptions of the settling pond operations, aimed especially at a study of the effects of waste effluent from these ponds on receiving streams, have been published (4). These reports conclude that clear effluent from the ponds is not toxic to fish or animal life in field tests or in controlled laboratory experiments.

Sulfur. Production of sulfur by the Frasch process requires injection of about 1200–1500 gal (5–6 tons) of superheated water per ton of sulfur produced. None of this water comes up through the injector-producer wells with the sulfur, so bleeder wells are drilled around the periphery of the deposit to tap the connate waters in the formation and to prevent a buildup of hydraulic pressure in the sulfur-bearing formation. Bleedwater equal in volume to the injected water is tapped through these bleeder wells. Even at small mines, bleedwater in amounts of several million gallons per day is produced and must be treated prior to disposal.

Salt and H_2S content of this bleedwater has already been described. In most cases, the bleedwater is discharged eventually to tidal streams or lagoons or to the open ocean, hence its saline content is not objectionable. The dissolved hydrogen sulfide content, from 270 to 1200 mg/liter, is a serious pollutant which must be removed before discharge.

Except for one operation on land and one offshore operation, Freeport Sulphur Company uses large retention reservoirs into which bleedwater is pumped, sometimes after spraying to oxidize and remove about 50% of the H_2S. The water is retained in these reservoirs for periods from 5 to 20 days (for different mines), during which oxidation and aeration reduce the H_2S content to less than 10 mg/liter. By further dilution with canal waters, the H_2S is reduced to an insignificant concentration.

One Freeport mine (Chacahoula) is situated in a fresh water habitat with sluggish streams. The bleedwater disposal problem appeared overwhelming until it was found that an underground salt water sandstone formation would provide sufficient capacity for injecting the bleedwater over the projected life of the operation. This has been done successfully.

At the offshore Grand Isle mine, 5 million gal per day of bleedwater is piped to jets located 15 ft below the ocean surface. Action of the jets, aimed at declinations of 7°, mixes it with 500 million gal per day of sea water, for a dilution of 100:1. At this point, the oxygen content of the diluted mixture is sufficient to reduce the H_2S content to 0.2 mg/liter, and further dilution and mixing occurs promptly to dissipate the H_2S completely. In all its operations. Freeport disposes of 13 million gal per day of bleedwater, most of which is treated as described above.

Texas Gulf Sulphur Company uses impoundments at two of its mines, essentially as described above but including preagitation at one to release the H_2S. Stripping the H_2S by use of boiler flue gas, containing 8–10% of CO_2, is used at another mine; and a closed system reaction with dilute sulfurous acid (H_2SO_3) to oxidize the sulfur, followed by settling for sulfur removal, is used at a fourth operation. The latter two processes are described in detail by Schwab *et al.* (3). Recovery of the sulfur is not economic.

Potash and Borate Minerals. In the extensive potash operations of New Mexico, the sylvite (KCl) is separated from the halite (NaCl) by either flotation or fractional crystallization. Wastewater from concentrating and refining operations is characteristically a brine saturated with NaCl, containing also flotation agents such as fatty acid amines, potato starch, fuel oil, and tall oils when flotation is utilized. These waste brines are pumped into retaining ponds which have porous bottoms, thus permitting brines to seep into underground water strata. Some of the waste brine is used to pump tailings from flotation plants to waste piles. Ultimately the brine seeps into the numerous sink holes in porous limestone from the bottom of the settling ponds. Such disposal is permitted in this isolated desert area, and operators foresee no tightening of regulations to prevent it in the future. As stated earlier, however, because of the severe scarcity of fresh water in the area, efforts are being made to develop methods for dry concentration or for utilization of saline water in producing a marketable potash product.

Potash recovery from solar ponds and flotation units at Wendover, Utah, involves disposal of wastewater which is a saturated solution of NaCl, KCl, and $MgCl_2$, averaging about 600 gal per minute. This is returned to solar ponds for water conservation and eventual recovery of the KCl content. Wastewater is thus continuously circulated through the solar ponds until, as described by the operator, it is "worn out." There are no regulations concerning wastewater practice, because the installation is so far out in the desert.

Announcement was made early in 1963 of plans to exploit the huge 3000-ft deep potash deposits in southern Saskatchewan by solution mining through drilled wells, to avoid the extreme costs of sinking shafts through the treacherous Blairmore water formation. Water would be pumped down through numerous wells, and KCl would be dissolved along with NaCl and recovered through the same or additional wells. The problem of minimizing solution of NaCl may be partially solved by special methods of placing a blanket of natural gas or of oil above the main potash bed to isolate beds of NaCl that lie above. The main cost problem would involve evaporating water from the brine thus brought to the surface.

Beneficiation of the borax produced from the large open pit at Boron, California, is accomplished by an entirely dry process involving high intensity magnetic separators to remove shale or other gangue. Water is used in the refining operation to leach the borax from remaining clay and other impurities. Wastewater from this operation contains suspended fine particles of clay and traces of dissolved borate minerals. It is disposed of in sealed-bottom evaporation ponds, the sealing being required by State Board of Health regulations that prevent any pollution of ground water, even far out in the desert where the operation is located. Verification of lack of pollution is made by the company by means of measurements in adjacent monitor wells.

The important Searles Lake, California, operations produce a variety of saline products—borates, potash, soda ash, salt cake, etc.—from brines recovered from wells in the area. Chemical methods involving evaporation and carbonation are used to recover the various products. Wastewater in quantities amounting to 20% of the incoming brine is simply returned to the highly saline waters of Searles Lake.

Salt. There are no serious wastewater problems encountered in the mining and beneficiation of salt. Production is accomplished by underground mining of rock salt in solid condition, pumping of brines from underground saline aquifers through wells, solution mining by pumping water down through wells to the salt formation where it dissolves the salt and bringing the saturated solution back to the surface through openings between pipe and casing in the same well or through adjacent return brine wells, and by solar evaporation of sea water or saline lakes.

Rock salt mines are typically dry operations, with the mined-out body lying well within the thicker salt bed, salt thus comprising both floor and roof of the rooms mined out. The salt as mined may be sufficiently pure for many applications, or it may require beneficiation if impurities are present. Dry separation methods have been perfected to accomplish this, or water may be used to dissolve the material with resultant refinement by evaporation with applied heat.

Where salt is recovered in the form of brine, from either brine pools or solution mining operations, the brines are usually used as such in various chemical operations, especially in the production of chlorine, caustic soda, and soda ash. Thus, there is no wastewater problem involved at the wellhead, since the entire product is used in manufacturing processes. Care must be exercised, however, that such brine wells are thoroughly sealed off near the bottom so no brine can escape upward into fresh water horizons.

In solar evaporation operations, important in the San Francisco Bay area and coastal areas of southern California, and in saline lakes of western desert areas such as Great Salt Lake, no wastewater problems are encountered. Along the coast, evaporation and crystallization of the NaCl is nearly complete, prior to crystallization of magnesium, bromine, and other salts. The concentrated brine is simply disposed of in the ocean, or is sold to chemical producers for recovery of magnesia and other compounds.

Kaolin. Water is employed in many of the kaolin operations in Georgia, where it is used in pit mining to break down the clay into a slurry for pumping to beneficiation plants several miles away, and in beneficiation to wash and separate the clay from sand, mica, and other heavier minerals. Thickeners, cyclones, and filtration are used in dewatering the product, and wastewater is finally disposed of in settling ponds, with clear water effluent draining into streams. Settling ponds are effective for the purpose of meeting State regulations that prohibit pollution of streams.

INDUSTRY TRENDS

In general, the United States is richly endowed with nonmetallic mineral resources, especially the major ones that have been discussed. As demand continues to increase for supplies of these materials to meet the needs of the growing economy, present operations can be expanded with comparative ease, and new ones started.

Potash production in New Mexico will become less important in the total supply picture as new operations in Utah and Saskatchewan get into full production, with additional mines to be added in the future, especially in Saskatchewan.

Phosphate resources in North Carolina will soon be developed to augment supplies from huge reserves still available in Florida, Tennessee, and the western states of Idaho, Utah, Montana, and Wyoming.

Spreading urbanization and construction of more highways, reservoirs, and recreational facilities will force sand and gravel and perhaps rock quarrying operations farther away from urban centers. This will result in higher priced material delivered to urban construction projects. A 1962 study of the Denver, Colorado, area, typifying this problem, showed that while production of sand and gravel since 1950 in the area was 50 million tons, total reserves were reduced by 250 million tons. Similar problems have been faced in the Florida phosphate area. The obvious answer is to educate zoning and conservation authorities on the need of regulating land use to permit recovery of such valuable resources under suitable controls. The pits and quarries can and should be reclaimed later for various useful purposes—agricultural, industrial, commerical, residential, parks, and even game sanctuaries. Florida phosphate operators are facing a serious problem in reclaiming the huge areas strip mined there. Outstanding progress is being made by all operators in fulfilling their pledge to carry out their activities in such a manner that the land involved would help meet the esthetic and practical needs of the community. Several histories of reclamation of gravel pits to highly useful purposes have been recorded. An outstanding example of reclamation of a rock quarry is the Queen Elizabeth Gardens in Vancouver, where a mined-out quarry was first converted to a trash dump and more recently to a beautiful rock garden and park.

Wastewater disposal appears to be well in hand in most mining operations. Regulations in many states now prohibit pollution of streams and lakes by the wastes from such operations. Almost universally, the ultimate method of treatment prior to discharging effluent to streams and other bodies of water is settling or aerating ponds. The cost of preparing and using land for such a purpose, together with the losses of water through evaporation and percolation, add up to substantial figures. In the future, as land and water values increase, the trend will move toward use of more water recovery equipment ahead of settling ponds—thickeners, screws, scalpers, cyclones, etc.—to minimize requirements for the final treatment in settling ponds.

ACKNOWLEDGMENTS

The author wishes to acknowledge assistance by many persons who responded to requests for data. Special thanks are extended to John D. Sullivan, Technical Director of Battelle Memorial Institute, and to C. E. Golson, of Arthur G. McKee & Company, for advice and assistance.

REFERENCES

1. Gillson, J. L. (Ed.), "Industrial Minerals and Rocks," 3rd ed. American Institute of Mining, Metallurgical, and Petroleum Engineers, New York, 1960.

2. Ruhlman, E. R., *U. S. Bur. Mines, Inform. Circ.* **7814**, 1958.
3. Schwab, J. W., Edmiston, D. C., and McBridge, G. T. Jr. *Sewage Ind. Wastes* **26**, 1370–1376 (1954).
4. Specht, R. C., *Florida Eng. Expt. Sta. Bull.* **32**, 1950.
5. U. S. Senate, Select Committee on National Water Resources, 86th Congress, 2d Session, Committee Print No. 8, "Water Resources Activities in the United States," 1960.

Mineral Products

Chapter 13

COKE AND GAS

by C. W. FISHER

Wastewater control for the coke and gas industries now concerns two distinct and different industries in the United States. In the early 1900's in the United States, and at the present time in several European countries, the "gas industry" meant "manufactured gas industry." For manufactured gas, coal or coke is the major raw material, thus closely relating the gas industry to coke plant operations. Now, however, natural gas and liquefied petroleum (LP) gas account for over 98% of the energy derived from gas in the United States. Thus, the gas industry is more closely connected to the petroleum industry; characteristics and means of handling wastewaters from the production of natural gas and LP gas will be discussed in the chapter on Petroleum. The present chapter is devoted mainly to the coal carbonization industry, reviewing sources of wastewaters and means of treatment or handling of these wastewaters.

THE COKE INDUSTRY

The production of coke by carbonization of coal consists of heating bituminous coal in the absence of air to final temperatures of 900°– 1100°C in an oven or a retort, driving off volatile products that are recovered as tar, light oil, and gas. Bituminous coal and lignite may also be carbonized at lower temperatures to produce chars and "low temperature coke," large amounts of tar, and lesser amounts of gas. At present, nearly all domestic coke is produced by the high temperature coking process. For this method of coking, horizontal slot-type ovens are used for over 98% of the production, the balance being produced in ovens of beehive type. In general, coke is prepared from a blend of grades of bituminous coal, to give proper quality of coke and to prevent damage to the ovens.

A typical beehive oven is a firebrick chamber with arched roof about 12 ft in diameter, where 5–10 tons of coal are carbonized in 48–72 hours. Coke is usually the only product recovered from these operations.

The slot-type or by-product coke oven is 40–43 ft long by 10–15 ft high and 14–20 inches wide, where 15–20 tons of coal are charged and carbonized in 12–24 hours. Groups of up to 100 of these ovens are arranged in a battery. Coal in the oven is coked by the combustion of fuel gas in flues built into the refractory brick wall separating each pair of oven chambers. Several varieties of by-product slot-type coke ovens are to be found in the United States. These include batteries having vertical heating flues with crossover flues connecting the heating flues of adjacent flue walls; batteries with vertical heating flues and a horizontal flue connecting the tops of the heating flues in each flue wall; and batteries with hairpin vertical heating flues. Each of these types may be built with the heating gas introduced through gun flues from the ends of the ovens, or of the underjet design with flues entering from the bottom of the battery. A few old batteries of ovens with horizontal heating flues are still in operation. The types of ovens are also referred to as Koppers, Koppers-Becker, Wilputte, Otto, or Semet Solvay, depending on designer or contractor.

TABLE I

OPERATIVE COKE OVENS AND PRODUCTION OF COKE IN THE UNITED STATES

Year	Slot-type ovens			Beehive ovens		
	Number of ovens	Number of plants	Coke produced, thousands of tons per year	Number of ovens	Number of plants	Coke produced, thousands of tons per year
1930	12,831	89	45,196	23,907	121	2,776
1940	12,734	89	54,014	15,150	93	3,058
1950	14,982	84	66,891	17,708	125	5,827
1960	15,320	73	56,219	7,583	43	1,010
1962	14,535	66	51,098	4,979	27	812

Adapted from U.S. Bureau of Mines Mineral Yearbooks.

Table I gives the number of slot-type and beehive ovens in the United States, and coke production for each type of oven since 1930. At present, over 90% of the coke is produced in ovens operated by plants owning or operating their own blast furnaces; thus, this industry is closely related to the iron and steel industry. For 1962, coke produced in the United States was utilized as follows (5):

Blast furnaces	90.0%
Foundries	4.7
Producer and water gas sets	0.2
Other industrial uses	3.7
Residential heating	0.5
Export	0.9
Total	100.0%

From the by-product coke oven, other materials are recovered, the yield and character of these by-products depending upon type of coal used, type of oven, and nature of coke being produced. Typical yields of by-products recovered for a coke oven plant are given in Table II.

TABLE II

By-Products from Coking of Bituminous Coal

Product	Yields, per ton of coal	Composition, volume %	
Coke oven gas	10,500 cu ft (Heating value, 530 BTU/cu ft)	Hydrogen	55
		Methane	30
		Nitrogen	6
		Carbon monoxide	5
		Ethylene	2
		Other	2
Crude tar	8.5 gal	Light oil	5
		Tar acids	3
		Tar bases	2
		Naphthalene	10
		Heavy oil	7
		Anthracene oil	10
		Pitch	63
Light oil	3 gal	Benzene	65
		Toluene	15
		Xylene	4
		Other and loss	16
Ammonia	5.5 lb	Usually recovered as ammonium sulfate or ammonium phosphate	

Many plants have facilities to process further the crude light oil into pure benzene, toluene, xylene, and solvent fractions. Several plants also have facilities for distilling tar and for recovering products from the tar distillates. Depending on economic conditions of sales, coke plants also may be designed to recover hydrogen, ethylene, sulfur, hydrogen sulfide, ammonium thiocyanate, naphthalene, phenol, pyridine, and other products.

THE GAS INDUSTRY

The gas industry in the early 1900's consisted of a limited distribution of natural gas and LP fuels, with widespread distribution of manufactured gas through city mains for residential use. Depending on process and raw material used, manufactured gas of the following major types was distributed: coke oven gas, oil gas, water gas, producer gas, carbureted water gas, and re-formed gas. Pipelining of natural gas has increased rapidly, and in 1962 only the states of Maine, Vermont, and Hawaii did not consume natural gas. LP gases consisting of ethane, propane, butane, isobutane, and mixtures of these gases have also had a rapid increase in usage. Natural gas and LP gases used as such or after re-forming have displaced nearly all manufactured gas distributed in the United States. Tables III and IV indicate consumption of natural gas and coke oven gas in the United States.

TABLE III

NATURAL GAS CONSUMPTION IN THE UNITED STATES
(BILLIONS OF CUBIC FEET)

Year	Total	Residential	Commercial	Industrial fuel	Field use	Carbon black
1930	1,942	305	71	577	723	266
1940	2,667	442	132	1024	700	369
1950	6,025	1198	388	2842	1187	410
1960	12,509	3103	1020	6408	1780	198
1962	13,752	3398	1199	7123	1892	140

Adapted from U.S. Bureau of Mines Minerals Yearbooks.

TABLE IV

SALE AND USE OF SURPLUS COKE OVEN GAS IN THE UNITED STATES
(BILLIONS OF CUBIC FEET)

Year	Surplus coke oven gas sold		Surplus coke oven gas used by producer
	Distributed in city mains	Industrial purposes	
1930	117	23	251
1940	152	30	342
1950	149	39	414
1960	30	30	460
1962	23	25	437

Adapted from U.S. Bureau of Mines Minerals Yearbooks.

SOURCES AND CHARACTERISTICS OF COKE PLANT WASTEWATERS

The basic flow diagram for a coke plant with normal by-product recoveries is given in Fig. 1. Coal, properly sized and mixed, is charged batchwise to the oven chamber from a larry car unloading through charging holes at the top of the oven. Upon being heated, the coal evolves volatile materials that escape through standpipes at the ends of the oven tops. The gases from all ovens in a battery are combined in a collecting

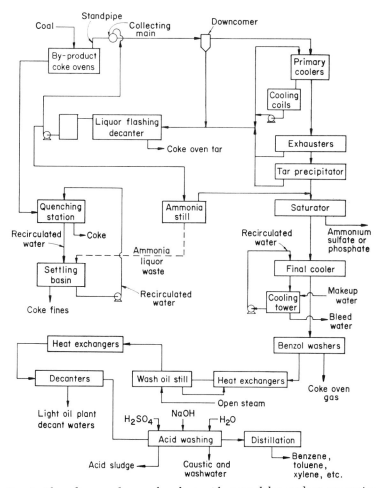

FIG. 1. Flow diagram for a coke plant with normal by-product recoveries.

main, where they are cooled to about 80°C by sprays of flushing liquor, thus condensing most of the tar. At the downcomer, condensed liquor is separated from the gases. The gases then pass through primary coolers of direct or indirect type where they are further cooled to about 30°C. Indirect cooling of the gas in shell-and-tube heat exchangers condenses out additional tar and crude ammonia liquor. Direct-type primary coolers utilize recirculated liquor for cooling the gas; the recirculated liquor is cooled in heat exchangers, and excess liquor and tar are withdrawn from the system for processing.

The recirculated flushing liquor, newly condensed liquor, and tar from all sources enter the flushing liquor decanter tank where tar is withdrawn as a heavy phase from near the bottom of the decanter. The tar may be further dehydrated by indirect heating, after which it is transferred to storage. Liquor from the top of the decanter is pumped back to the sprays in the gas collecting main, and the excess is transferred to the ammonia liquor storage tank for processing in the ammonia still.

The ammonia still includes a bubble plate column where free ammonia, hydrogen sulfide, carbon dioxide, and hydrogen cyanide are stripped from the liquor by direct contact with low pressure steam, and a unit where dissolved ammonia salts are decomposed by addition of milk of lime and then stripped. The overhead vapors are usually returned to the coke oven gas stream ahead of the ammonia saturator.

Wastewaters from the ammonia still have high pollutional values, due to their phenol content. Most coke plants treat these waters to remove phenol. Some plants send the treated or raw dephenolized wastewater to the coke quenching station as makeup water for cooling of coke. Each ton of coal carbonized produces 20–30 gal of crude liquor. Use of open steam in the ammonia still increases this volume by about 20%. These waters have the approximate composition indicated in Table V.

Coke oven gas from the primary coolers then passes to exhausters which draw the gas from ovens and compress it to about 2 psig for trans-

TABLE V

APPROXIMATE COMPOSITION OF CRUDE LIQUORS TO AND FROM THE AMMONIA STILL

Liquor	To ammonia still	From ammonia still, in plant having no dephenolizer	
Total ammonia	7000	0.04–	2.5
Free ammonia	4000	0 –	0.04
Fixed ammonia	3000	0 –	2.5
Cyanide, as HCN	20– 100	10	– 100
Chloride	1100–6000	1100	–5000
Sulfate	150–1000	150	–1000
Phenols	400–3000	400	–2500
pH	–	9	– 12.5
BOD	–	2000	–4000

Results expressed as mg/liter, except pH.

mittal through the remaining by-product recovery equipment. This equipment consists of tar precipitator, saturator for removal and recovery of ammonia and other basic materials, final recirculating water coolers, and benzol washers for recovery of light oils. The coke oven gas may then be used or sold as a fuel, with or without treatment for removal of hydrogen sulfide, depending upon the requirements of the users.

Recirculated water is used for most final coolers, with the sensible heat of the water removed in a cooling tower. Makeup water is required, and a small bleed is removed from the system to limit the concentration of dissolved solids. These waters have high pollution values, with phenol concentrations from 250 to 2000 mg/liter and HCN from 150 to 270 mg/liter. Therefore, where plants require a bleed from the system, these waters should be diverted to the coke quenching station.

Crude light oil is removed from the gas in benzol washers by a hydrocarbon absorption wash oil. The crude light oil is then recovered by open steam stripping of the enriched wash oil in a wash oil still. Vapors leaving the top of the still are cooled and condensed in a series of heat exchangers, the condensate going to separators or decanters. The water layer from these decanters has the following average characteristics:

Volume, gal per ton of coal	5–20
pH	6–8.5
Phenols, mg/liter	30–150
Ammonia, mg/liter	5–30
5-day BOD, mg/liter	300–800

The oil layer, designated as crude light oils, is sold as such or may be further refined for recovery of benzene, toluene, xylene, and solvent naphtha. Before final distillation, most plants acid wash, water wash, and caustic treat the crude light oil for removal of unsaturates and sulfur compounds. The acid washing step produces sludge which requires special treatment or safe disposal in a pit, or the sludges may be burned. All methods of acid sludge disposal require care to prevent pollution of air or public waterways. Effluents from the water and caustic washes average less than 0.2 gal per ton of coal carbonized and are sent to the coke quenching station or to plant sewers.

Some large coke plants have installed hydrogenation plants for treatment of the crude light oil in place of the acid and caustic washing. The hydrogenation process also has the advantage of eliminating the acid sludge, caustic, and washwater streams.

After the coal has been carbonized, doors at each end of the oven are removed and a ram discharges the coke into a quenching car. The hot coke is transported to a quenching station where it is cooled by direct water spray. Coke quenching uses 500 gal of water per ton of coke quenched, of which about 150 gal is evaporated. The remaining water goes to a settling basin for recovery of coke fines, and is usually recirculated. Makeup water may be either fresh water or, as at several plants, process wastewaters diverted here for evaporation. Total recirculation of water is recommended for eliminating pollution from this operation; and, as economics and operating practices permit, other process wastewaters should be utilized as makeup water for coke quenching.

TREATMENT AND DISPOSAL OF COKE PLANT WASTEWATERS

The largest single source of wastewater from a by-product coke plant and the waters having the highest pollutional values are wastewaters from the ammonia still. Removal of phenols from these waters has been given much attention, because phenols are detectable by taste in water in a concentration of 0.1 mg/liter, and chlorophenols can be detected in concentrations of about 0.005 mg/liter. It should be emphasized that many other organic materials, such as decaying vegetation and algae, produce taste and odor in drinking water; surveys have shown that taste and odor problems in drinking water bear no relationship to phenol concentrations in ranges up to 0.1 mg/liter. However, it is important that the phenol content be reduced to a low level in any wastewaters that may be used as a source of drinking water. Of possible phenol removal methods, three are generally used to treat ammonia liquor still wastes: liquid extraction, vapor phase dephenolization, and biological treatment.

LIQUID EXTRACTION

The liquid extraction process uses a selective solvent, such as benzene or a light oil, to extract phenols from the crude ammonia liquor. These solvents have the advantage of being readily available at the coke plant and can be regenerated in existing equipment. The liquid extraction process treats the ammonia liquor before it enters the ammonia still, thus any solvents dissolved in the ammonia liquor are recovered as part of the vapors from the still. Dephenolization by oil extraction is an old process that has been considerably improved in efficiency of phenol removal by refinements in the design of the liquid-liquid contacting equipment. Koppers Company, Inc. has used the Koch Kaskade in its latest plants. The Wilputte Coke Oven Company, a division of Allied Chemical Corporation, has used the Podbielniak centrifugal extractor for the plants it has constructed.

The flow diagram of a typical Koppers light oil extraction dephenolizing process (2) is shown in Fig. 2. Crude ammonia liquor is pumped through a filter, cooled to about 40°C, and fed to the top of the dephenolizing tower. Approximately 4 volumes of liquor pass countercurrent to 5 volumes of ascending light oil. The phenol-rich light oil flows from the top of the tower to a decanter where entrained ammonia liquor is removed and returned to the system. The light oil flows by gravity through two caustic washers where phenols react to form sodium phenolates. After the phenolate in the lower caustic washer reaches a maximum concentration, it is removed. The contents of the upper washer are then transferred to the lower and replaced by a fresh solution of 25%

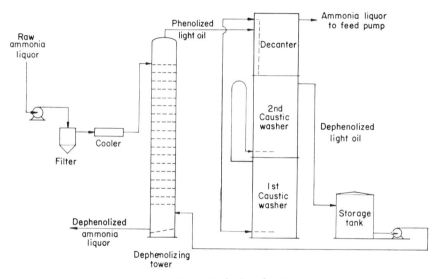

FIG. 2. Koppers light oil dephenolization process.

sodium hydroxide. Material from the bottom washer is evaporated to a tar acid content of about 50%, and is usually sold as such. This process reduces the phenol content of crude ammonia liquor from an entering concentration of 1500–2000 mg/liter of phenol to an outlet concentration of 10–30.

The Wilputte dephenolization plants (1) use a Podbielniak centrifugal extractor, operating with the first extractor for continuous countercurrent contacting of cooled raw ammonia liquor with light oil. The second centrifugal unit is a reactor for continuously contacting phenolrich light oil with caustic solution. Dephenolized light oil is recyled to the centrifugal extractor. Phenol removal efficiencies of 99% are obtainable with this type of unit.

Other solvents used for dephenolization of ammonia liquor by liquid extraction processes are petroleum oils, creosote oils fortified with tar bases, and tricresyl phosphates.

Low temperature coal carbonization and certain coal hydrogenation processes produce wastewaters having high pollutional properties similar to high temperature coke plant ammonia liquor wastes. In addition, these waters contain considerable quantities of dihydric phenols, found only to a limited extent in waste liquor from high temperature carbonization. For removal of dihydrics, the Phenosolvan process was developed in Germany and England. This process uses one of several esters, ketones, or ethers, such as butyl or isobutyl acetate, for the solvent in a liquid extraction process similar to those described above.

Extracted phenols from all absorption processes can be recovered by washing with a caustic solution as described above. The phenols may then be "sprung" from the sodium phenolate solution by use of gases containing CO_2, to yield a crude phenol. Some plants recover phenols by distillation of solvent from these residual crude phenols.

VAPOR PHASE DEPHENOLIZATION

The vapor phase process for dephenolization of ammonia liquor by evaporation of phenols from wastewaters has been installed at a number of coke plants. Hot ammonia liquor from the base of the free ammonia still is sprayed over a packed column or dephenolizing tower, divided into two sections. In the upper section, ammonia liquor is contacted countercurrently with steam; the steam is recirculated by means of a blower to the lower section where phenols are removed by reaction with sodium hydroxide. A 10% caustic solution is added batchwise at short intervals or is continuously recirculated over trays or packing. Dephenolized liquor is returned to the ammonia still, and sodium phenolate solution from the base of the column is pumped to storage. Phenol removals from the ammonia liquors from 95 to more than 98% are possible by this method.

BIOLOGICAL TREATMENT

Biological treatment of waste ammonia liquors from coal carbonization processes has been practiced at numerous plants in Europe and to some extent in the United States. This includes sending ammonia still wastes to a municipal sewage treatment plant. Activated sludge and trickling filter plants have handled these wastewaters in concentrations from 0.1% to over 5%, most plants operating with a concentration of ammonia still wastes below 2.5% in the waters received for treatment. At such concentrations, no toxic effects are noted at the sewage treatment plant. Reductions in phenols of 99.5% and higher are normal, with only a few micrograms per liter (parts per billion) remaining in the final plant effluent.

Biological oxidation units also have been used successfully for treatment of concentrated ammonia liquor wastes (3). Certain precautions are required to give satisfactory degradation:

A feed of nearly constant composition must be maintained to the system. It is recommended that storage capacity equal to 5 or more days of feed liquor be provided so that variations in operation of the ammonia still can be evened out.

Nutrient phosphorus must be added to the system.

Feed to the unit should be above 70°F and near neutral pH for best operations.

Wastewaters must be free from tars and oils.

Biological activated sludge or trickling filter treatment reduces phenols from 800 mg/liter to below 1 mg/liter. Other dilution waters normally available in the plant then make the combined waste acceptable for discharge to most receiving waterways.

Other Treatment Methods

Chemical oxidation of ammonia still waste with chlorine, ozone, and chlorine dioxide has been studied on a small scale (4). Phenols can be oxidized almost completely, and BOD's reduced more than 60%. To date, costs of treatment by chemical oxidation alone have been excessive, and the process is not used on concentrated wastes. Chemical oxidation may be more applicable for secondary treatment of waste containing low concentrations of phenol.

Adsorption of phenols on activated carbon also has been demonstrated, but operating costs appear high.

Most plants in the United States provide one of the above methods for treating ammonia still wastes to reduce phenols and other objectionable materials. Several plants use ammonia still wastewaters, with or without dephenolization, as makeup water for coke quenching.

It should be noted that liquid extraction and vapor phase processes for treating ammonia liquor wastes remove 97% or more of the phenol. However, waters from these operations still have high oxygen demand values, and require utilization within the plant or adequate dilution or secondary treatment before final discharge to a public waterway.

Subsurface disposal or deep well injection is another method that may be used for disposing of coke plant wastewaters. For successful disposal, a suitable geological reservoir beneath or in the immediate vicinity of the plant site must be available. Specific reservoir data needed are: areal extent, thickness, permeability, porosity, depth, barrier zones, faults, pinchouts, and outcrop. Where suitable underground reservoirs are available, the initial investment and operating costs for this method of disposal may be less than would be required for surface disposal.

Decanted waters from the light oil refining processes account for the second largest volume of process wastewaters. These waters also have high pollutional values, as noted earlier, and contain phenols, ammonia, and dissolved organics that have high oxygen demand. Several coke plants divert these effluents to the coke quenching station for destruction; others send them to sewers where they are diluted or treated along with other plant wastewaters. These wastes are biodegradable providing the precautions are taken that were described earlier for treatment of ammonia still wastewaters.

The two wastewaters described above, plus final cooler bleedwaters and sludge from acid washing the light oil, constitute over 99% of normal process wastewaters in a coke plant. Thus, adequate treatment or handling of these wastes is essential for good quality control of effluents from a coke oven plant.

GAS INDUSTRY WASTEWATERS

The natural gas and LP gas industries do not have major water pollution problems. Wastewaters arise during the drilling of wells and from producing wells where petroleum oil and salt waters are found in conjunction with the gases. These wastes are handled like petroleum wastes.

The major water use of the gas industry is for cooling, in connection with gas compression and storage. With normal care in design and operation of the compressor stations, these water uses need not create a pollution problem.

TRENDS IN THE COKE AND GAS INDUSTRIES

The high temperature coke industry within the United States has limited prospects for increase in quantities of coal carbonized within the next 10 years. Over 90% of the coke produced is used in blast furnace operations, and at the present time innovations are being made in blast furnace operation which decrease the amount of coke required per ton of pig iron produced. Other methods of iron and steel production are under development that would not require oven coke in their operations.

Considerable research and development is under way at the present time in the United States on other methods for increasing coal usage.

These include low temperature carbonization, briquetting, coal gasification, and hydrogenation of coal and coal tars. All of these may produce wastewaters that require treatment before they are suitable for discharge to a public waterway or for recycling within the process. Means of adequately treating these waters should be developed during the basic process studies.

In the near future, the need for increased water reuse, as a result of expansion in industry and population growth, will require higher degrees of treatment for many wastewaters before discharge. Additional research and development are required to provide economically feasible methods of adequately treating these waters. At present, one of the most promising methods for further treating coal processing wastewaters is biological treatment, such as lagooning in oxidation ponds, spray irrigation, activated sludge, aeration, and anaerobic digestion. Area requirements for waste treatment facilities frequently limit the type of treatment which can be considered and developed.

REFERENCES

1. Bowman, R. O., *Blast Furnace, Coke Oven, Raw Materials Comm.* **17**, 226–235 (1958).
2. Crane, J. D., *Blast Furnace, Coke Oven, Raw Materials Comm.* **19**, 379–387 (1960).
3. Horne, W. R., and Hurse, J. E., *Purdue Univ. Proc. Ind. Waste Conf.* **18** (1963).
4. Ohio River Valley Water Sanitation Commission, "Phenol Wastes—Treatment by Chemical Oxidation," 1951.
5. U. S. Bureau of Mines Mineral Yearbooks.

Chapter 14

IRON AND STEEL

by HENRY C. BRAMER

The iron and steel industry, as treated here, includes pig iron production, steel making, rolling operations, and those finishing operations common in steel mills, i.e., cold reduction, tin plating, and galvanizing. Most steel firms operate iron ore mines, ore beneficiation plants, coal mines, coal cleaning plants, and coke plants; many have fabricating plants or produce a variety of specialty steel products. These operations are treated in other chapters, particularly under Coal Mining, Metal Mining, Coke and Gas, and Metal Finishing Products.

THE IRON AND STEEL INDUSTRY

Most of the iron and steel industry in the United States is centered in the integrated facilities of large corporate enterprises; the eight largest producers are among the 100 largest industrial corporations in this country. A comparatively small producer in this industry represents a very large industrial complex. The installed steelmaking capacity in the United States in 1962 was 125 million ingot tons; a record production of 117 million ingot tons was achieved in 1955. Steel production in the United States was 98 million ingot tons in 1962.

Generalizations about steelmaking operations are difficult, and exceptions can be found in any mill. Steel mills in operation today range from new, modern mills built within the last decade to older marginal facilities built early in this century. Capital requirements in steelmaking plants are great and long periods of production are usually necessary to recover investments; changes in technology thus tend to come about slowly in comparison with many other industries.

MANUFACTURING OPERATIONS

Manufacturing operations of the iron and steel industry may be grouped as pig iron manufacture, steelmaking processes, rolling mill operations, and finishing operations. A single mill is not likely to incorporate all of the many combinations and variations of these operations that are possible. Most mills specialize in the production of broad categories of steel products; in a large mill, however, the product list is long.

The manufacture of pig iron is accomplished in the blast furnace. Steelmaking processes include pneumatic processes, open hearth processes, and electric furnace processes. Rolling mill operations include rolling of blooms, slabs, and billets; scarfing and other preparations of semifinished steel; rolling of shapes, bars, strip, and plates; wire drawing; tube drawing and pipe forming; and pickling or other oxide removal operations. Finishing operations include tin plating, galvanizing, cold reduction, and coating.

Blast Furnaces. The blast furnace process consists essentially of charging iron ore, limestone, and coke into the top of the furnace and blowing heated air into the bottom. Combustion of the coke provides the heat necessary to attain the temperatures at which the metallurgical reducing reactions take place. The incandescent carbon of the coke accounts for about 20% of the reduction of the iron oxides; the carbon monoxide formed between the coke and the oxygen of the blast accounts for the remaining reduction accomplished. The function of the limestone is to form a slag, fluid at the furnace temperature, which combines with unwanted impurities in the ore. Two tons of ore, 1 ton of coke, ½ ton of limestone, and 3½ tons of air produce approximately 1 ton of iron, ½ ton of slag, and 5 tons of blast furnace gas containing the fines of the burden carried out by the blast; these fines are referred to as flue dust.

The blast furnace auxiliaries consist of the stoves in which the blast is preheated, the dry dust catchers in which the bulk of the flue dust is recovered, primary wet cleaners in which most of the remaining flue dust is removed by washing with water, and secondary cleaners which include electrostatic precipitators and bag filters.

Sintering plants are operated as part of the blast furnace departments. Recovered flue dust, fine ores, and recovered rolling mill scale are sintered to yield sufficiently large and dense agglomerates that these materials can be charged to the blast furnace with minimum carry-over in the blast. Sintering is accomplished on moving grates by ignition of the residual fuel in the flue dust plus added coke dust or crushed coal.

Steelmaking Processes. Modern steelmaking processes may be classified as pneumatic processes, open hearth processes, and electric furnace processes. The pneumatic processes include the first of the modern steelmaking processes, the Bessemer converter, which found commerical application in 1860, as well as the basic oxygen furnace, which is the newest of the various steelmaking processes. The Bessemer and side-blown penumatic converters utilize air blasts that literally burn out the unwanted impurities in pig iron to produce steel. The basic oxygen furnace utilizes pure oxygen introduced into a vessel and directed at the surface of the iron bath; the vessel is lined with a basic refractory brick.

The basic open hearth process has been the principal steelmaking process in the United States since 1908, and at present accounts for nearly 90% of installed capacity. The process consists essentially of heating the charge in a covered hearth with fuel gas introduced with an excess of air. The products of combustion pass through brick checkers which store much of the sensible heat in the gas. By periodically reversing the gas flow through the checkers, the incoming gas is preheated and the high temperature necessary in the furnace is maintained. The basic reaction involved is that of oxidation; however, the arrangement of the furnace makes possible inspection and sampling as well as controlled additions to the charge.

The electric furnace processes for steel making, while representing a comparatively small percentage of total ingot tonnage, is important in the production of stainless, tool, and special alloy steels. Electric furnace processes differ basically in furnace design, principally in the manner in which the electric current is used to heat the charge. Direct heating induction furnaces and electric arc furnaces are used in steel making.

Rolling Mill Operations. Steel produced by any of the various processes is poured into ingot molds and allowed to cool; the molds are stripped, and the ingots are placed in soaking pits for proper conditioning prior to rolling. Ingots are rolled into blooms, slabs, or billets depending upon the final product. The semifinished steel is prepared for finishing in a number of ways, all of which remove surface defects. Chipping, grinding, and scarfing are the principal methods employed. Scarfing refers to the use of oxygen torches to remove surface defects and is accomplished by hand on cold steel or mechanically on hot steel as part of the rolling operation.

Finishing mills include a wide variety of mills intended to produce specified steel products; such mills include plate mills, mills for rolling rails and structural shapes, bar mills, wire mills, tube mills, and continuous strip mills. The continuous hot strip mill will be described briefly, because the tonnage produced on such mills is relatively great and much of the waterborne wastes of a steel mill originate there.

Conditioned slabs are brought to rolling temperature in continuous reheating furnaces, then pass through a scale breaker and high pressure water sprays to dislodge the loosened scale. A series of roughing stands and a rotary crop shear produce a section that can be finished to a coil of the proper weight and gauge. A second scale breaker and high pressure water sprays precede the finishing stand train in which the final size reductions are made. Cooling water is applied through sprays on the runout table, and the finished strip is coiled.

Most hot-rolled strip is pickled to remove surface oxides. Pickling is the process of removing scale through the chemical action of inorganic acids, and may be either a batch or a continuous operation. Pickling lines for hot-rolled strip operate continuously on coils that are welded together, passed through the pickler, then sheared and recoiled. The steel passes through the pickler countercurrently to the flow of acid solution. Most mild steel is pickled with sulfuric acid; stainless steels are pickled with hydrochloric, nitric, and hydrofluoric acids. Various organic chemicals are used in pickling to inhibit acid attack on the base metal, while permitting preferential attack on the oxides; wetting agents are used to improve the effective contact of the acid solution with the metal surface.

Finishing Operations. Cold-reduced, flat-rolled products are made by cold rolling pickled strip; the thickness is reduced 25–99% in this operation and a smooth, dense surface is produced. The product may be sold as cold-reduced, but is usually heat treated. Cold reduction generates heat that is dissipated by flood lubrication in which palm oil or synthetic oils are emulsified in water and directed in jets against the rolls and the steel surface during rolling. Cold-reduced strip is cleaned with alkaline detergent solutions to remove the rolling oils prior to coating operations. Electrolysis is frequently used in such cleaning operations.

Tin plate is made from cleaned, annealed, cold-reduced strip by either the electrolytic or hot-dip process. In this country, about 80% of the tin plate is produced by the electrolytic process. The hot-dip process consists of passing the black plate through a light pickling operation and then through the tin pot which consists of a flux, molten tin, and a bath of palm oil. The electrolytic process utilizes tin anodes and the steel strip is made the cathode; the processes vary according to the composition of the electrolyte and include acid, alkaline, and halogen solutions. The electrolytic processes consist of alkaline cleaning, rinsing, pickling, rinsing, plating, rinsing, fusion, quenching, chemical treatment, rinsing, drying, and oiling in sequence. The coils are welded together to provide a continuous feed through the operation and are sheared following the plating operations.

Hot-dip galvanized sheets are produced on either sheet or continuous lines. The process consists essentially of a light pickle in hydrochloric acid and application of the zinc coating by dipping through a pot containing molten zinc. Variations in continuous operations include alkaline cleaning, continuous annealing in controlled atmosphere furnaces, and different fluxing methods.

In recent years, steel products coated with various synthetic resins have become commercially important. Other steel products are produced with coatings of various metals and inorganic materials. Finishing operations for stainless steel products requiring a bright finish consist of rolling on temper mills or mechanical polishing.

CHARACTERISTICS OF STEEL MILL WASTES

Wastes from the various operations in steel making vary widely in characteristics and in volume. These wastes generally have physical and chemical effects on receiving streams different from the oxygen-consuming characteristics of municipal sewage and organic industrial wastes. Because the waste streams vary so widely and are usually separated by the distances between the several operations, composite effects are of little significance; treatment and disposal generally must be considered for the separate wastes.

WATER USE IN THE INDUSTRY

The water requirements of steel plants vary widely, depending primarily upon the quantity and quality of the available supply. The use of as little as 1500 gal of water per ton of product has received much attention in one instance where recirculation is extensively practiced, due primarily to short supply. A figure of 65,000 gal per ton of product has also been widely quoted and has been valid in certain installations that have had practically unlimited water supply. The use of 30,000–40,000 gal of water per ton of product has been typical of many large plants; actual consumptive use of water, i.e., water withdrawn but not returned, is probably less than 1000 gal per ton of product. A recent industry survey indicated a maximum water use of 49,000 gal per ton of product and an average use of 17,000 gal per ton.

Water use in the various departments of a typical integrated mill is approximately as shown in Table I. Most of the water required by a steel plant is used for indirect cooling, and needs no treatment, provided it is not excessively hard; chlorination is often desirable to prevent slime formation. The water used in blast furnace gas washing and in hot mills for roll cooling and scale transport is not necessarily of high quality; it is usually used as pumped. In the various finishing operations such as cold reduction, stainless strip rolling, electrolytic tin lines, and galvanizing, purer water is required and treated water is often used.

WASTEWATERS

The various wastewaters from a typical steel plant are considered here individually, roughly segregated according to the operations from which they result. It must be remembered, however, from the previous de-

TABLE I

WATER USE IN AN INTEGRATED STEEL MILL

Department	Volume	
	Gal. per ton of finished steel	Per cent of total
Blast furnace	10,000	25
Open hearths	5,000	12½
Coke plants	5,000	12½
Hot mills	10,000	25
Finishing mills	8,000	20
Sanitary, boiler, and other uses	2,000	5
Total	40,000	100

Taken from Nebolsine (1) with slight modifications.

scriptions of the various operations that no such clearcut segregation exists in actual practice. Indeed one of the major problems in installing waste treatment facilities in older mills is the segregation of waste streams from integrated operations.

Gas-washer Waters. The water used in washing blast furnace flue gas contains from 1,000 to 10,000 mg/liter of suspended solids, depending upon the furnace burden, size of the furnace, operating methods employed, and type of gas-washing equipment. Following a "slip" in the furnace, the concentration of solids in washer water may exceed 30,000 mg/liter. The use of fine ore and high blast rates result in the highest concentrations of solids in the washer water; the top pressure used in the furnace is also an important factor. The efficiencies of dry dust catchers and wet washers vary considerably and account for many of the differences found in various installations. Conventional wet washers use an average of about 3000 gpm of water; the newer venturi scrubbers use 600–1000. The wash water from electrostatic precipitators adds little to the washer flow, but increases the concentration of the finest particles in the waste stream. Blast furnaces producing ferromanganese have a high percentage of semicolloidal dust particles in the washer water.

The fume from pneumatic steelmaking processes, open hearth and electric furnaces, and hot scarfing operations is often eliminated by electrostatic precipitators or venturi scrubbers which produce waterborne wastes. These suspensions are generally similar to gas-washer water, but the particles are much finer.

The flue dust particles in washer water are probably 50% finer than 10 microns and approximate the composition of the furnace burden; the specific gravity is about 3.5 on the average. Effects on the receiving streams include objectionable color, and interference with aquatic life through formation of bottom deposits and impedance of light transmission; in extreme cases sludge banks are formed that interfere with navigation. Gas-washer waters, especially from furnaces operating on ferromanganese, contain appreciable though highly variable concentrations of complex cyanides and may have a toxic effect on aquatic life.

Scale-bearing Waters. Scale-bearing water originates in the various rolling mill operations and consists of the water used to dislodge scale and to cool the rolled product, plus the water used to transport scale through the flumes beneath the mill line. The characteristics and quantities of scale-bearing water vary widely depending upon the particular rolling operations. The total iron loss in the form of scale averages about 2½%, from the blooming mill through the final rolling operation.

Scale produced in the rolling of blooms and slabs in primary mills is relatively coarse material and most of it settles out of suspension readily. The scale particles from such mills are 90% or more coarser than 200 mesh. Scale produced in a billet mill is considerably finer; 25% of such particles may be finer than 200 mesh. The water use in primary mills ranges from 2000 to 7000 gpm, depending upon the design of the mill and the rolling practices. The scale particles are mixtures of various iron oxides, with the higher oxides predominating in scale from primary mills. The specific gravity of mill scale is about 5.0, hence such particles, particularly the coarse material, tend to clog sewers and to deposit in receiving streams. These are, in general, the only effects of primary mill flume water.

The scale produced in finishing mill rolling operations has, in general, the same composition and specific gravity as that from primary mills. It differs, however, in particle size and quantity, and in its effects. Considerably greater variation occurs among installations than in the case of primary mills. Ten to 20% of the scale particles from finishing mills is smaller than 200 mesh. The coarse particles are still relatively fine, and the finest particles may be 5 microns or less in diameter. Water use in finishing mills ranges from 5000 gpm or less in bar mills and cold reduction mills to 25,000 gpm or more in the newest hot strip mills. Finishing mill flume water may settle in the receiving streams and form bottom deposits or sludge banks, and may increase the turbidity of the stream or impart an objectionable color if the scale particles are extremely fine.

Acid Waters. Spent pickling solutions and acid rinsewaters differ widely in quantity, composition, and concentration, depending upon the manner of pickling, production rate, type of steel being cleaned, and the degree to which control over the operation is practiced. Spent pickling solutions of various types may be produced in different, separated operations at a large mill. Acid rinsewaters have the same relative proportions of iron salts and free acid as pickling solutions, but are much more dilute; 10–15% of the acid used in pickling is discharged in rinsewaters. Spent pickling solution discharges may inhibit bio-oxidation processes in streams and may be injurious to aquatic life if the quantity released in relation to the stream flow is sufficient to lower the pH of the stream significantly.

Sulfuric acid comprises about 90% of the total of acids used in pickling steel. Spent sulfuric acid pickling solutions contain free acid, ferrous sulfate, undissolved scale and dirt, and the various inhibitors and wetting agents, as well as dissolved trace metals. The spent solutions from continuous strip picklers contain 5–9% free acid and 13–16% ferrous sulfate; from batch operations the spent solutions may contain 0.5–2.0% free acid and 15–22% ferrous sulfate. Ten to 15% of the acid used in pickling is discharged in the rinsewater as highly diluted free and combined acid. Spent sulfate pickling solutions are discharged at 170°–190°F and can amount to 100,000 gal per day in a large mill.

Hydrochloric, nitric, phosphoric, and hydrofluoric acids are used in pickling stainless steels. These acids may be used alone, in various combinations, or in combination with sulfuric acid. Stainless steel pickling practices vary widely in the industry. A typical pickling operation for stainless steel plates consists of a 10% sulfuric acid bath at 160°F, followed by a 10% nitric acid, 4% hydrofluoric acid bath at 150°F. A typical continuous pickling line for stainless steel strip consists of a 15% hydrochloric acid bath at 160°F followed by a 4% hydrofluoric acid, 10% nitric acid bath at 170°F. Phosphoric acid is often used in pickling when a phosphate coating is desired. Hydrochloric acid is being used increasingly for mild steels in the new vertical tower pickling installations. These spent solutions contain free acids and the various iron salts, as well as undissolved scale and dirt, inhibitors, wetting agents, and trace metals. Compositions vary widely according to the specific operation and plant practice.

Oil-bearing Waters. Rolling oils, lubricants, and hydraulic oils are present in the effluents from many operations in a steel mill and occur as both free and emulsified oils. Volumes of the waste streams and the concentrations of oil vary widely according to operating practices and housekeeping methods. Emulsified oil in an effluent can be esthetically objectionable and may add a significant BOD. Free oil is particularly objectionable in a stream because very small quantities can result in widespread surface films; larger quantities foul boats and docks and result in unsightly accumulations along stream banks. Severe oil pollution can have serious adverse effects on aquatic life, birds, and land animals.

So-called soluble oils are present in the waste discharges from cold reduction mills, electrolytic tin lines, and a variety of machine shop operations. Natural palm oil and synthetic proprietary substitutes are used in these operations and form stable emulsions when mixed with water at elevated temperatures, especially when kerosene and various detergent cleaning compounds are used. Concentrations of soluble oils vary according to the degree of recirculation practices; volumes of the waste streams likewise vary widely. Typically, the effluent from once-through use in a cold reduction mill will contain 200 mg/liter oil, 25% of which is a stable emulsion.

Lubricating oils and hydraulic fluids are present in the effluents from all rolling operations and most other machine operations. These oils exist mostly as free, floating films, and the quantities depend primarily upon machine maintenance and manual lubrication practices, i.e., upon housekeeping.

Miscellaneous. Other wastewaters from steel mills include alkaline cleaning solutions, water used in granulating slag, and cooling water. Alkaline cleaning solutions are used to remove rolling oils prior to finishing operations. Caustic soda, soda ash, silicates, and phosphates are common cleaning agents. Spent cleaning solutions contain saponified oils and dirt and have substantial residual alkalinity. Total volumes are small, ranging from 1,000 to 10,000 gal per week for individual operations; these quantities are usually dumped batchwise. The effects on the receiving stream are probably not adverse, especially if the volumes of acid wastes are relatively large, as is usual.

The quenching of blast furnace slag produces small quantities of water containing slag particles. Effluent from a slag pit may range from 100 to 200 gpm and is usually of a clear appearance. The highly abrasive nature of the suspended slag particles is the principal objection to such effluents; the bulk gravity of slag particles ranges from 0.8 to 1.5 because of expansion in the granulating process.

Cooling water discharges comprise the largest percentage of steel mill effluents and are usually 10°–15°F warmer than the water withdrawn from the source of supply. The rise in temperature is the only change in water used for indirect cooling, and is usually not significant if the effluent is discharged into a reasonably large stream. Discharged cooling water can have an adverse effect at certain plants where the receiving stream is small and supports a temperature-sensitive fish population. More often than not, the cooling water discharge is of better quality than the water withdrawn from the stream, because of the treatment used for corrosion control.

DISPOSAL OF STEEL MILL WASTES

Methods of waste disposal in the steel industry vary widely from plant to plant. The age of the mill is probably the most important single factor accounting for these variations. In older mills, space for large treatment facilities is often not available; the space required may well be of more potential value for production facilities than the total direct costs of a waste treatment plant. Other factors influencing the variability in methods include the effluent standards that are applicable, the attitudes of management, and the competitive position of the particular operations involved, as well as the characteristics of the waste streams.

GAS-WASHER WATER

Blast furnace gas-washer water is usually treated by plain gravity sedimentation in mechanically cleaned circular clarifiers or in simple rectangular sedimentation basins. Circular clarifiers are used almost exclusively in newer installations.

A typical modern installation may consist of a 75-ft diameter clarifier, handling gas-washer water at 6.9 mgd from a blast furnace rated at 1200 tons per day. The effluent would contain approximately 80 mg/liter suspended solids; the underflow of 180 tons per day of wet dust would be pumped to the sinter plant for additional thickening and filtration on leaftype vacuum filters.

Older installations might be typified by two 13 ft × 111 ft rectangular sedimentation basins handling gas-washer water at 3.5 mgd from a blast furnace rated at 880 tons per day. The effluent concentration might average 250 mg/liter suspended solids. Sludge would be dredged from the basins by clamshell buckets at the rate of about 22 tons of wet dust per day and hauled to the sinter plant in railroad cars.

The clarified gas-washer water may be recirculated either wholly or in part. Recirculation is practiced when supply conditions dictate water economy, and usually requires secondary treatment such as chemical flocculation. The effluent from simple rectangular basins is not ordinarily suitable for recirculation without such extra treatment.

The use of separate clarifiers for each blast furnace or pair of furnaces may result in the discharge of untreated wastes whenever clarifier operation is interrupted. A more satisfactory arrangement consists of collecting the gas-washer water from all blast furnaces, with treatment in centrally located clarifiers. Interconnection of the clarifiers insures continuous treatment even if the operation of one clarifier is interrupted for an extended period.

Some plants operate the washer water clarifiers in series, the underflow of each being added to the influent of the next. A single line to the sinter plant and the agglomerating effect of added sludge are possible benefits of this scheme.

Where effluent requirements are stringent or where existing equipment is called upon to handle greater than design flows, chemical flocculation or the various polyelectrolytes may be used, usually in secondary treatment units. Polyelectrolytes alone have usually not resulted, in plant practice, in the rather spectacular improvements indicated by laboratory experiments. With improved methods of determining and controlling optimum dosages and with probable price reductions, these materials will doubtless become more commonly used.

The design of circular clarifiers and rectangular sedimentation basins for gas-washer water requires specialized techniques; the conventional criteria for sanitary wastes are not satisfactory. The methods outlined in the following section on scale-bearing waters are generally applicable for gas-washer water clarification.

SCALE-BEARING WATERS

Rolling mill flume water has long been partially clarified in small, simple sedimentation basins known as scale pits, in order to prevent sewer clogging. These pits are usually small in relation to the water flow, and the deposited scale is cleaned out periodically with clamshell buckets. In newer mills, scale pits are larger and are designed with the objective of water pollution control; continuous mechanical cleaning is often incorporated.

Flume Water Clarification. A scale pit typical of older practice was 18 ft wide, 30 ft long, and 8 ft deep, to handle flume water at the rate of 3500 gpm from the slab rolling section of a hot strip mill. Effluent concentration averaged 200 mg/liter of suspended solids; there was no provision for removing oil. The pit effluent went directly to a river. Flume water from the finishing end of the mill contained only fine scale, not likely to clog the sewer, and went to the river untreated.

When the mill cited above was rebuilt, flume water treatment was improved to provide more effective pollution control. The scale pit was tripled in size and handles all water from the mill; oil is removed continuously through split-pipe skimmers. The scale pit effluent goes to a

35-ft diameter clarifier for additional solids removal and oil separation, and the clarifier effluent is returned to the mill for reuse. Little or no wastewater from this mill is now discharged.

Treatment following once-through use in newer mills usually consists of primary clarification in a scale pit, and secondary clarification and oil removal in relatively larger rectangular sedimentation basins. Scale pits are typically cleaned by dredging with clamshell buckets, and secondary clarifiers are usually cleaned continuously by scrapers on endless chains. Many variations of this basic scheme are found in various rolling mills; in fact, few installations are identical. Often the secondary clarification includes chemical treatment, typically with additions of lime, ferric sulfate, and polyelectrolyte coagulating agents. Chemical treatment is most often used with circular clarifiers as the secondary basins. When chemical treatment is used, the water is generally reused in the mill; it may be passed through cooling towers, especially in the warm weather months.

The recovered scale is sintered for use in the blast furnace or open hearth furnaces. Mill scale is comparable to high grade iron ore and is thus a salvaged material of considerable value. Generally speaking, the recovery of mill scale from primary scale pits shows an economic return; more than 90% of recovered scale is obtained from these pits. Scale removal from secondary pits must be justified on the basis of pollution control or as necessary for water reuse.

Steel Mill Wastewater Sedimentation. Research sponsored by the American Iron and Steel Institute has resulted in design procedures that are applicable for steel mill sedimentation equipment, including scale pits, secondary basins for scale removal, and gas-washer water clarifiers. These procedures predict basin performance in terms of an empirical measure known as the sedimentation index (SI), expressed in minutes. The sedimentation index may be interpreted as the settling time, under specified laboratory conditions, that will result in sedimentation equal to that of a particular basin at a specified flow rate. Values of SI are approximately 0.10 for simple scale pits, 1.0 for secondary mill scale basins, 10.0 for small gas-washer water clarifiers, and 30.0 for large washer water clarifiers. This work has shown that there are optimum ratios of width and depth to length for rectangular basins, and that large circular clarifiers have less volumetric efficiency than smaller clarifiers at comparable flow rates. Overflow rates and superficial linear velocities are not adequate criteria for the design of steel mill sedimentation equipment.

Rolling mill flume water and blast furnace gas-washer water should be sampled with care when such samples are to be used as the basis of basin design for required effluent concentrations. Composite samples should be taken over periods of typical operation; samples should be randomized so as not to coincide with process cycles such as slab rollings or blast furnace chargings. Settling rate tests should be made soon after collection because many of these suspensions cannot be effectively reconstituted after settling has occurred. Existing installations similar to contemplated new installations can often be used as sample sources for design purposes, but differences in raw water quality due to location and season of the year should be borne in mind.

PICKLING SOLUTIONS

Few industrial wastes have received as much attention as spent pickling solutions in terms of research and process development effort. There are more than 100 patented processes for spent pickling solution treatment; only two or three have actually been operated commercially. The recovery of by-products from waste treatment processes seems attractive, but has not proved economically sound. Relatively dilute solutions of cheap bulk chemicals are involved and the quantities are large in comparison with most possible markets for by-products.

Spent Sulfate Solutions. Processes and methods for the treatment of spent sulfate pickling solutions may be classified as follows:

Neutralization	Electrolysis
Evaporation	Ion exchange
Refrigeration	Deep well disposal
Differential solubility	Land surface disposal
Chemical conversion	Miscellaneous
Extraction	

Neutralization with lime is the treatment method commonly used by steel mills. This method has the advantage of lowest capital cost, but operating costs are high because there no credits obtainable. The principal disadvantages of lime neutralization are high cost and land area necessary to lagoon the neutralized slurry, which is equal in volume to that of the pickling solution plus the lime slurry. The slurry from conventional lime neutralization cannot be dewatered effectively but remains plastic for a long time. Lime neutralization with controlled air oxidation of precipitated iron produces a more compact slurry which can be dewatered, requiring much less land for lagoons. High calcium lime is usually used for neutralization although other alkaline agents such as dolomitic lime, limestone, carbide sludge, and spent cleaning solutions can be used.

Many evaporation schemes that have been proposed result in the recovery of iron sulfates and free acid from spent pickling solutions. The manufacture of copperas is accomplished by adding scrap to heated pickling solutions to convert all free acid to ferrous sulfate, evaporating sufficient water to precipitate $FeSO_4 \cdot 7H_2O$, separating the crystals by centrifuging, drying the product with flue gas, and packaging. The commercial production of copperas provides only a partial answer to the disposal problem, as 5% of the steel industry's potential output completely satisfies the market demand. Other evaporation processes propose to recover ferrous sulfate as either the heptahydrate or the monohydrate, and free acid for return to the picklers, on the basis of the solubility diagram of Fig. 1. These processes differ, in the evaporation methods, and

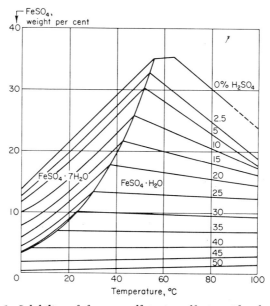

FIG. 1. Solubility of ferrous sulfate in sulfuric acid solutions.

include tubetype evaporators, filmtype evaporators, and submerged combustion. Refrigeration schemes are based on similar solubility relationships. Differential solubility has also been proposed, using water-soluble organic liquids to reduce the solubility of ferrous sulfate, and recovering the organics for reuse. In any of the above processes, further steps can be added to produce iron oxide and sulfuric acid from the ferrous sulfate. While technically feasible, the production of acid from the sulfate is not likely to be economically attractive soon.

Various chemical conversion processes have been developed including the manufacture of ammonium sulfate from either pure ammonia or coke oven gas; the conversion of sulfates to chlorides with gaseous HCl and production of iron oxide by roasting, with the re-formed HCl returned to the process; the production of ferric sulfate using sulfur dioxide; and the manufacture of ferric chloride and sodium sulfate with sodium chloride.

Spent sulfate pickling solutions can be used to extract manganese from low grade ores, to extract magnesia from dolomite, and to produce ferric phosphate from phosphate rock. Electrolytic processes have been developed for the production of high purity iron, with acid recovery; several of these processes use ion exchange membranes. Conventional ion exchange processes have been developed for recovery of most of the free acid from pickling solutions; ion exchange offers the most likely solution for rinse-water treatment in the few instances where this may be necessary.

Modern well drilling methods and the development of high pressure pumps have made disposal in deep wells possible where suitable underground strata are available. Disposal on land surfaces includes discharge into artificial lagoons for solar evaporation or into limestone quarries or slag dumps for slow neutralization. In at least one plant, spent pickling solutions have been poured onto molten slag for flash evaporation, with outstanding success. In many areas contract haulers dispose of pickling solutions into limestone quarries, after lime neutralization.

Despite the effort devoted to finding practical methods for treating and disposing of spent pickling solutions, only neutralization, copperas manufacture, deep well disposal, and land surface disposal are in general use in this country. By-product recovery remains an intriguing, technically feasible, but as yet uneconomical possibility.

Other Acid Solutions. Many of the processes for disposing of spent sulfate solutions are applicable to solutions of the other acids with little or no modification. In general, more severe corrosion problems are encountered in handling these solutions, but the value of the acids and their salts is greater than the corresponding sulfates. Lime neutralization is the most general treatment method for stainless pickling solutions; the high cost and problem of sludge disposal are again the principal difficulties. Ion exchange processes have been developed to recover values from stainless steel pickling solutions, but are not in widespread use.

OIL-BEARING WASTES

Oil-bearing wastes in steel mills originate principally in rolling operations and may generally be considered in two categories: lubricating oils from hot mills and soluble oils plus free oils from cold reduction mills and finishing operations. The hot mill effluents contain relatively much scale as compared with oil; the cold mill effluents contain only a little scale as compared to the oil content.

Hot Mill Oily Wastes. The flume water from all hot rolling operations contains lubricating and hydraulic oils, generally present as free oil bound to a certain extent with scale particles. Most of this oil is readily separated by gravity and may be skimmed in the primary scale pits or in secondary sedimentation basins. That oil which is bound with scale particles has the effect of reducing the settleability of the particles; this oil may be separated by settling or floating the oil-scale agglomerates, or may not be recoverable by gravity separation if the agglomerates have a bulk density approximately equal to that of water. Oils are nearly always recovered from the surface by a split-pipe skimmer operated periodically as oil accumulates.

Gravity separation of oil from hot rolling operations is usually adequate for once-through use of the water on the mill and may suffice for recycling if an efficient secondary basin is used. More often, reuse of water on the mills requires chemical treatment or air flotation. In one hot strip mill, the primary scale pit effluent is sent to a circular clarifier, where additional oil is separated by gravity and the clarifier effluent is returned to the mill; occasional staining of the finished steel occurs when abnormally great amounts of oil are present in the flume water. In another mill, all scale pit effluents go to a secondary terminal treatment in American Petroleum Institute (API) oil-water separators with air flotation, as used in the petroleum industry. In still another plant the secondary treatment consists of addition of lime, ferric sulfate, and a polyelectrolyte in a circular clarifier; the oil is absorbed by the ferric floc which settles out of suspension.

Most hot mill effluents contain 10–20 mg/liter of oil if efficient skimming is provided and adequate capacity is provided for gravity separation. Secondary treatment can reduce the oil to 1–5 mg/liter in the effluent.

Soluble Oil Wastes. The effluents from cold reduction mills are usually given preliminary treatment in sumps located under the mill floor. Oil separation in these sumps is nearly always by gravity and the floated oil is removed by manual operations. Some oil recovery is practiced in all such plants; the separated oil is pumped to storage tanks and is given nominal treatment to remove suspended matter and water prior to sale to reclaimers. The effluent from the sumps contains free oil and scale to a greater or less extent depending upon the sump size and the efficiency of the oil recovery operation; in all cases the effluent contains emulsified oil in concentrations from 50 to 100 mg/liter. The sump effluent may be discharged directly to a stream, discharged after secondary treatment, or recirculated to the mill with or without secondary treatment, depending upon mill practice and the pollution control criteria.

Secondary treatment of cold reduction mill effluents may consist of chemical treatment and air flotation in a basin similar to an API oil-water separator. Ferrous sulfate and lime with dissolved air flotation is a relatively common treatment method. Aluminum sulfate and calcium chloride have been used as emulsion-breaking agents and some of the polyelectrolytes show promise in treating these wastes.

In many mills the soluble oil recovery units are operated by outside contractors. The designs of these units are proprietary and are based upon the best recovery of usable oil rather than upon minimum effluent concentrations for pollution control purposes. The effluents of these units are usually suitable for recirculation to the mill. Some such units incorporate secondary treatment and produce effluents containing as little as 10–15 mg/liter of oil; such an effluent is usually suitable for discharge to a stream.

OTHER WASTEWATERS

Other steel mill wastewaters such as alkaline cleaning solutions, slag pit effluents, and sanitary wastes present few special problems, but are important in planning pollution control comprehensively. Alkaline cleaning solutions may be used as additional alkaline agents in spent pickling solution neutralization, or may simply be diluted prior to discharge if the quantities are relatively small. Slag pit effluents are treated by rotary screening if discharge is to a navigable stream or a recreational stretch of a stream. Sanitary wastes may be conventionally treated in a mill-operated facility or sent to a municipal sewage treatment plant. The greatest problem encountered with sanitary wastes is in segregating them from process waste streams, especially in older mills; the cost of sewer segregation is usually the greatest cost of treating these wastes.

Cooling water effluents from steel mill operations may be treated in conventional cooling towers when necessary. Usually this is not necessary as a pollution control measure. Cooling towers may be used, however, where cooling water is recirculated to the mill, but are frequently necessary only during the warm weather months.

IRON AND STEEL INDUSTRY TRENDS

Trends in the steel industry are being influenced by acceleration of the rate of technological advancement, changes in the economic climate of the country, and by increasing competition from foreign steel producers and domestic producers of substitute products.

Manufacturing Methods

Blast furnace operations are likely to change only in degree and detail in the immediate future. Direct reduction processes are not likely to replace the blast furnace soon in this country. Somewhat larger furnaces will probably be built; beneficiated ores will be used to a greater extent as a result of improved sintering methods; higher top pressures and blast rates, oxygen enrichment, use of powdered coal, and natural gas injection are among the practices which will become increasingly common.

The basic oxygen furnace will probably replace the open hearth furnace as the primary steelmaking process. Continuous casting with vacuum degassing will likely take the place of the sequential operations of ingot molding, soaking pit treatment, rolling of blooms, reheating, and rolling of slabs and billets.

Increasing rates of production will undoubtedly be the guiding principle as new mills are built and older mills are modernized. The 80 inch strip mill is rapidly becoming the industry standard and production goals are constantly being raised on these mills. Automation of rolling mills is becoming more and more common; automatic operation of the rolling process is general, with a few mills under complete computer control. Pickling with hydrochloric acid in vertical towers, with acid regeneration, bids fair to replace much of the strip pickling with sulfuric acid and may solve a good portion of the spent pickling solution disposal problem.

Finishing processes are constantly being developed as the steel industry looks to competition from other materials. Thin tin plate, steel foil, steel clad with other metals, and a variety of formed and coated products are among the products that foreshadow future developments.

Water Reuse

Reuse of water in the steel industry will increase in the future. Some of this increased reuse will be for the purpose of conservation in localized situations of water shortages, as in circumstances where the low flow period reduces surface streams to a critical point or where the groundwater faces serious depletion. The principal factor influencing reuse will probably be the increasing requirement for high effluent quality, and the criterion for the extent of reuse will be economics. The completely closed process water system is, of course, the final answer in industrial wastewater treatment. Even under conditions of abundant supply, complete recirculation can become economical when effluent quality requirements bcome sufficiently high. Such systems will probably provide the solution to wastewater control problems in the steel industry increasingly in the future.

INDUSTRY GROWTH AND COMPETITION

The steel industry faces a period of increasing costs of production, production facilities in excess of current demand, and vigorous competition from overseas and at home. Costs of production are being lowered by automation and new high-rate production facilities, while overcapacity will probably be soon reduced by retirement of marginal facilities and by normal obsolescence. Foreign steel producers now have the most modern equipment and production techniques, and have largely overcome the domestic producers' former principal advantage, i.e., the ability to produce high quality products to exacting specifications. Aluminum and paper products are providing imaginative competition in the container, consumer goods, and light construction materials fields. While the long-term outlook for steel manufacture is promising, a period of great change and readjustment faces the industry.

RESEARCH

Research by the steel industry in the field of wastewater control is carried out by each individual steel company and by industry-sponsored groups through the American Iron and Steel Institute. On occasion, several companies have joined in special projects such as stream surveys and pilot plant evaluations of waste treatment processes.

Much of the steel industry's research in this area tends to be short-range, aimed at solving current problems. The industry-sponsored research programs of the American Iron and Steel Institute are more long-range in nature, looking toward future requirements for wastewater control; these programs now integrate research in the fields of water and air pollution.

Current and recent research includes studies directed toward optimizing sedimentation basin design, developing oil-water separation techniques, studying flocculation phenomena, providing instrumental means for effluent analysis and control, studying the origins of tastes and odors in drinking water, gathering background data on surface stream water quality, and developing methods of chemical analysis.

Research needs of the future in the industry are in the general areas of effects of minor effluent components, prevention of esthetic nuisances, determination of the necessity for and equity of control measures, and continuing efforts to minimize the net costs of wastewater control.

REFERENCE

1. Nebolsine, R., *Iron Steel Engr.* **31**, No. 4, 78–88 (April 1954).

Chapter 15

NONFERROUS METALS

by JOHN A. TALLMADGE

Current usage divides all metals into three groups: iron and steel including alloy steels; ferroalloys; and nonferrous metals. Wastewater from the first two groups is discussed in the chapter on Iron and Steel. This chapter deals with wastewater control in the nonferrous production industry. It does not include the mining phase of production or the metal finishing phase, as these are presented in other chapters on Metal Mining and Metal Finishing Products. The subject matter of this chapter is confined to the processes and related operations intermediate between production of metal ores and the finished product. These intermediate processes are usually those involved in the extraction or refining of commercially pure metal from ores and the fabrication of the metal into usable shapes.

THE INDUSTRY

METAL PRODUCTION AND CONSUMPTION

Because statistical data relating to metal production in the United States vary with each metal, comparisons of production are complicated. Production rates may be reported for various steps in the process (mining, refining, alloying); in various units (pounds, short tons, long tons); and on different equivalents (metal, ore, oxide, concentrate). The data may or may not include secondary recovery from scrap and minerals used in compound or mixture form without purification to metal.

The 1961 production rate of metals is compared in Table I in consistent units of short tons of equivalent metal. The total consumption is some indication of metal usage, as in fabrication, alloying, and chemical reaction. The primary production data are the amount of metal or equivalent purified, regardless of whether the ore was domestic or imported.

The four major nonferrous metals are aluminum, copper, zinc, and lead. Most of this chapter is related to these four metals, as they constitute well over 70% of all nonferrous metals produced. As shown in Table I, the production rate of these metals is small compared with that of the iron and steel industry. Because they are used primarily as ferroalloys, manganese, chromium, and nickel are discussed in the chapter on Iron and Steel. Only brief mention will be made of sodium, tin, and magnes-

255

ium. None of the metals with annual production below 20,000 tons is discussed except as it may present unusual problems. Uranium is discussed in the chapter on Atomic Energy, and some of the others are discussed in the chapter on Inorganic Chemicals.

TABLE I

CONSUMPTION RATE FOR METALS, 1961

		United States			World
Rank	Metal	Total consumption	Primary production	Secondary production	Primary production
1	Iron	128,000	65,000	66,000	289,000
2	Aluminum	2,300	1,900	340	5,200
3	Copper	1,650	1,550	410	5,100
4	Zinc	1,200	900	180	3,600
5	Lead	1,000	470	450	2,700
6	Manganese[a,b]	770[c]	570[d]	—	6,700[c]
7	Chromium[a,b]	350[c]	170[d]	—	1,400[c]
8	Nickel[a]	120	10	10	400
9	Sodium[e]	110	110	—	—
10	Tin	80	Small	20	210
11	Magnesium	45	40	10	120

United States consumption rate

10 to 20		5 to 10		0.5 to 2		less than 0.1	
12	Molybdenum[a,b,c]	15	Titanium[f]	20	Vanadium[a,b]	26	Gold
13	Uranium	16	Tungsten	21	Rare earths	27	Thorium
14	Antimony	17	Silver	22	Mercury		
		18	Cadmium	23	Bismuth		
		19	Cobalt[a,b]	24	Columbium		
				25	Tantalum		

Taken from U. S. Bureau of Mines Yearbook, 1961.
All data in thousands of short tons.
[a] Used mainly for ferroalloys.
[b] Little pure metal produced.
[c] Estimated from ore data.
[d] Based on ferroalloy production.
[e] Not including metal salts.
[f] Not including metal oxide.

PROCESSES USED

The processes described in this chapter are concerned with either the extraction of pure metal from the ore or fabrication of the metal. Production of concentrates in order to separate minerals from useless rock, usually by gravity separation or flotation, is considered in the chapter on Metal Mining.

Extraction of pure metal includes a variety of purification methods, such as dissolving metal compounds by leaching, production of oxides, reduction of the oxides to metal by smelting, and refining by electrolysis. Smelters and refiners are primary or secondary, depending on whether they use natural ores or scrap as their principal source for metals.

Fabrication of metals includes such operations as alloying, casting, extrusion, forging, rolling, wire-drawing, and heat treating, and provides sheets, wire, tubing, and other industrial shapes. Operations such as assembling, plating, and coating are considered in the chapter on Metal Finishing Products.

Major Nonferrous Metals

Production of aluminum from bauxite ore includes an aqueous extraction of aluminum oxide (alumina), followed by electrolytic reduction of molten alumina. Almost 50% of the aluminum produced is made into sheets, including plates and foil; about 25% into extruded tubing; and about 20% into castings. Much of the rest is made into rolled shapes.

Copper is extracted from sulfide concentrates and from "cement" copper by smelting in a reverberatory furnace to produce anodes of about 98% copper, followed by electrolytic refining using aqueous sulfate solutions. Most of the ores used are sulfides. Copper oxides are converted to "cement" copper by leaching the ores with sulfuric acid and precipitating the copper with scrap iron. About 55% of the copper is fabricated in wire mills and about 40% in brass mills.

Zinc sulfide concentrates are reduced to zinc by smelting in distilling retorts or in electrolytic plants using aqueous solutions. In addition, many smelters recover zinc from scrap and some from lead blast furnace slag. About 40% of the slab zinc is used for zinc-base die castings, 40% for galvanizing, and about 10% in brass mills. Some zinc ores are used to make zinc oxide pigments, without reduction to the metal.

Lead sulfide concentrates are reduced by smelting in reverberatory furnaces to produce lead anodes, followed by electrolytic refining using aqueous solutions. About half the lead consumed comes from scrap; over 60% of the scrap is derived from lead storage batteries. Approximately 35% of the total lead consumed is used in lead storage batteries, 15% in tetraethyl lead, and 10% in red lead and other pigments. Most of the rest is used in various metal products. About half the lead used in storage batteries is antimonial lead.

OTHER METALS

Sodium is made primarily by electrolysis of fused sodium chloride obtained from rock salt. Since most of the metallic sodium produced is used in making tetraethyl lead, sodium plants are located near chemical plants in Ohio, New York, Tennessee, Louisiana, and Texas.

Although there is some secondary smelting of tin in the United States, there is little mining or primary production. About 40% of the domestic consumption is for tin plate, 20% for brass products, and 20% for solder.

Most of the magnesium produced in the United States in peacetime is made by electrolysis of fused magnesium chloride, in Texas. The magnesium chloride is obtained by reaction of hydrochloric acid with magnesium hydroxide obtained from sea water. Magnesium is used primarily in aluminum alloys (40%), structures (30%), and as a metal reducing agent (20%).

PLANT SIZE

The primary production of each of the four major nonferrous metals is derived from only 13–30 plants. However, hundreds of plants are involved in secondary production and thousands in casting operations. Some indication of the relative size of various nonferrous metal plants is shown in Table II.

The size of the plant is important because the control of wastewater in small plants is frequently quite different from control in large plants. Although effluents from larger plants have larger waste loads, treatment and disposal is often under better control at large plants.

WASTE CHARACTERISTICS

As the primary concern of this book is wastes in aqueous or other liquid form, solid and gaseous wastes are not discussed under waste disposal, but are mentioned briefly in this section.

Many of the nonferrous metal industries require substantial amounts of power for electrolytic refining; wastewater problems for power generation are discussed in the chapter on Power. Substantial amounts of water are used in these industries for other cooling and condensation needs. However, contamination of such waters is small compared with other wastewaters, and cooling water problems for these industries are similar to, or less severe than those in other industries such as power generation. Therefore, except for unusual conditions, waste cooling water problems are omitted from this chapter.

Wastes are described below in order of production tonnages for each metal. This order is not meant to imply that wastes discharged from the

TABLE II

NONFERROUS METAL PLANTS IN THE UNITED STATES, 1958

Type of operation	Average employment	No. of plants with employment of			Total no. of plants
		1–49	50–249	250 or more	
Primary[a]					
Aluminum	869	1	0	19	20
Copper	485	1	10	19	30
Zinc	446	1	5	14	20
Lead	274	0	8	5	13
Other	92	15	11	3	29
Rolling and drawing					
Aluminum	253	85	63	37	185
Copper	384	30	34	41	105
Other	116	94	33	16	143
Casting					
Aluminum	31	835	95	25	955
Copper	22	599	69	7	665
Other	50	270	60	15	345
Summary					
Primary production	420	18	34	60	112
Secondary production	37	315	64	8	387
Rolling and drawing	240	209	130	94	433
Casting	31	1704	224	47	1965

Taken from U. S. Census of Manufacturers, 1958.
[a] Smelting and refining.

largest industry are of the largest quantity or constitute the greatest problems. On the contrary, copper wastes currently seem to present more problems than aluminum wastes.

ALUMINUM

Alumina from Bauxite. As much of the bauxite used in the United States is imported from the Caribbean area, nearly all the alumina plants are located near the Gulf of Mexico seaports or inland waterways. Of the 8 plants operating in 1959, 6 were near the coast of Louisiana, Texas, or Alabama, and 2 were in Arkansas near the domestic bauxite mines. Individual plant capacities were approximately either 400,000 or 800,000 short tons of alumina per year.

In the Bayer process, which is used for bauxite ores of low silica content, alumina is solubilized as sodium aluminate using sodium hydroxide, and the residue is discarded as red mud. Because the sodium hydroxide is recovered and recycled and because the calciner stack gases are primarily water vapor, the only waste produced in large quantities is the mud slurry. Another wastewater arises from dumping spent cleaning acids, but the quantities are so small that the waste acid is easily neutralized either by pumping to red mud lakes or by treating with lime.

The total intake of water for all uses, including recycle, was about 12 mgd at the 6 plants operating in 1952, representing about 0.7 gal/lb of alumina (1). Aside from cooling water, the largest use of water at these plants is for makeup water to the mud lake to compensate for evaporation losses.

One estimate of the total amount of mud slurry discharged at all plants is 1 mgd. Solids present in the red mud contain some aluminum silicate and also the impurities removed from bauxite, which are primarily silicon, iron, and titanium oxides (7). The solid concentration in the mud varies from 15 to 50%. The total solid discharge rate is comparable to the amount of impurities in the bauxite, or about 0.15–0.30 lb/lb of alumina produced; rates of 400–2000 tons of solids per day have been reported. While these mud wastes are not toxic, they contribute a substantial amount of silt to nearby waterways if not removed.

Primary Production of Aluminum (Electrolytic Smelting). Aluminum electrolysis plants are located near cheap sources of power. Of the 21 plants in operation in 1951, 12 are in the power areas of the Northwest (7), Niagara Falls (2), Ohio River Valley (2), and TVA (1); 7 are near alumina plants in Texas, Louisiana, Alabama, and Arkansas; and the 3 others are located in Montana, Indiana, and North Carolina. Individual plant capacities are about 100,000 short tons of aluminum per year although the range is from 40,000 to 250,000 tons per year.

The electrolysis of aluminum from a salt bath of alumina and fluorine salts results in off gases containing 0.1–0.2% fluoride, primarily as HF in gaseous form and sodium salts in the particulate matter. Discharges of 0.015–0.03 lb fluorine/lb aluminum have been reported (2, 3). At one time, these gases were passed to the atmosphere, but they were toxic to nearby vegetation and livestock. Now the gases at almost all reduction plants are scrubbed with water to remove 90–99% of the fluorine. Gas scrubber effluents are the main wastewaters in refining of primary aluminum. Solid dumpings from pot lines, which contain fluorine, are potential wastewater problems only where leaching is substantial and uncontrolled.

Although about one-fifth of the water circulated at these plants is used for cooling or sanitary purposes, most of the water circulated is used for scrubbing. The total amount of water circulated for scrubbing in 1952 was 80 mgd at 11 reduction plants, with usage as high as 28 gal/lb of aluminum reported at one plant. Currently, however, much of the scrubber water is recycled; the consumption rate for scrubbing has been lowered at one plant to 0.04 gal/lb of aluminum produced. Therefore, the fluorine concentration in the effluent depends considerably on the amount of scrubber water recycled. Where they are discharged without treatment, these fluorine solutions constitute potential wastewater problems.

Secondary Recovery of Aluminum (Smelting Scrap). While the yearly recovery of aluminum at secondary smelters is only about 15% of primary production, there are, due to small capacities, a large number of these smelters. They are located primarily in industrial centers, as in Illinois, New York, Ohio, and California. These smelters employ melting facilities and reverberatory furnaces and, for the most part, produce aluminum-base alloys.

Although individual smelting plants produce only small amounts of waste, they often pose waste problems because of their location in heavily settled areas, and because many discharge waste without treatment. The two wastes which present the largest current or potential problems are airborne wastes, namely, furnace fumes and corrosive chlorine fumes, the latter of which is discussed under fabrication.

Some of the plants treat the furnace fumes, the objectionable part of which is primarily metal oxide in particulate form. Since these wastes are usually deposited in solid rather than aqueous form, smelters produce little undesirable wastewaters. The few plants that recover occluded alumina from waste refinery flux produce a silt which, if leached in an uncontrolled manner, might produce corrosive wastewater. As these silt dumps are usually located in sparsely settled areas, they probably do not present a serious problem.

Fabrication. As shown in Table II, there are about 1000 plants involved in casting aluminum and almost 200 in rolling and drawing operations. Due to a wide range of sizes and types of locations, there is a considerable variety in quantity and composition of wastes produced—both in the substantial amounts of wastewater from cooling and in other wastes.

In almost all casting operations, a purge gas—usually chlorine—is used to degas the aluminum from electrolysis; this prevents formation of hydrogen bubbles in the billets or final products. In some large fabrication plants, the resultant gaseous waste is scrubbed to remove chlorine gas, and a toxic, corrosive wastewater is formed. However, most fabricators emit the waste gas without scrubbing; thus, these corrosive gases now constitute an air pollution problem, and represent a potential wastewater hazard.

The major waste liquids from rolling, drawing, and extrusion arise from lubricant solutions, of which two general types are used. The insoluble oils, such as kerosene, are used under mild conditions, hence little decomposition occurs; wastes from these lubricants usually include solid material and some water. The soluble oils, which are emulsions of special oils in water, are used under such high conditions of temperature and pressure that decomposition of the oil becomes appreciable over a period of time. Although these emulsions are provided in continuous flow by closed recycle systems, oil decomposition leads to dumpings of the emulsion batches several times each year.

Summary. The major wastewaters arising from the aluminum industry are the mud slurries from bauxite purification, the fluoride effluent solutions from electrolytic plant scrubbers, the chlorine effluent solutions from casting degassing, and the contaminated lubricant oil solutions from rolling and drawing operations.

COPPER

Leaching of Oxide Ores. Because chemical leaching of ores is unusual in mining operations, wastewaters from leaching are discussed here. Wastewaters from sulfide ore flotation are described in the chapter on Metal Mining. Located near copper mines to minimize transportation costs, the 9 largest leaching plants are in Arizona, Michigan, Montana, Nevada, New Mexico, and Utah. About 10% of the primary copper production is derived from leached ores, and the median size leaching plant produces the equivalent of 8000 tons of copper per year.

Impurities in copper oxide ores cannot be separated readily by flotation; thus, copper from these ores is usually extracted by countercurrent leaching with aqueous sulfuric acid. The dissolved copper is then recovered from the copper sulfate solutions by contact with scrap iron in iron launders, where black "cement" copper of 65–90% copper content is precipitated. The resultant wastewater is the spent liquor, which is mainly a solution of ferrous sulfate. The waste solutions formed contain several grams per liter of ferrous sulfate as well as enough acid to have a pH of about 4.

Total water use in 1955 for all leaching plants was about 2 mgd makeup and 8 mgd recycle, over 90% of which was for process and washing purposes. The median flow rate for 7 plants was about 12 gal of water makeup per lb of copper. Over 90% of the water used was self-supplied groundwater. Saline groundwaters, with solids content as high as 2000 mg/liter, are useful because their high sulfate content allows a reduction in sulfuric acid requirements.

Primary and Secondary Smelters. The production rate of secondary copper is as large as that of primary copper. However, whereas primary copper is processed only at a few smelters (14 in 1955), secondary copper is recovered at a large number of locations. Secondary copper, of which half is derived from new scrap and half from old scrap, is recovered from unalloyed copper at primary smelters and from brass and bronze alloys at brass mills and foundries as well as at secondary smelters (5 in 1959). About one-fourth of the secondary copper is recovered at primary smelters. The median production rate of copper smelters in 1955 was 60,000 short tons of copper per year. The largest was 5 times this size and the smallest was only $\frac{1}{14}$ this size.

Most of the copper ore used is domestic; about three-fourths of this ore is mined in Arizona and neighboring states, and the remainder mainly in Michigan, Montana, and Tennessee. Thus, most of the mines are located in the arid, sparsely populated parts of the western United States. Most primary smelters are at or near the mines, and are frequently integrated with mine operations, so they too are in the arid west; in 1955, 6 were in Arizona, 4 in the neighboring states of Utah, New Mexico, and Nevada, and 4 in other southern or western states (one each in Texas, Tennessee, Montana, and Washington).

Many other metals are associated with ores of the major three metals, copper, lead, and zinc. Among these are iron, arsenic, antimony, molybdenum, bismuth, cadmium, gold, silver, and metals of the platinum group. Unless these are solubilized during the extraction or smelting processes, the presence of most of these metals is of little consequence as far as wastewater problems and disposal are concerned.

The two major smelter wastes, slag and sulfur dioxide, arise in the reverberatory furnaces. Here, copper compounds are reduced to copper metal and most metal impurities go into molten slag. The oxides of iron, silicon, aluminum, calcium, and magnesium, as well as the naturally occurring potassium and sodium silicates in the feldspar gangue minerals, are wholly discarded as waste slags, which are usually disposed of in molten form in dumps. Since they contain few soluble, noxious constituents, they normally do not present a wastewater problem. In at least one smelter, the slag is granulated by washwater before dumping; as a result, many slag particles are entrained in this washwater.

Roasting of copper sulfide ores produces substantial amounts of sulfur dioxide fumes (9–12%) in the stack gases, which form highly corrosive acids in the presence of water vapor. As a result, much of the vegetation near the smelters has been killed. The first attempts to minimize this problem involved construction of tall chimneys to improve fume dispersion, but these were not successful because of air flow patterns. However, this serious gaseous waste problem has been eliminated at many locations by conversion of the sulfur dioxide into a valuable product, sulfuric acid. Thus, regardless of treatment, these gaseous wastes do not pose a wastewater problem. Slag, sulfur dioxide, and entrained solids are the main wastes from smelter operation; of these, only entrained solids occur as wastewater.

The five secondary smelters are located in heavily populated industrial areas of New Jersey, New York, and Texas. Wastes associated with secondary copper production are similar to those described above, except that little sulfur dioxide is emitted.

The median amounts of water circulated and consumed at smelters in 1955 were 5 and 0.7 gal/lb of copper, respectively; the minimum consumption was 0.2 gal/lb. The amount of water used at each smelter is related to the abundance of water in the area. For the 7 smelters located where the annual runoff did not exceed 1 inch of rainfall on the drainage basin, the median water use was 1.6 gal/lb; at the other 11 smelters, where the annual runoff was more than 10 inches, the median water use was 21 gal/lb.

Refineries. Twelve of the 15 primary refineries operating in 1959 used the electrolytic process; 6 of these were large plants in east coast industrial centers (New York, New Jersey, Maryland) where imports are readily received, and the other 6 were each located in a different western state, generally not distant from the smelters. The 3 other refineries, situated near the Great Lakes, purified Lake Superior copper in furnace processes. The median annual plant output was about 150,000 tons; the range was from 80,000 to 260,000 tons.

Electrolytic refining is used to remove from copper impurities that lower its electrical conductivity and alter its other properties. These impurities accumulate in the anode mud and in the acidic copper sulfate electrolyte solution. By careful purifying procedures, the levels of soluble impurities in the electrolyte are kept low enough to prevent interference with the deposition of pure copper; in this way, a closed circuit electrolyte is maintained and no foul solution need be discarded as waste.

The impurities present in anode mud include arsenic, antimony, nickel, selenium, and tellurium, as well as gold and silver. The precious metals are present in sufficient amounts to pay for their recovery and also to defray the major part of the refining costs; the other impurities are also recovered. Because the anode mud and other impurities in refineries are usually extracted and marketed as valuable by-products, they cannot be described as waste streams.

Water used for cooling molds and hot copper cast shapes, such as anodes and wire or ingot bars or cakes, sometimes contains scale and other solid contaminants in the form of entrained solids. However, most of the cooling and process water used in these plants does not become contaminated. The median water circulation rate is about 2 gal/lb of copper at these plants; the consumption rate is smaller. No major wastewaters arise from copper refineries.

Brass and Wire Mills. Brass is an alloy of about ⅔ copper and ⅓ zinc, with specialty brass alloys containing other metals. About 95% of the fabrication of copper occurs in brass and wire mills. There are many more of these fabrication mills than there are primary production plants. As shown in Table II, there are about 100 rolling and drawing mills and over 650 plants involved in casting operations. On the average, annual production rates for these plants are much smaller than for most copper smelters and refiners, especially in casting, where almost all plants are small. In contrast to primary production, most of these fabricators are located at or near industrial centers.

The distribution of the larger plants is indicated by the location of the 58 rolling and drawing mills having over 100 employees: 18 are in Connecticut, 7 in Pennsylvania, 6 in Michigan, 4 each in New Jersey and Ohio, 3 each in New York, Illinois, and California, and 9 of the other 10 are in other industrial areas. About one-third of the domestic production of brass and copper products is in Connecticut.

In the rolling and drawing of tubes and wires in several steps, the metal tends to become hard, and annealing is required after every two or three steps. The oxide scale formed in annealing is removed by dipping the metal products in sulfuric acid baths, followed by rinsing in water. The major wastewaters in the copper and brass industry are these rinses; they contain a considerable amount of dissolved copper, zinc, chromium, and sulfuric acid. The acid or "pickle" baths, although they are dumped only infrequently, provide wastewaters containing the same toxic compounds; spent liquor wastes may be considered related to rinsewater wastes, but are of higher concentration and much lower volume.

Oil-bearing wastewaters are formed from lubrication, similar to those formed in the aluminum industry. These are frequently discharged into municipal sewers or rivers with little or no treatment. Characteristics and disposal of this type of waste are discussed under aluminum.

Other wastes of the copper and brass industry are the solid scrap, almost all of which is recovered for reuse, and zinc fume from the electrolytic melting furnaces, most of which is discharged in stack gases without treatment. The zinc fume losses, which are about 4–7 lb/ton of brass product, constitute a gaseous waste problem. However, recovery, when it is used, does not produce any appreciable wastewater other than a small amount of easily removed entrained solids.

Casting operations are characterized by the large number of small shops; about 600 locations have less than 50 employees. Their wastes include zinc fume from melters, lubricants, and entrained solids in wastewaters. Most of the wastewaters produced are discharged into municipal sewers or nearby rivers.

Pickle Rinsewaters from Fabrication. Rinsewater and acid bath dumps are discussed together because both contain the same noxious compounds —copper, zinc, chromium, and acid—and are related in other ways. Of these two wastes, rinsewaters contain the larger mass of contaminant— 90% of the total in one study. Although acid bath dumps are more concentrated, the flow rates of the relatively dilute rinsewaters are large, averaging 200–1000 gal/ton of product. In 1956 in Connecticut, over 18 mgd of wastes were discharged from a total of 21 nonferrous metal plants, most of which consisted of rinses from brass mills.

.The magnitude of total load from both wastes can be estimated from a 1941 Connecticut survey (9) which indicated that, for each ton of product, the amount discharged as waste included 5 lb of copper, 4 lb of zinc, the chromium equivalent of 5 lb of sodium dichromate, and 30 lb of sulfate. About one-fifth of the sulfate was in the form of sulfuric acid.

Rinsewater concentrations vary with time and with the individual plant, but some not atypical values are indicative. One tube mill with a 500,000 gal/day washwater flow had average concentrations, in mg/liter, of 80 sulfuric acid, 70 copper, 70 zinc, and 20 chromium; a wire mill with a 20,000 gal/day washwater flow had average concentrations, in mg/liter, of 1300 sulfuric acid, 800 copper, 1400 zinc, and 600 chromium. Maximum concentrations were 2–3 times as high. The pH of these wastes often ranged from 4 to as low as 2.

Pickle baths are batch vessels of about 1000 gal capacity, filled with a 5–10% sulfuric acid solution. During the time they are used for pickling, the acid content becomes depleted and the metal content accumulates. When spent, the pickle liquor is discarded and a new batch of acid is prepared. Dumping cycles vary, but are frequently once a month.

Bright dip baths, used to remove stains on the finished tube or wire, operate similarly to pickle baths except that 3–8% sodium dichromate is added to fresh batches, and dumping cycles are usually every week or every few days. Typical compositions of pickle baths at the time of dumping are, in mg/liter: 80,000 sulfuric acid, 10,000 copper, and 10,-000 zinc, with maximum values 2–4 times these concentrations. Bright dip baths, when dumped, have similar copper content, somewhat lower acid and zinc content, and substantial chromium content (20,000 mg/liter).

Discharge of these wastes without treatment is toxic to aquatic life and harmful to sewers and sewage plants; dilution is seldom adequate. Acidity of water below a pH of 6 is often lethal to the aquatic life that forms food for fish. The presence of copper, zinc, or chromium above 2 mg/liter is lethal to fish; furthermore, natural purification of a stream is inhibited. In a Japanese study, the lethal concentration for salmon was reported as 0.05 mg/liter copper or 0.6 mg/liter zinc. Permissive metal concentrations are usually set between 0.02 and 1.0 mg/liter. These metal sulfate wastes are acidic and corrosive, so they reduce the life of municipal sewers and corrode sewage treatment plant equipment. These wastes also interfere somewhat with the biological treatment of sewage and are not completely removed by municipal sewage treatment processes (5).

Pickle washwaters from the copper industry have most of the undesirable qualities possessed by steel industry pickle wastes—and copper, zinc, and chromium are considerably more toxic than iron.

Summary. Mussey (6) has reported that, on the average, more water is used to produce a ton of copper than a ton of any other major metal. Based on a 1956 survey, which did not include a direct comparison with other metals nor water use in copper fabrication, his survey indicated that 70% of the total water use of 330 mgd was for mining and concentrating the ore and the remaining amount for reducing the concentrates to refined copper.

The most objectionable liquid wastes in the production and fabrication of copper are the iron sulfate solutions from leaching of oxide ores and the pickle rinsewaters from wire and brass mills. Another, but minor, wastewater is the process water effluent containing entrained solids.

ZINC AND LEAD

Zinc and lead wastes are similar to wastes from the copper industry; the major ores are sulfides and the primary production of metal is by smelting and electrolysis, except that most of the zinc is refined by

distillation. Ores of zinc and lead often occur in the same deposit, sometimes with copper deposits.

Zinc. Most of the zinc smelted is derived from domestic ores of zinc
or lead and zinc. Of the 14 largest mines, most are located in one of
three areas: middle Atlantic, Tennessee and Virginia, or the Rocky
Mountain states. The Anaconda copper mine in Montana also produces
a considerable amount of zinc.

With only a few exceptions, smelting and refining are combined at the
same locations and are not at mine sites. All but 5 of the 20 smelters
are in Illinois, Texas, Oklahoma, Montana, or Pennsylvania and the
average annual capacity of smelters is about 50,000 tons of slab zinc.
The major wastes are the suspended dust and sulfur dioxide in the roasting furnace fumes. Cyclone separators remove as much as 99.5% of
the particulate matter. At most plants, the resultant gases are used to
produce sulfuric acid; at others, the waste gases are discharged without
treatment.

Although a few refineries purify zinc by electrolysis, most use the retort
method, which is a combined distillation and condensation process
carried out in batches or continuously. Gaseous zinc waste is minimized
by nearly complete recovery of zinc from the fumes. Zinc production at the 11 secondary smelters is only about 15% of primary production; the wastes are similar to those at primary retort refineries.

In electrolytic refining, the crude zinc oxide from roasting is leached
by acidic solutions to extract soluble zinc. Impurities in the resultant
zinc sulfate solutions are removed by precipitation in thickeners, and the
pure solution is then electrolyzed to form metallic zinc. Thus, the
potential wastewaters from these refineries are the spent electrolyte solutions and the slurries from the thickeners. The slurries formed by neutralization with lime contain iron, silica, antimony, and arsenic; slurries
from other treatment steps contain cobalt, cadmium, and copper. These
slurries usually do not present wastewater problems as they are either
treated to recover cobalt and other metals or discharged into lagoons
where further settling occurs. Little or no zinc appears in wastewater as
the spent electrolyte solutions and the supernatant liquid from slurries
are usually recycled for reuse in the leaching step.

Zinc is fabricated in the industrial states. It has three major uses:
die casting, half of which is in Michigan and Illinois; galvanizing, half
of which is in Ohio, Illinois, and Pennsylvania; and brass alloying, one-
third of which is in Connecticut. Zinc wastes in casting and galvanizing
are minimized by recover and reuse of scrap, although some gaseous

fumes are discharged and wastewaters contain some entrained solids. The main wastewater problem from the zinc industry is the discharge of soluble zinc in rinsewaters of brass mills, which has been discussed under the copper industry.

Lead. The production and fabrication of lead is a complex operation involving considerable amounts of reclaimed scrap and the import of one-third of the lead ores used in smelters. Although mining of lead is active in about half the states, two-thirds of the domestic ore is mined in Missouri, Idaho, and Utah.

Most of the smelters and refineries are located near the mines. As in primary production of zinc, these two process steps are often combined; the 11 smelters and 8 refineries are located at a total of 13 sites. The wastes of these primary producers are similar to those of the primary producers of copper. The two ways of smelting are: the ore hearth method, which produces lead in one step using high purity ores found in the Missouri area; and the 2-step sintering and blast furnace method, which uses complex ores containing several recoverable metals to make crude lead oxide and then lead and mixtures of other metals. Waste gases containing sulfur dioxide are emitted from sintering and ore hearthing; most are used for sulfuric acid manufacture, although some are discharged without treatment. As smelting is a dry, high temperature process, no wastewaters are formed directly. The waste solids given off, especially those from the blast furnace, are reprocessed to recover metals in ways in which some water is used but little pollution results. For example, zinc and lead are recovered from the slag and the higher density matte and speiss formed are sent to copper plants for recovery of arsenic, antimony, and copper (4).

Aqueous solutions are used in both electrolytic refining and the by-product recovery steps of furnace kettle refining. However, because of the presence of valuable materials in these solutions, they are refined and recycled; thus, no appreciable amount of wastewater is formed. In a similar way, the electrolytic slimes and anodes are processed for recovery or reuse of valuable materials.

Secondary lead recovery is, in tonnage, as large as primary lead production. Because of the other compounds and the larger number of sites involved, it is potentially more important from the waste viewpoint. There are over 250 secondary plants located in industrial centers; most of the 50 largest plants are located in sea coast areas or near the Great Lakes. Recovery from storage batteries has potential problems involved with the antimony in antimonial lead alloys and the discarding of unwanted parts by burning and dumping, as well as the high toxicity of lead itself.

The relatively high value of lead and its well-known toxicity have led to high recoveries and usually to adequate health precautions. Lead battery fabrication has similar aspects. Adequate control is also exercised by industries which are large consumers of lead, such as the paint and tetraethyl lead industries. Except perhaps in some smaller plants, wastewater problems in the lead industry are not serious.

OTHER METALS

Magnesium. In the production of magnesium hydroxide, the water effluent contains fewer salts than the influent sea water used as raw material. Furthermore, magnesium salts are not toxic in the usual concentrations found in water. Little wastewater is formed during production of the metal by electrolysis; recovery of the metal and of the chlorine gas evolved is almost complete.

Gold. Of the annual domestic production of 1.5 million troy ounces of gold (50 tons), about $\frac{1}{7}$ is extracted from gold ores by cyanidation, mainly at the Homestake Mine in South Dakota. About $\frac{2}{7}$ is made by amalgamation, and the rest from placers or base metal ores, but only the cyanide method produces a potential wastewater hazard. This hazard is due to the high toxicity of cyanide, and arises not only from the sodium and calcium cyanides used to form complexes with gold, but also from the cyanide sometimes used in the flotation circuits of mineral beneficiation plants.

After the gold cyanide complexes are split or electrolyzed to remove the gold, the cyanides are frequently recycled, thus minimizing waste discharge. Waste cyanide solutions can be oxidized to nitrogen and carbon dioxide by the same methods used for electroplating wastes, described in the chapter on Metal Finishing Products.

SUMMARY

The major potentially objectionable wastewaters arising from primary production and fabrication of nonferrous metals are the mud slurries from bauxite, fluorine solutions from aluminum refining, oil-bearing wastes from lubrication in fabrication, iron sulfate solutions from copper oxide leaching, pickle washings from brass mills, entrained solids from many operations, and cyanides from gold extraction. Of all these, pickle washwaters from brass mills are probably the most objectionable in quantity and toxicity.

WASTE DISPOSAL

From a long-range view, the best solution to waste problems is waste elimination by process changes. Wastes may be eliminated in existing plants by reuse of the noxious material or by recovery of by-products for sale; in new plants, choice of an alternate process may eliminate production of the undesirable material. Examples of these approaches in the nonferrous metal industries have been mentioned. Even where these approaches are not used, process changes to minimize waste formation have reduced treatment costs and decreased the amount of waste discharged to the surroundings. Treatment and disposal should be considered only where process alternatives are not available or where a temporary expedient is needed.

Where wastes are noxious materials that can be converted to harmless form by chemical reactions, treatment may involve such decomposition. In the nonferrous industries, however, noxious materials usually persist through treatment, and ultimate disposal becomes significant. Treatment of such wastewaters often involves separation of the deleterious substances from water by chemical reaction and phase change to gas or solid form, usually designed so that more concentrated mixtures of the noxious material are produced. Less frequently, treatment may involve concentration to another liquid phase; examples of these concentration treatment methods include ion exchange and the separation of immiscible liquids. On the other hand, disposal of these materials involves the permanent or semipermanent relocation of the waste. Frequently called "ultimate disposal," this includes dispersion of wastes by dilution and storage of solid materials or slurries on land. Therefore, for these persistent materials, treatment in itself is not adequate, but must be followed by some form of disposal.

Waste disposal may be accomplished, in one or more steps, with or without treatment—either of which may be satisfactory or unsatisfactory, depending upon such conditions as nature of the surroundings and concentration and amount of waste. An example of unsatisfactory treatment, indicative of some parts of the nonferrous metal industry today, occurs when a gaseous waste is converted into a noxious liquid waste, as in the scrubbing of fluoride gases in the aluminum industry. This treatment is unsatisfactory at many locations because it is incomplete; satisfactory disposal in these cases requires subsequent treatment and disposal of the new form of the waste.

Before considering disposal practices for specific wastes, three aspects common to most of the nonferrous metal industry should be examined: effect of surroundings, plant size, and waste concentration.

The primary production of these metals often occurs in arid, sparsely populated areas, whereas much of the secondary production and fabrication is located in or near heavily populated industrial centers where water is often more plentiful. Much of the primary aluminum, however, is produced in sparsely settled areas having plentiful water. A popular method of treatment and disposal in sparsely populated areas is lagooning, because of low land values. This method, however, is often considered too expensive within heavily populated industrial areas, even though smaller plants are the rule. Partly because of the more favorable attitude on the part of large companies, which usually operate larger facilities, it is generally true that treatment of wastes from primary production is better accepted than adequate treatment for wastes at small fabrication plants. It also is generally true that waste disposal in these industries is more of a problem in industrial centers where water is plentiful, but where treatment costs are higher and the accumulation of wastes from several industries is more likely to occur. These, of course, are generalizations for which notable exceptions occur and which will probably be changed in time.

Wastewaters contaminated by metal ions in large concentrations offer the best possibility of economic extraction of the metals for reuse or sale as by-products; treatment costs are often low, as in precipitation of iron sulfate by evaporation in the copper industry. Dilute solutions, because of their large water volume, are so costly to treat that the practice of discharge of these solutions to large waterways is widespread. This dilution method is possible only if sufficiently abundant water flows are near, and only as long as it is condoned by the public and the government. Where valuable metals are involved, as in electrolytic copper wastes, it is usually economical to concentrate the solutions and to recover the metals. If dilute solutions cannot be stored and reused, the alternative is expensive treatment; dilute wastes arising from the washing of pickled metal are a current example of this problem. Other rinsewaters and cooling waters used in fabrication also pose the problems of dilute solutions.

The treatment method most frequently used in the nonferrous metal industries is sedimentation of solids; it is used for entrained particulate matter as well as for precipitates formed by evaporation and by treatment with alkaline chemicals. Disposal methods most frequently used for wastewaters of this industry are discharge into rivers and oceans and discharge of solids onto land areas.

ALUMINUM

Mud Slurry from Bauxite. Bauxite mud slurries arise from thickeners arranged to wash the solids countercurrently to recover caustic for reuse. At several alumina plants, the mud wastes are impounded in large artificial lagoons, called lakes, where the insoluble solids settle out to 50–60% solids by weight and the supernatant liquor is returned to the alumina plants for reuse. The solid sediment is allowed to accumulate in the lake bottoms; thus, discharge of mud slurries into waterways is avoided.

At other plants, slurries are diluted and discharged directly into large waterways, using special care at the discharge point to avoid rapid settling in the river bed. Where the waterway is full of silt, as is the Mississippi River, such discharges do not change the character of the water except to add to the silt content; such effluents may, however, be quite noticeable in clearer waterways.

The choice of discharging or impounding mud slurries depends on economic factors, primarily availability of land and the caustic concentration in slurry mother liquor. Where land is available at a reasonably low cost, discharge of mud wastes to rivers is usually not economical unless the final slurry is reduced to a total caustic content of less than 1–5 gm/liter, expressed as sodium carbonate.

Where the aluminum silicate concentration in the red mud is appreciable, the mud is mixed with limestone and soda ash, sintered, and leached with water in order to recover aluminum as sodium aluminate solution. The resultant brown mud slurry is then discarded in the ways used for red mud. This recovery of aluminum from red mud is part of the "combination process," which has made possible utilization of low grade bauxite ores with a silica content as high as 15%. It is currently not economical to recover the titanium or iron from either red or brown mud slurries.

Fluoride Solutions from Electrolytic Plant Scrubbers. As a result of considerable cooperative effort by the large aluminum companies throughout the past 20 years, air pollution by fluoride fumes has been almost entirely eliminated by efficient scrubbing. Unless the liquid effluent of the scrubber is treated effectively, however, a wastewater problem is created.

At several plants, the resultant fluoride solutions are treated with lime in thickeners to neutralize the hydrofluoric acid and to precipitate most of the fluorides and sulfates as calcium salts. Most of the alkaline supernatant water from these thickeners is recycled to the scrubbers but some is discharged to rivers. The thickener sludge is impounded and dried by natural evaporation. Scrubbers have been designed to operate with low liquid flow rates; as a result, scrubber effluents as concentrated as 20 gm F/liter have been obtained in some tests.

At some plants the fluorine is recovered for reuse. In one method, the gas fumes are scrubbed with aqueous sodium hydroxide to produce a sodium fluoride solution; this solution is treated with sodium aluminate to precipitate cryolite for use in the electrolytic cell. The second method, used at two of the newer plants, is a dry scrubbing process which operates with a lower cost of recovery. At locations where there is no governmental restriction or where there is sufficient water for dilution below toxic levels, some plants discharge fluoride solutions without treatment. Scrubbers in these plants are operated with large water flow rates in order to produce effluents of low fluoride concentration.

Chloride Solutions from Casting Fumes. Chloride effluents from scrubbers are rare, since casting fumes are discharged without scrubbing at most plants; at some, the chlorine concentration in the fumes has been minimized by process improvements in handling and fluxing. Scrubbers are usually provided only at large casting fabricators and only where the chlorine discharge concentration is too high for the particular locale, as in heavily populated areas.

Where water is used to scrub the fumes, the wastewater effluent is usually discharged without treatment. In the usual case where fumes are scrubbed and scrubber effluents are treated, a thiosulfate reduction method is used. In this process, fumes are scrubbed with sodium hydroxide solution, most of which is recycled; the discarded portion is treated with sodium thiosulfate to reduce sodium hypochlorite to sodium chloride, which is then discharged as salty water.

Lubricating Oils from Fabrication. Insoluble oils used in mild pretreatments, such as kerosene, decompose little with use. These oils are frequently recovered for reuse by filtration and distillation because the small amounts of occluded water are easily separated. Those requiring disposal are burned for fuel oil or sold as road oil.

Emulsified oils, used under the extreme pressure and temperature conditions of rolling and drawing, break down and decompose with continual use. Because of decomposition and because of the low concentration of oil in the emulsion, recovery of this waste oil has not been attempted. Emulsified oil wastes are, at some plants, diluted and discharged without treatment; the relatively infrequent occurrence of these discharges (1–3 months at one plant) allows slow outflow at times chosen to minimize effects of pollution. However, many state laws require processing of oil wastes; one state has an upper allowable limit of 10 mg of oil per liter. At some plants, emulsions are converted to solutions by addition of chemicals, and then discharged into sewers. Most treatment methods used, however, are based on breaking the emulsion chemically, with alum, magnesium sulfate, or low pH, separating the two phases, burning the oil, and discharging the wastewater after neutralization with lime or caustic. Both soluble and insoluble oil wastes are often discharged by small fabricators without treatment, unless restrained by restrictive regulations.

Summary. Several materials are recovered from aluminum industry wastes, including aluminum from red mud silicates, fluorine from electrolytic plant fumes, and insoluble lubricating oils. While effective treatment of all types of wastes is technically possible and each is practiced at some plants, many wastewaters are discharged without treatment— especially in small fabrication operations.

COPPER

Iron Sulfate Solutions from Leaching. Leaching wastes are formed in the iron launders used to extract copper from oxide ore and to recover copper from tailings of sulfide ore, low grade ore, and mine waters. Because these operations are located mainly in the arid Rocky Mountain area of Arizona and its neighboring states, treatment of this waste is necessary to prevent making streams unpotable and unfit for agricultural or recreational use.

Most of the ferrous sulfate wastes are treated with lime to make them alkaline. The solutions are then transferred to lagoons where soluble ferrous hydroxide oxidizes to ferric hydroxide, which precipitates, aided somewhat by water evaporation. In this way, iron is disposed of by land storage and clean effluents are produced. At some locations, the effluents are reused.

Waste treatment is avoided by the Inspiration Consolidated Copper Company in Arizona by elimination of the waste. The copper sulfate leach solution is electrolyzed to deposit copper at the cathodes, and the resultant regenerated sulfuric acid liquid is recycled. In this way, production of iron sulfate waste is avoided. The copper recovery rate is about 40,000 tons per year.

Integrated Waste Treatment for Primary Production. Where more than one wastewater is produced, the possibility of combining them in some way should be examined. An example of integrated treatment, using leaching wastes and ore tailings, is used by the Anaconda Company at Deer Lodge County, Montana. The essential feature of this joint treatment is a combination of the alkaline tailing waste with the acidic leaching waste to form a neutral iron-free effluent for discharge. Two tailing waste sources are used: sand and slime sediment formed from lagooning tailing wastes in previous years, and wastewater from currently used tailing disposal lagoons; both contain residual lime. The leaching wastewater, having a pH of 4, first passes through the old tailings lagoon where it is partially neutralized by contact with the residual lime. By thus passing over the area, it controls dusting which otherwise presents an air pollution problem. After collection, the water flows through a ditch where clear water from the active tailing lagoon, of pH 11, is added to produce a pH of about 7. At times of high leach flow or cold weather, milk of lime is added to complete neutralization.

This combined stream flows into a 400 acre settling pond which permits oxidization of the ferrous hydroxide to ferric hydroxide. In settling, ferric hydroxide carries down with it any other solids suspended in the stream. The ultimate discharge to the Clark Fork River is clear, with a pH between 6.8 and 7.4.

Entrained Solids. Small solid particles frequently occur in water effluents from smelting, refining, and fabrication processes. Examples of such wastewaters are those from slag granulation in copper smelting and those used for cooling copper pigs and billets. Similar effluents arise in other metal industries.

The finely divided slag particles and the copper oxide scale from cooling pigs can be easily removed in concrete sedimentation tanks or earth dam settling basins. The hold time in these basins also serves to reduce the cooling water temperature. Such treatments are generally designed to permit water reuse. At many locations where reuse is not practiced, water containing these solids is discharged without treatment into nearby waterways. Disposal of settled solids is accomplished by periodic cleaning of the basins and dumping of the solids in slag pits.

Pickle Rinsewaters from Fabrication. At plants where pickle bath rinsewaters and dumps are segregated from other wastes, rinsewaters have been treated successfully by neutralization and precipitation. A good example of segregated wastes treated in this way exists at the Scovill brass mill in New Milford, Connecticut, where rinsewaters contain 10–20 mg/liter each of copper and zinc and have a pH of about 2.5. To even out large fluctuations in flow rate that occur (0–800 gpm), these dilute wastes are first collected in an equalization lagoon; based on the average flow rate of 400 gpm, this lagoon has an 8-hour capacity.

A steady 400 gpm flow from the equalization lagoon is pumped to a 1000 gal mixing tank where slaked lime is added to neutralize the acid and to raise the pH to 11–12. The spent pickle liquor, when dumped, is sent to a separate storage tank from which it is pumped slowly, over several days, to the mixing tank where it is combined with rinsewaters. These strong wastes are dumped when the mill is shut down, using the same pump and parts of the piping used for rinsewaters. Provision is made for a pretreatment reduction to the trivalent form of the hexavalent chromium in dichromate pickle liquors; this is done by addition of sodium bisulfite and acid to the liquors in the storage tank.

The high pH liquid from the mixing tank is separated in a clariflocculator, composed of a flocculator in the center of an annular clarifier; at average flowrates, these two parts have detention times of 20 and 170 minutes, respectively. The slurry underflow is discharged to one of two sludge lagoons, of 250 day combined capacity; top water from the sludge lagoon is returned to the equalization lagoon and compacted sludge is removed periodically. The clear effluent of pH 11–12 and containing 1–2 mg/liter each of copper and zinc is diluted fourfold by mixing with other process water effluent, and discharged to the nearby river. These treatment facilities have for several years produced a final effluent containing acceptable levels of copper, zinc, and pH.

Attempts to reduce the size of treatment facilities by process changes in the mills themselves have been successful. Two examples from the New Milford plant are indicative. In one approach, by changes in cycle time and drain angles, more of the pickle liquor is allowed to drain back into the acid bath before rinsing. This improvement in rinse procedure results in a decrease in the amount of acid waste produced and a reduction in the flow rate of rinsewater required, both of which allowed construction of a smaller waste treatment plant than would otherwise have been possible. The other approach also involved rinse procedures; countercurrent rinses were used and the rinsewater flow rate was controlled by pH. As a result, the wastes produced are fairly consistent in concentration, so smaller variations in lime addition are required; fluctuations in flow are decreased by the equalizing lagoon.

A waste treatment plant designed in conjunction with new brass mill facilities has capital and operating costs that are usually lower than the treatment costs for an existing brass mill of equivalent capacity. This reduction in treatment costs can be achieved if the effect of the proposed brass mill layout and operation on treatment is considered, such as in process changes, as noted above, and in segregation of wastewaters. The New Milford treatment plant, designed in conjunction with the new brass mill using wastewater segregation and suitable process changes, is an example of successful use of this cost reduction approach.

Many brass mills discharge their wastes directly into nearby rivers, using dilution to reduce metal content; as a result, however, several receiving streams contain concentrations of metals and acids which are lethal to fish. Reasons given for lack of treatment include high cost and lack of land for lagoons. In Connecticut, nearly all the 24 brass mills built before the New Milford mill discharge without treatment, even though pollution laws have been enacted. This absence of pollution control is due, in part, to lack of sufficient enforcement personnel.

Processes for the recovery of copper and zinc from rinsewaters containing about 10 tons per year of each metal have been found to be technically feasible in bench scale tests. However, according to one cost estimate, the processes are not economically feasible at the present time. These recovery methods are discussed under copper industry trends.

Summary. Treatment processes for the removal of contaminants from copper industry wastewaters are technically feasible and are in operation at some locations, but much of the wastes are currently discharged without treatment. The lack of treatment seems to be more prevalent with pickle rinse wastes from fabrication than with other copper wastes, but some iron sulfate leaching effluents are untreated and many entrained solids are discharged without much attempt at removal. Recovery of reusable material from these pickle washwaters does not seem economically feasible under present conditions.

INDUSTRY TRENDS

INDUSTRY CHANGES

Metal Production. In the years since World War II, aluminum production has expanded rapidly due to new uses such as structures. Copper production increased considerably during this same period, in line with general industrial growth; but because of world competition and other factors, lead and zinc production decreased.

As indicated in Table III, it is expected that the well-established copper, zinc, and lead industries will increase only about 35–50% from 1961 to 1975. Because manganese and chromium are closely related to steel, these industries will probably grow at a faster rate along with steel. The production rate of aluminum is expected to triple in this same period, continuing the rapid growth shown in the 1950's, after recovering from a relatively level production rate in the early 1960's.

No major process changes are anticipated in primary production, although use of lower grade ores will result in more impurities to dispose of. The greatest process changes in the industry in the near future will most likely be in fabrication, as competition with nonmetal products and

TABLE III

ESTIMATED GROWTH OF NONFERROUS METAL INDUSTRY

Metal	Consumption in the United States		Estimated increase, %
	1961 Actual	1975 Estimated	
Aluminum	2,300	7,200	210
Copper	1,450	2,000	40
Zinc	930	1,400	50
Lead	1,000	1,350	35
Manganese[a]	770	1,350	75
Chromium[b]	350	790	125

Taken from U. S. Bureau of Mines Yearbook, 1961.

All data in thousands of short tons.

[a] Assuming manganese ore of 45% manganese.

[b] Assuming chromite of 29% chromium.

other metals will tend to encourage development of new products and more efficient, lower cost operations.

Waste Disposal. There is little doubt that pollution regulations will become increasingly strict and compliance more rigorously enforced. In portions of the industry where substantial advances in wastewater control have already been made, as in large smelters and refineries involved in primary production, few major changes are anticipated. Successes in by-product recovery, waste reuse, and minimizing of discharges will probably be followed by minor improvements in these developments and some effort toward waste elimination rather than waste reduction. Choice of processes for new plants will be weighted to those which avoid the source of wastes.

Wastes which are currently discharged with little or no treatment will receive more attention, especially in areas which are heavily populated or which are changing from rural to urban. In addition to population growth pressures, many areas in which water has been considered plentiful, such as the eastern half of the United States, will find increasing pressure against pollution in order to supply industrial needs. More and more of the smaller firms which do not have personnel qualified to handle pollution problems will seek help in reducing pollution. Some may adopt existing methods, such as small smelters recovering sulfuric acid from sulfur dioxide fumes, and some will discharge into city treatment plants; but new processes will probably be developed to meet the special needs of smaller firms, of which fabrication is an important sector.

Substantial accomplishments are also to be expected in the difficult area of dilute solutions, such as those which arise with washwaters and cooling water, because metal ions are toxic and other contaminants are noxious in very low concentrations. Although treatment is costly and by-product recovery is often not feasible for these wastewaters, the U. S. Public Health Service has started development of methods for obtaining pure effluents, or ultimate treatment.

Aluminum Industry. In the future, more of the mud slurries from baux-ite purification will be treated by sedimentation. As large volumes of sediments are accumulated, recovery of titanium and perhaps iron will be reevaluated; if recovery is feasible, the mud slurry discharge can be further reduced.

In electrolytic plants, fluoride precipitation and reuse will become more widespread and other process changes to reduce fluoride loss will be developed. In large fabrication plants, tighter control will be exercised over chlorine usage, as by improvements in fluxing; chlorine effluent solutions may be applied more widely to by-product uses, such as sterili-zation of feed waters. Treatment of emulsion lubricating oils will prob-ably be adopted by more fabricators, until more stable lubricants are developed that can be recovered for use. Where substantial development problems arise, however, the cooperation within the industry used to eliminate fluorine from electrolytic fumes should be used again to ex-pedite solutions.

Wastewaters from secondary smelters and small fabricators may be-come more toxic for a time, as scrubbing of gaseous halide wastes is adopted. Already, however, wastes from these plants, unless provided for at municipal treatment plants, pose special problems at each of several locations. These problems should be studied and tested as a joint, cooperative program by the plants concerned and perhaps also by larger firms, unless governmental study is preferred.

Copper Industry. In the future, all iron sulfate leaching wastes that are currently discharged without neutralization will be treated to remove iron. Treatment will be assisted by continued cooperation between in-dustry and governmental agencies. Recovery of iron will probably be uneconomical for a number of years; however, the accumulations of ferric hydroxide residue may some day be used for iron recovery.

As pollution regulations become more restrictive, more of the en-trained solids will be removed from the wastewaters. Sedimentation will continue to be the method used, although in heavily developed areas, new settler designs may be necessary to provide for minimum land re-quirements.

The processing of toxic fabrication wastes will undergo the most rapid changes, because treatment is currently inadequate. The toxic discharges of copper, zinc, chromium, and acid bearing wastewater from brass mills will, at least initially, be reduced by use of the existing treatment method of lime precipitation, rather than by use of new methods such as ion exchange. For smaller plants, some modifications in treatment procedure, such as batch operation, may be needed to adapt this method to smaller waste flows. However, more effort should be devoted to increasing the installation of new treatment plants; methods should be developed that do not severely disrupt economic conditions, but can be used to speed up construction of treatment facilities.

With the accumulation, in slurry lagoons, of copper and zinc hydroxides from more widespread treatment, recovery of these metals will probably become more attractive. One of the more likely approaches is the roasting process developed for the Connecticut Water Resources Commission at Yale University. In this process, metal hydroxide slurries from lime neutralization are filtered, mixed with soda ash, dried, and roasted to metal oxides; the oxides are extracted with water to remove chromate and are dissolved in acidic spent electrolyte; copper from the resultant solution is deposited on waste brass chips from which zinc is dissolved, and the final solution is electrolyzed to produce metallic zinc and spent electrolyte for recycle. Alternately, copper may be deposited from rinsewater on chips before the metal hydroxides are precipitated. Found technically feasible in bench tests but uneconomical for a single brass mill, this recovery process may be applied to a cooperative system using slurries from several mills as estimates indicate a cooperative plant is economically feasible.

Further effort should also be directed at process changes to minimize waste loads. Improvements in rinsing procedures and in rinse design are among the many fruitful approaches that will probably be adopted more widely.

RESEARCH NEEDS

For both public and industrial interests, the best long-term solution to wastewater problems is elimination of the cause of wastewater and thus the need for treatment and disposal. This requires process research, devoted to new or modified processes that offer potential economic advantages over existing methods or to new processes for economic evaluation.

The possibility of developing dry processes in place of wet processes should be investigated for alumina manufacture and the pickling of copper and brass tubing and wires. The disadvantages of this approach are that conversion of existing plants is usually costly and time consuming and that the research necessary is expensive. Alternately, process changes to minimize wastes in existing processes should be studied; this approach has been applied to fluorine fumes in aluminum electrolysis and to rinse procedures in brass mill wastes. Further refinements should be studied in these areas and the approach should be extended to reduction of oil-bearing wastes from fabrication, entrained solids, and other wastes.

The main research need in the nonferrous metal industry is improvement in treatment processes, with respect to cost and to reduction in effluent impurity concentrations. Assuming that large companies will try to reduce costs of any of their existing treatment plants, other research should be directed to developing by-product recovery from treatment effluents and to alternative, less expensive processes.

By-product recovery should be investigated for titanium and iron recovery from bauxite mud slurries; this would not eliminate the mud slurry discharged but would reduce its amount considerably. Several processes for recovery of copper and zinc from brass mill wastes have been suggested and evaluated, such as roasting, ion exchange, brass chip extraction, and electrolysis. The economics of these processes should be reevaluated periodically, so they can be adopted as soon as they are economically attractive. Recovery of iron from the ferric hydroxide produced in copper leaching effluents is another possible area for study. Although solvent extraction is better suited for more valuable materials, it might be useful in by-product recovery of these metals.

One method of reducing treatment costs is to modify plant processes to produce wastes in more concentrated form, thus reducing capital costs substantially and, to some extent, operating costs. One suggested process change, which has been found surprisingly effective in metal finishing, is redesign of rinse methods to reduce water usage and thereby increase waste concentrations. Wastes so concentrated have frequently been re-used, either partially or entirely, thus eliminating the waste. Research on rinse design methods is needed for further applications.

Another concentration method is ion exchange, suitable for soluble ion wastes such as pickle liquors. This method is effective in reducing contaminant concentrations to low levels, but disposal of regenerant solutions is necessary. Research on the applicability of ion exchange should be directed toward ultimate treatment on very dilute wastes, where its costs may be competitive with other concentration methods; for example, in the removal of cyanides.

Other separation and treatment methods may be more effective or cheaper than existing processes. Froth or foam flotation has been tested to separate metal hydroxide precipitates from water; Baarson and Ray of the Armour Company found it to be effective at a pH near 7, but the economics are not well known. Bacterial action might be useful for treating oil-bearing wastes.

In summary, almost all the research which is needed is that to determine technical and economic feasibility of treatment, disposal, and waste elimination processes; in other words, process research for large scale separations by both chemical and physical means.

Governmental agencies should set allowable waste limits and enforce them by a specific timetable of deadlines, but they should also continue to encourage industry to do research necessary to solve its waste problems. Where changes in waste treatment offer potential profit or a reduction in costs, the industry involved should be informed of these possibilities by governmental agencies and should sponsor needed research. Cooperative programs, as used successfully by the aluminum industry in eliminating fluorine from electrolysis fumes, should be encouraged as well as action by individual companies. Where new and additional costs are necessary to provide adequate treatment, cooperative research programs are essential. It is preferable that they be sponsored by industry but in cases where little or no action is taken, as may occur with small fabricators, governmental agencies should, for the public interest, sustain some of the needed research.

Acknowledgment

The assistance of Professor A. P. Wichmann in the preliminary preparation of several parts of this chapter is gratefully acknowledged.

References

1. Conklin, H. L., "Water Requirements of the Aluminum Industry," U. S. Geol. Surv. Water-Supply Paper 1330-C, 1956.
2. Erga, O., Terjesen, S. G., and Utvik, A. O., in "Extractive Metallurgy of Aluminum" (G. Gerald ed.), Vol. 2, pp. 83–94. Wiley (Interscience), New York, 1963.
3. Henry, J. L., in "Extractive Metallurgy of Aluminum" (G. Gerald, ed.), Vol. 2, pp. 67–81. Wiley (Interscience), New York, 1963.
4. Kirk, R. E., and Othmer, D. F. (eds.), "Encyclopedia of Chemical Technology," Vol. 8, p. 227. Wiley (Interscience), New York, 1952.
5. McDermott, G. N., Moore, W. A., Post, M. A., and Ettinger, M. B., J. Water Pollution Control Fed. 35, 227 (1963).
6. Mussey, O. D., "Water Requirements of the Copper Industry," U. S. Geol. Surv. Water-Supply Paper 1330-E, 1961.
7. Reese, K. M., and Cundiff, W. H., Ind. Eng. Chem. 47, 1672–1680 (1955).
8. Reese, K. M., Garcia, A. F., and Lewis, R. A., Ind. Eng. Chem. 47, 2066–2072 (1955).
9. Wise, W. S., Dodge, B. F., and Bliss, H., Ind. Eng. Chem. 39, 632–639 (1947).

Chapter 16

PETROLEUM

by H. F. ELKIN and R. J. AUSTIN

Petroleum industry operations, from production to marketing, result in wastewaters of various compositions, but all are characterized by their content of oil. The objectionable nature of oil pollution has long been recognized, and the problem has been under continuous study and attack by the American Petroleum Institute, other industry organizations, and individual companies. Other industries, including metal finishing, vegetable oil production, meat production, and organic chemical manufacture, also produce oily wastes, and have utilized techniques developed by the petroleum industry.

THE PETROLEUM INDUSTRY

The petroleum industry has four major subdivisions: production (or mining), transportation, refining, and marketing. To these might be added the special field of petrochemical manufacture, but this is properly a segment of the organic chemicals industry, in which petroleum serves as the basic raw material. Some companies operate in only one or a few of the major subdivisions named; others span all, in a complex network of departmental organization.

Production. The production of petroleum involves its recovery from underground sources, in the form of crude oil. Natural gas is obtained from the same or separate wells, but its recovery and purification are relatively free from wastewater problems. Smaller quantities of oil are produced from oil shales, obtained by hard-rock mining, and recovered by distillation or other processes.

The 1962 production of crude oil in the United States was 2,676,000,000 barrels of 42-gal capacity. World production was approximately 3½ times this figure. Employment in domestic crude oil and natural gas operations exceeds 250,000.

Wastes from production operations include muds lost during drilling operations; oily losses during drilling and production; and, most significant, brines, which usually unavoidably accompany the crude oil. If adequate stream flow is available, brines may be disposed of by dilution, after oil removal, although troublesome pollution may result. Discharge underground is a more common practice, and may be used to maintain pressure on the producing well. Ponding for evaporation is sometimes feasible, but may cause contamination of potable aquifers.

Transportation. The transportation of petroleum includes moving crude oil from producing area to refinery, and distribution of finished products to market. Pollution problems arise primarily from accidents and equipment failure. Accidents are, to some degree, unavoidable, but their occurrence should be minimized and procedures for salvaging or destroying spills should be known to all personnel involved.

Transporters of petroleum and its products have sometimes caused pollution through accidents or failure to follow approved procedures. This situation has largely been corrected. Water ballast in empty oil tankers can be reasonably freed from oil before discharge to the ocean or other waterway; such pumping of oily water as is necessary can be done far enough from shore that the contamination is dissipated before it causes harm. Wastes from the cleaning of transportation equipment require special treatment, but it is not complex.

Refining. The oil refining industry in the United States has experienced a steady growth over nearly 100 years. A variety of products are produced, numbering in the hundreds; however, the major products are fuels, lubricants, greases, and semiraw materials for the chemical and petrochemical industries. About 8 million barrels per day of crude oil are used in manufacturing these products. Although the industry is experiencing a steady yearly growth, the number of oil refineries has declined from 352 in 1948 to 287 in early 1963. Within the refineries themselves, the trend is to larger units; and within the industry, the trend is to refineries of higher capacity. In 1962, over 130,000 people were employed in petroleum refining; refinery capacity on January 1, 1963, was 10,297,-000 barrels/day. With the population increase experienced in recent years there have been important changes in area market requirements as well as significant development of new market areas.

Modernization of facilities has included the development and installation of wastewater treatments of improved effectiveness. Expansion of refining capacity has been accompanied by a reduction of over-all water usage.

The principal operations within a refinery are fractionation by pressure and vacuum distillations, thermal and catalytic cracking, re-forming, polymerization, and alkylation. Operations such as acid treatment of lube stocks, sweetening of gasoline, extraction, and stripping are incidental to the preparation of stocks to specifications. Water is used in these operations primarily for indirect cooling, and does not come into contact with hydrocarbons. However, water used in washing stocks and steam recovered as condensate from processing operations comprise process wastewater, and are usually contaminated.

Marketing. The marketing of petroleum products may cause stream pollution by spills or other losses during transportation, and by minor losses at bulk stations and individual retailers. The latter are difficult to control because of their small size, large number, wide distribution, and the fact that most discharges are to municipal sewerage systems and are not easily observed. There are over 200,000 retail service stations in the United States, and total employment in marketing operations exceeds 500,000. Adequate control of wastewater is usually realized by preventing oily wastes from entering the sewer, as by collecting used crankcase oil; and by providing oil traps in the sewer to collect oils that enter despite the precautions taken.

REFINERY WASTE CHARACTERISTICS

Wastewaters from refineries usually contain oil, which may be separable, emulsified, or dissolved; chemicals, including acids, alkalies, sulfides, mercaptans, ammonia, and phenols; and suspended solids. The wastes may originate in process or cooling equipment leaks and spills, condensate from steam stripping operations, washwater from crude oil desalting and product treating, releases during shutdown or startup of equipment, draw-offs from storage tanks, equipment cleaning waters, cooling tower blowdown, water conditioning plant wastes, storm runoff, and miscellaneous sources such as area or equipment washdowns, pump gland cooling water, fire fighting, and sanitary wastes.

The major function of water in a refinery is for cooling, while relatively small quantities are used for boiler feed, direct processing, fire protection, sanitary use, and other purposes. In a "typical" 50,000 barrel/day refinery, generating more than 1 billion BTU per hour, as much as 50% of this thermal load is removed by water. Assuming a 30°F temperature rise in the cooling water, 40,000 gpm of water is required to remove this heat.

Water is used both consumptively and nonconsumptively in petroleum refining operations. Evaporation and windage losses from cooling towers and discharge of process steam to the atmosphere are major consumptive uses. Discharge of once-through cooling water, cooling tower blowdown, and discharge of steam condensate are typical nonconsumptive uses. Average freshwater intake requirements for domestic refineries have been estimated at 200 gal/barrel of crude oil charged. Gross water use, or water intake plus water recirculated, varies from about 800 to 3000 gal/barrel of crude oil refined. However, actual water consumed or "lost" averages from 2 to 5% of the total water used, or 30 to 60 gal/barrel of crude.

The extent of recirculation and reuse of water in refineries, as in other industrial operations, is largely dependent on the availability of a supply of satisfactory quality. Increasing recirculation and reuse of water results in an obvious decrease in refinery water intake and net effluent discharge, but paradoxically is accompanied by an increase in actual consumptive use because of the resulting evaporation.

Second to cooling, the major use of water is for boiler feed. The resulting steam is used for stripping and distillation, and because the steam comes in contact with petroleum products, the process condensate may be contaminated. Process wastewater is usually defined as any water or steam condensate that has been in direct contact with oil, either liquid or vapor, and can therefore contain oil or chemical contaminants. This includes spent caustic and acid solutions, product and crude washwaters, crude desalting water, and condensates from steam stripping, distillation, and steam cleaning or regeneration of catalysts and clays. Storm runoff waters may be contaminated or uncontaminated depending on the refinery area drained.

Both separable and emulsified oil may be found in any of the above wastewater sources. Sulfides may occur in crude desalting water and from gasoline condensate receivers at distillation and cracking units. Phenolic wastes may be found in condensate waters from catalytic cracking, in gasoline washwaters following caustic treating, and from lube oil and solvent production processes utilizing phenols.

The American Petroleum Institute (API) Manual on Disposal of Refinery Wastes (1) lists as sources of acidity in refinery wastewaters: distillation of crude oil and intermediate products, acid treatment and acid sludge handling, and catalytic cracking and equipment cleaning which contribute to formation of hydrogen sulfide and other acidic compounds. Alkalinity in wastewater, in the form of sodium, calcium, and ammonium hydroxides and carbonates, may originate in caustic treatment of distillates, sweetening and gas purification processes, corrosion control with neutralizing agents, water treatment plant wastes, refrigeration units that use ammonia, and conversion of nitrogen during catalytic cracking.

A broad range of oxidizable solutes, including some of the components described above, may occur in refinery wastewaters, and contribute to the over-all oxygen demand. Sources are distillate and cracking condensate accumulator draw-offs, cooling water from barometric and contact condensers, spent chemicals from distillate treating, petrochemical manufacture, water draw-offs from crude and intermediate storage tanks, and sanitary sewage. Taste and odor in wastewaters are caused principally by materials such as phenolic, naphthenic, nitrogenous, and organic sulfur compounds. The chief sources of these wastes are treating operations for removal of sulfur, nitrogen, and oxygen compounds from crude and distillate products, decomposition products from distillation and catalytic cracking, barometric condenser water, and crude desalting washwater.

It is not possible to generalize on the over-all quality of refinery wastewater. No two refineries are alike in size, type of crude oil charged, complexity of processing, and type, age, and efficiency of water use and waste control facilities. The quantity of pollutants, expressed in terms of the conventional unit of production, barrels of crude oil refined, may therefore be grossly misleading. For example, a complex integrated refinery may "rerun" oil two to three times in producing a wide range of products, while a simple topping and cracking refinery reprocesses only a portion of its original crude charge. Obviously, the complete or integrated refinery has a wider range and larger quantity of waste materials in its effluent than a simple distillation-cracking plant of comparable initial crude capacity.

Limited data on typical refinery effluent quality was developed in the 1961 API Water Use Survey (5). On the basis of crude runs only, refinery effluents, on an average, contained 100–200 lb BOD and 150–300 lb COD per 1000 barrels of crude oil refined. These relationships are based on limited survey data and are not adjusted for complexity of refining.

WASTE DISPOSAL

In-plant Procedures

Unit operating procedures include a number of steps related to waste control, and referred to as in-plant procedures. These involve specific operations and, frequently, specific equipment for the sole purpose of accomplishing waste control in the most effective and least expensive manner. Often, these in-plant procedures are used to prevent entry to the sewer system of substances that would complicate or render essentially useless the final waste treatment operation. Other in-plant procedures involve recovery of raw materials, intermediates, and final products within a particular unit area; reuse of water, as by cooling towers; reuse of a chemical in a series of treatment steps in which initial use requires the highest concentration and the requirements of successive uses are met by reagents of lower strength; and treatment procedures that condition a waste for discharge to the sewer or remove it from the system for special or selective disposition or for regeneration.

Oil is usually collected from a drainage system at each refining unit, in a number of sumps conveniently located about the unit to serve specific areas. Such a system collects drainage from pump gland oil systems, sampling telltales, water from deck drainage, incidental spillage, and incidental or controlled leakage from the unit's emergency blowdown system. The sumps are generally float controlled to discharge water to the main sewer system automatically; accumulated oil is normally discharged to slop tanks by manual control. This system is limited to the collection of oil of relatively low volatility. Wastewater from the sumps is usually collected in a closed system that discharges to the refinery main sewers, from which the oil is collected in master separators. It is not uncommon for refining units to be equipped with boxes that do a rough job of separating oil from the process wastewater. These boxes or separators may not conform to the API separator design, but are constructed and sized arbitrarily to accomplish the one purpose of removing free floating or readily separable oil.

Most important of the reuse systems is the cooling tower, which may increase the consumptive use of water, but reduces the amount of water taken from the raw water supply, and reduces the volume of wastewater to be treated. The cooling tower operates as a closed system, consequently, it is effective in minimizing oil losses to the refinery sewer.

Steam condensate is frequently collected from reboilers and used as feed water for the steam generating plant, or as a part of the makeup for the cooling tower system. Foul condensate, which is water formed from steam used in process operations such as distillation or serving as inert atmosphere or quench in the regeneration of catalyst, appears as process wastewater from reflux drums. This water may be used directly in crude desalters; however, it is more common to strip it relatively free from sulfides before such use.

Caustic soda is used in the treatment of many crude stocks to remove hydrogen sulfide and mercaptans. Incidental to this treatment is the formation of caustic cresylates. Other stock treating operations employ caustic cresylates to accomplish sweetening. There is usually an accumulation of caustic cresylate to be discarded from the system. There are limited market outlets for the spent caustic solutions, which partially relieve the refiner of the need to provide special treatment for these wastes. However, such markets, besides requiring specification material, are irregular. Consequently, the refinery employs maximum reuse of caustic solutions, together with regenerative processes where possible.

Sulfuric acid is used as a catalyst in alkylation, and in the treatment of certain fuel products and some lube stocks. Many refiners sell or trade these spent acids and acid sludges to acid manufacturers. Sometimes, the spent acids are sold for use in other industries, where they may be used directly or fortified with acid of full strength. The corrosive nature of spent acids prohibits their disposition to the refinery sewer system; and treatment by neutralization would be not only an unbearable economic burden to the refinery but an unnecessary economic waste.

Stripping and Oxidation. In the distillation of crude oil and in catalytic cracking, sour condensate waters are produced. These wastewaters contain varying concentrations of sulfides, mercaptans, ammonia, and phenolics, depending upon the type of crude oil, the cracking conditions, and the amount of steam used. The most common method of treating sour condensate water is by steam stripping in a tower. Sulfides, mercaptans, and ammonia leave the tower in the overhead gases, and the major part of the phenolics is drained to the sewer system in the tower bottoms. Distribution of the components between overhead and bottoms is controlled by design and manner of operation. Hydrogen sulfide and mercaptan are relatively easy to strip. Complete ammonia removal is difficult, and requires large amounts of steam. Some refiners use a combination of fuel, gas, and steam for stripping these waters.

In recent years, oxidation of sour waters in towers has become practical. Sour water is fed into the bottom of the tower with sufficient air to oxidize the sulfur compounds and ammonia. The reaction is exothermic. Usually the sulfur compounds are oxidized to thiosulfate and the ammonia to water and nitrogen; phenolics are not affected. The degree of oxidation is controlled by the contact time provided in the tower. Oxidation to sulfate can be accomplished by using higher pressure and extended contact time. Spent caustic solutions containing sulfides and mercaptides are also oxidized in towers; in some instances, concurrently with the sour waters.

Combustion. Combustion is used to a limited extent as an in-plant disposal practice for selected wastes. Hydrofluoric acid alkylation and spent aluminum chloride sludges are sometimes burned in special incinerators. The resulting air pollution, however, cannot be tolerated in most areas. Combustion of spent caustic solutions, including sulfide, mercaptide, and cresol types, has found limited application because of air pollution, corrosion of the incinerator, and difficulties of handling the slag, which is mostly sodium carbonate, formed in the combustion chamber. In some refineries, where petrochemical manufacture is a part of the operations, spent or waste solvents are incinerated as a means of disposal.

However, chlorinated hydrocarbon disposal by this means requires absorption towers for removing the hydrogen chloride formed. The small size of this operation may permit discharge of the absorbed acid to the sewer system or permit the expense of neutralization.

The burning of oily sludges and salt-bearing acid sludges in power station furnaces has been practiced in the past, and is feasible where oil or coal is used as fuel. Air pollution control, however, limits this practice.

Solvent Extraction. Solvent extraction as a means of waste treatment finds limited use in an oil refinery. It is sometimes used on phenol-bearing wastes, such as caustic cresylates and sour water stripper bottoms. Control of the wastewater pH is required, to put the phenolic material in the acid form. The cresol-bearing solvent is recovered by extraction with strong caustic solution, to produce a marketable product.

Housekeeping. Around any manufacturing operation, good or bad housekeeping is apparent to the observer, and is reflected in the waste treatment problem. Good housekeeping includes repair of leaks as soon as possible, avoidance of oil discharge with the necessary elimination of water from process units, proper disposition of solids and spent chemicals, careful handling of emulsions, and awareness by all personnel that waste treatment begins at the process unit. The design of process units must include facilities that promote good housekeeping. Telltales or sampling lines should be installed in a manner that allows collection at the unit of line flushings. Facilities for cleaning up after charging new catalyst should be provided so that such materials are not flushed to the sewers; these materials can cause sewer line blockage, promote emulsification, and stabilize emulsions. The latter effect disturbs oil-water separation, which affects adversely the receiving waters or interferes with performance of secondary treatment facilities. Proper operation of adjunct facilities, such as are provided on gasoline treating plants for oil-water separation and on coking units for coke-water separation, is important in the housekeeping problem. Improper operation of these facilities impedes performance of downstream waste treatment equipment and produces a generally unsightly apearance in the effluent.

TERMINAL TREATMENT

Oil refineries usually employ separate sewer systems for oily water or process waste, spent cooling water, storm drainage, and sanitary sewage. Considerable study is required to determine, for a particular refinery, the degree of separateness of these systems or the manner in which all of them may be brought together at a single outlet.

Sanitary sewage is usually collected in a separate system and discharged to city sewers. If municipal facilities are not available, septic tanks may be employed, with the overflow going to drainage fields. If secondary treatment is used for the refinery effluent, the overflow from sanitary sewage septic tanks may be discharged to the nearest oily water sewer.

Gravity Separators. Gravity separation is the final treatment step for oil refinery wastewaters. For process wastewaters or the oily water sewer system, an oil-water separator designed in accordance with the API Manual (*1*) is commonly used. This is a gravity separator in which oil accumulates on the surface and heavy solids settle to the bottom. Oil skimming and bottom sludge removal are required periodically. Storm drainage and spent cooling water are frequently routed through separators of this type. In these two services, however, the separators are usually of less costly design than those used for oily water, i.e., they provide less settling time because these waters are almost oil-free. Separators on these streams serve primarily as protective devices in the event of accidental spillage or an emergency situation in which oil may be released because of a fire or tank failure. Gravity separation may provide the total treatment needed for simple refineries; however, where there is a complex of operations involving lube oils and petrochemicals, additional treatment may be required. It may consist of chemical flocculation, air flotation with or without chemicals, or biological oxidation by means of trickling filters, activated sludge, or ponding for an extended time.

Chemical Flocculation. Chemical flocculation consists of the addition of a reagent to a wastewater to form a precipitate removable by settling. Aluminum sulfate, ferric chloride, and aluminum chloride are the most common reagents used to accomplish chemical flocculation. In some instances, substances present in the wastewater, such as calcium bicarbonate and magnesium carbonate, may be made to form precipitates and so serve as flocculating agents. When the pH of the wastewater is controlled within the proper range, hydrated reaction products of the flocculating agents result; these relatively insoluble compounds, initially present as colloids, agglomerate as flocs. During agglomeration, they become associated with other colloidal and suspended matter. As the floc particles grow, their apparent density increases and they settle, carrying with them whatever insoluble matter may have become trapped during the growth period. Polyelectrolytes are frequently used to hasten the flocculation process.

Chemical flocculation is effective in reducing the suspended matter content of wastewater, including insoluble matter in a finely divided state. Oil content can be reduced to its solubility level by this process. Some BOD is removed in the process, but the removal is limited to oxygen-demanding substances present initially as colloids or other particulates. Flocculation is effective in removing turbidity; it has no effect on color caused by substances in solution, but on color caused by colloidal materials it can be effective to the extent that it induces agglomeration of the color bodies.

Air Flotation. In the air flotation process, wastewater is saturated, usually under pressure, with a gas such as air, and is then released to a vessel at atmospheric or reduced pressure. The supersaturation is relieved by formation of tiny bubbles of gas. The bubbles, while forming and rising through the water, attach themselves to particulate matter and convey it to the surface, from which it can be skimmed. Air flotation offers the advantage of a faster rate of separation than gravity separation, and space requirements for a particular treatment job are generally less. The combination of air flotation with chemical flocculation is more effective than air flotation alone; it produces about the same degree of treatment as chemical flocculation, but does it faster, minimizes some of the effects that upset simple chemical flocculation, and accomplishes at least a minor degree of oxidation.

Air flotation, with or without chemicals, can yield a greatly improved effluent insofar as appearance and oil content are matters of concern. Where oxygen demand requirements are not important, it can serve as the final treatment for refinery effluent.

Biological Oxidation. Bio-oxidation is used extensively in the treatment of refinery wastewaters. Both trickling filters and activated sludge have been adapted to the treatment of selected waste streams and to total effluents, and bio-oxidation ponds also are widely used. A high degree of treatment can be attained with any one of these methods, comparable to that obtained in the treatment of food wastes and sanitary sewage. However, a longer period of time is required on refinery effluents. In some plants, biotreatment has been limited to selected streams, usually those containing phenolic compounds. However, as water usage declines, refinery effluents become of poorer quality, and the need for treatment is greater, even though the absolute amount of polluting materials may be less than it was when effluent volumes were greater. Furthermore, regulatory requirements grow more stringent. Consequently, the trend is strongly toward treatment of the total effluent, excluding only storm and surface drainage from oil-free areas.

Selection of type of biotreatment depends largely on costs and space available for the treatment plant. It is advisable to study all three methods in pilot plants, if possible; or at least those that can be adapted to the area and terrain. Pilot plant information is needed to evaluate treatability of the effluent, to determine its variability in composition, and to estimate the surge capacity needed to level out fluctuations that adversely affect the performance of trickling filters and the activated sludge process.

The bio-oxidation pond requires considerable area for its installation. Where area is available and terrain favorable, it is the method of lowest cost, both in installation and operation. The pond has good buffer capacity to withstand shocks from overloads and toxic substances. If the pond can be made sufficiently large, supplementary aeration is not required; however, greater flexibility in size and operation exists if a limited amount of aeration capacity is installed initially. Reliable and precise methods are not available for designing such installations. Pilot plant studies can be helpful in estimating the requirements. Ponds are in operation without aeration, where the holding time is as much as 180 days. Such systems, however, suffer deterioration of effluent quality at times, because of algae cycles during which algae grow excessively, die and cause high BOD and color, then grow again. This is a summer ailment, and can be alleviated by providing withdrawal lines at several points so effluent can be removed at the end of the bacterial section and ahead of the algae areas. Aerated ponds with as little as 3 days holding time are producing high quality effluents, comparable to trickling filters or activated sludge.

Oxidation ponds should be divided into compartments. A presettling basin of at least 24 hours holding time should be used to retain oil and sludge; this permits easier removal than if it is allowed to collect in the larger ponds.

A clear-cut basis is lacking for selection of a trickling filter or activated sludge unit for treating the total effluent from a refinery. Approximately equal performances can be attained with these two units. Installation costs are usually greater for a trickling filter than for an activated sludge unit; however, operating costs are greater for the latter. The trickling filter is considered to withstand the effects of overloads and toxic materials better than activated sludge. The amount of oil that either type of unit can tolerate is not clearly defined, although a limiting concentration of 100 mg/liter has been reported. It is likely that this varies with concentration of solids in the aeration basin of the activated sludge unit and with the condition of the biological film on the trickling filter medium. In the latter, there could be a wide range in tolerable oil concentration between low rate and high rate filters, and between the rock and plastic media.

Chemical Oxidation. Chemical oxidation has found but limited use in the treatment of refinery wastes. Oxidation, in towers, of spent caustic solutions containing sulfides and mercaptides, and of sour condensate containing $(NH_4)_xS$ is being employed. The operation is carried out as a continuous process, with solution and air fed to the bottom of the tower. The reaction is exothermic and provides its own heat once it has been started. Sulfur compounds are converted to thiosulfates in a temperature range from 150 to 250°F and pressure from 10 to 60 psig. Temperature and pressure vary with composition of the waste and degree of oxidation desired. Conversion to sulfate can be attained by using higher temperature and pressure, and increasing the contact time in the tower.

Oxidation by ozonation or chlorination is seldom used on refinery wastes because of costs. Use of these agents on biotreated effluents offers a possible tertiary treatment in extreme conditions. This could be justified only for taste and odor compounds that are refractory to the usual biomethods. However, the taste and odor compounds are among the last components in the mixture to react with these oxidizing agents. The relatively large amount of oxidant consumed in oxidizing residual BOD, plus that required to establish mass action conditions needed to effect oxidation of the taste and odor constitutents, makes the process prohibitively expensive.

DISPOSAL METHODS

Underground Disposal. Deep well disposal is being increasingly used for selected industrial wastes. It has been used for brine disposal in oil field regions for many years. At the refinery, wells can be employed to dispose of sour condensate streams, spent caustic solutions, and spent acids. A suitable geological formation is required, having adequate permeability and porosity, and covered by a relatively large impermeable cap or formation. There should be no geological faults in the area, and the receiving formation must be substantially below the depth of present or future potable water wells in the area. The well must be properly cased and sealed so that upper formations are safe from contamination.

Waste solutions charged to the well must be free from suspended matter in order to avoid plugging the sidewall of the borehole. Fresh water or acid may be injected into the well initially, to establish a front or barrier between the waste and the original formation water; this is to prevent reactions between components of the waste and the underground water that would yield precipitates and plug the formation, and applies particularly in the vicinity of the injection area. At remote points in the formation, more reliance can be placed upon these reactions generating and maintaining an adequate fresh-water front.

Dilution. "Dilution as the solution to pollution" is an old attitude of declining merit, not because it is bad philosophy, but because its capacity is exhausted in many areas. Nevertheless, its potential should be assessed and used within reasonable bounds. Conventional waste treatment processes are prevented by economics from accomplishing a degree of treatment that would make dilution unnecessary. Dilution may offer only limited possibilities for meeting the oxygen demands of a waste and, at the same time, afford considerable capacity for accepting a waste having high dissolved solids. The characteristics of the waste and the properties of the waters into which the waste is to be discharged must be carefully weighed when treatment requirements are being balanced against dilution potentialities.

Evaporation. Evaporation has little to offer in solving refinery waste disposal problems in most of the United States. In arid regions, however, it can be an important asset when ponds without outlets are used, i.e., seepage and evaporation ponds. Evaporation rates are as much as 30 inches per year in excess of rainfall in parts of the United States. Ponds having areas of 400 to 1000 acres afford a disposal capacity of 0.9–2.25 mgd by evaporation alone. This is adequate capacity for refineries ranging in size from 40,000 to 100,000 barrels/day.

SLUDGE DISPOSAL

One of the most difficult problems in the treatment of refinery wastewaters is the handling and disposal of sludges, including sludges derived directly from waste treatment as well as those originating in oil processing operations. In designing for either waste treatment or oil processing, it is difficult to assess the potential of these operations for producing sludges and to predict their characteristics. Too frequently, sources of sludge are ignored, not recognized, or dismissed as being of no consequence. Segregation of sludges offers possibilities of minimizing difficulties and expense in arriving at ultimate disposition. For convenience, sludges can be considered under 4 general types: oily, oil-free, chemical, and biotreatment.

Oily Sludges. Oily sludges are derived from oil-water separators, tank bottoms or cleanings, air flotation treatment of wastewaters, and cleaning or dredging from lagoons or oxidation ponds. Sludges as taken from any of these operations consist of slurries of oily solids in water with an average composition of about 97% water, 1% oil, and 2% solids. If final disposition is to be in some remote area, thickening may be required in order to minimize transportation costs. Generally, thickening to about 20–30% oily solids can be accomplished by quiescent settling or use of a thickening unit. Centrifuging may be used to accomplish a higher degree of water removal, after thickening of the sludge to 10–15% oily solids to produce a satisfactory centrifuge feed. Sludges from the sources indicated are obtained at irregular intervals, with the result that centrifuge feed varies from day to day and erratic results are obtained. Tank bottoms frequently contain heavy emulsions that require special attention in preparing centrifuge feed. Sludge and skimmings from air flotation units may introduce special difficulties. Thus, feed preparation for the centrifuge can present a variety of problems, and addition of demulsifiers, polyelectrolytes, or light oils is commonly employed to aid preparation for centrifuging. The dewatered and relatively oil-free solid can be disposed of by incineration, or used as landfill.

Oil-free Sludges. Solids from water conditioning may consist of silt, calcium carbonate, magnesium hydroxide, and minor amounts of organic matter, along with precipitated treating agents. Composition varies with the water source. They should not be discharged to the oily water sewer system because they can promote emulsification and inhibit oil-water separation. In some refineries, these solids are thickened and dewatered by centrifuging. The dewatered solids are suitable for landfill; occasionally they may find a limited market.

Chemical Sludges. A variety of chemical sludges result from oil refining operations. Spent aluminum chloride complex, sulfuric acid alkylation sludge, calcium fluoride from HF alkylation, and acid sludge from the treating of lube oil stocks are examples of sludge that require special handling. Sludges from lube oil stock treating and H_2SO_4 alkylation are treated for acid recovery in the refinery, or sold to acid manufacturers. Spent aluminum chloride complex has been disposed of by burial with crushed limestone, or hydrolyzed and used as a source of aluminum in chemical flocculation. Where possible, such sludge is simply drowned, to avoid HCl liberation, and sent to a pit containing alkaline waste, in which the aluminum hydroxide is allowed to accumulate. Calcium fluoride sludge is an end product from treating HF alkylation plant wastewater. It is removed from the final settler as a slurry, drained free from water, and buried.

Biotreatment Sludge. Sludges from the treatment of refinery wastes by trickling filters or the activated sludge process can be digested anaerobically in the same manner as sanitary sewage sludge. Sludges from oxidation ponds and aeration basins, however, contain considerable oily matter and respond poorly to anaerobic digestion. Disposition of these sludges can be accomplished by dewatering, centrifuging, and incinerating; spreading in a suitable area for complete drying; or using as landfill.

INDUSTRY TRENDS

A steady growth in oil refining output in the United States has been recorded in the past decade and is expected to continue in coming years. Crude runs to domestic refineries increased from 1730 million barrels per year in 1946 to 2730 million barrels in 1955 and to 2953 million barrels in 1960. The President's Materials Policy Commission estimated that domestic consumption of petroleum products would amount to 5 billion barrels annually by 1975. The future increase in domestic rate of demand for oil products has been estimated by various authorities to range from 3 to 5% annually. The lower estimate is predicated on increased production of natural gas liquids and increased yield of additional lighter products from crude oil.

Despite this consistent growth pattern, over-all fresh water requirements and over-all net pollution load per barrel of crude oil processed have steadily decreased for a number of reasons:

Many outmoded and inefficient refineries have been shut down, and areas which they previously supplied are now serviced by pipelines. There are approximately 100 fewer refineries in operation today than there were 20 years ago.

Expansion of existing refineries with modern processing equipment has satisfied most of the increased demand for oil products. Shutdown of older, large water using units in these existing plants has reduced over-all net pollution loads.

Improved waste treatment and reuse of wastewater in existing refineries has become more common, with planned modernization and accompanying economies.

The relatively few new refineries built in recent years in the United States have been adequately equipped with modern waste treatment facilities as a part of their original construction.

Only about 40% of the total crude oil refining capacity in the United States is located in areas where effluents are discharged to freshwater streams and lakes that are usable for municipal water supplies or other critical purposes.

Burroughs (2, 3) has summarized process improvements and other technical developments in recent years which have significantly aided over-all refinery pollution abatement, including the following:

Widespread use of catalytic cracking, re-forming, and hydrogenation, which yield products low in sulfur and require minimum subsequent treatment.

Extraction and similar processes for the manufacture of lubricating oil, which reduce or eliminate the need for chemical treatment.

Continuous processes for removing sulfides and mercaptans from products, which minimize the production of spent chemicals requiring disposal.

Continuous removal of hydrogen sulfide from products, gases, and certain wastewater streams, and its subsequent conversion, in many locations, to elemental sulfur.

Sale of sulfide-bearing spent caustic soda and other spent chemicals for use by other industries.

Return of spent sulfuric acid to the manufacturer for fortification or replacement.

Injection of certain wastes into underground disposal wells and disposal at sea (with the approval of appropriate authorities).

Although the common misconception of an impending water shortage still prevails, studies of oil industry water use thoroughly negate such predictions. Ten-year survey data in 1950 and again in 1960 indicate that domestic crude oil processing capacity increased 93% with only a 21% rise in fresh-water intake. A detailed analysis of 104 existing refineries, excluding new ones, reveals a 51% increase in capacity with only a 5% increase in fresh-water intake.

The use of recirculating cooling water, air cooling in place of water cooling, reuse of wastewaters, and gradual replacement of older and less efficient processing units with fewer but larger modern units have all contributed to this impressive conservation accomplishment. Remaining problems are generally centered in older existing plants where modernization of equipment has not yet been economically justified and where existing plant layout, above and below ground, presents costly and difficult problems for waste reduction.

Although the aforementioned water conservation measures have been widely adopted in recent years by domestic refiners, water availability, as to both quantity and quality, has been only a minor factor in site selection. Factors other than water availability will undoubtedly continue to control future refinery locations. Tidewater location for access to deep water and ocean transport, proximity to crude oil supply and to marketing locations, and cheap and abundant supplies of natural gas for fuel have been dominant factors in refinery location. The advent of large crude and product pipelines and of more efficient waterborne carriers has minimized the need for refinery construction in population growth areas.

Another measure of domestic refining waste reduction accomplishment is provided in the 1960 API survey, wherein domestic refiners reported expenditures of $97 million and $156 million for facilities to treat intake and effluent waters, respectively. An annual cost of $33 million is required to operate these facilities. A sample of 80 refiners reported investing $37 million for new waste treatment equipment during the 5-year period preceding the survey. A projected additional expenditure of $30 million in the near future was also reported by domestic refiners.

Although these cost figures are certain to increase as refiners continue their waste control efforts and as river basin water quality improvement planning is implemented, dollars alone cannot accurately describe the extent of industry accomplishments to date or planned. No cost survey can accurately reflect the significant, but less obvious, benefits of in-plant process improvements and increased attention to good housekeeping practices which are reflected in reduced pollution loading in the effluent. Likewise, no plant has problems or solutions identical with another, and widely varying investment costs may be required to produce comparable waste reduction at different plants. It is a reasonable assumption that the more apparent and economical waste reduction programs have largely been implemented, and that remaining effluent improvements, as in most industries, will be more costly and difficult per unit benefit obtained.

Pollution abatement in the petroleum refining industry in the coming decade will continue to receive material assistance by process modernization, in-plant modifications, and water recirculation and reuse. Intermediate and secondary waste treatment procedures, already firmly established in the industry, will be even more widely employed where receiving waters demand high quality effluents. Biological oxidation will probably remain the dominant secondary treatment where its use is justified and until some of the more esoteric experimental tertiary treatments are perfected and proved effective.

Although research in wastewater control in the oil industry is conducted by individual refiners on specific problems, broad gauge common areas of interest are investigated through sponsored programs of the American Petroleum Institute. Recent and current API research has studied improved gravity separator design, the characteristics and modifying influences of refinery effluents on tastes and odors in receiving water, and made exploratory studies on nonbiological oxidation procedures.

REFERENCES

1. American Petroleum Institute, "Manual on Disposal of Refinery Wastes." Vol. I, "Waste Water Containing Oil," 7th ed., 104 pp., 1963.
1A. American Petroleum Institute, "Manual on Disposal of Refinery Wastes." Supplement to Vol. I, "Dispersion of Refinery Effluents in Receiving Waters," 1963.
1B. American Petroleum Institute, "Manual on Disposal of Refinery Wastes." Vol. II, "Waste Gases and Particulate Matter, 5th ed., 68 pp., 1957.
1C. American Petroleum Institute, "Manual on Disposal of Refinery Wastes." Vol. III, "Chemical Wastes," 4th ed., 93 pp., 1960.
1D. American Petroleum Institute, "Manual on Disposal of Refinery Wastes." Vol. IV, "Sampling and Analysis of Waste Water," 1957.
1E. American Petroleum Institute, "Manual on Disposal of Refinery Wastes." Vol. V, "Sampling and Analysis of Waste Gases and Particulate Matter," 1954.
1F. American Petroleum Institute, "Manual on Disposal of Refinery Wastes." Vol. VI, "Solid Wastes," 1st ed., 51 pp., 1963.
2. Burroughs, L. C., "Water Use by Petroleum Refineries." American Petroleum Institute Misc. Paper, 1963.
3. Burroughs, L. C., "Recent Developments in Control of Air and Water Pollution in U.S. Refineries." Paper No. 25, Sixth World Petroleum Congress, Frankfort, 1963.
4. Otts, L. E., "Water Requirements of the Petroleum Refining Industry." U.S. Geological Survey Water-Supply Paper 1330-G, 1963.
5. Stormont, D. H., *Oil Gas J.* **61**, No. 8, 86 (February 25, 1963).

Manufactured Products

Chapter 17

INORGANIC CHEMICALS

by W. R. TAYLOR

This chapter on inorganic chemicals and the one following on organics together constitute a review of the chemical industry. Certain other chapters, particularly those on mining, coke and gas, and petroleum, also contain information pertinent to chemical operations. The products discussed in this and the following chapter are used in almost all other industries. This chapter reviews the inorganic chemical industry products and raw materials, and the nature of the wastewater problems encountered and techniques for solving them.

The effluents discussed in most of the other chapters are characterized by similarity. Individual plants within these industries produce the same general product or series of products from the same raw materials and by approximately the same methods. Techniques and methods of wastewater treatment applicable to one plant are generally usable in another plant of the same industry without substantial change.

The manufacture of inorganic chemicals can hardly be called a unit industry. The products are of an inorganic nature, but the individual plants are characterized by dissimilarity. A great variety of products is manufactured, and any given product may be made by a number of processes, from different raw materials, and with effluents of entirely different characters.

THE INORGANIC CHEMICAL INDUSTRY

To indicate the diversity of products manufactured by the inorganic chemical industry, Table I lists the major products as of 1962, arranged in order of decreasing production down to an annual figure of 100,000 tons. This list includes only manufactured chemicals; materials which are mined and purified, such as NaCl and KCl, are not included. It is interesting to note that among the top 10 inorganic chemicals from the standpoint of tonnage, only sodium carbonate and phosphoric acid have liquid waste problems of significance.

Multiproduct plants are common in the industry, sometimes by the nature of the process, and sometimes because of utilization of by-product streams which would otherwise be wasted. A plant producing chlorine by electrolysis of salt brine also produces sodium hydroxide in a fixed ratio.

A soda ash plant may advantageously operate in conjunction with a calcium products plant to utilize calcium values in the side streams.

Inorganic-organic industry combinations are frequent; such halogenated hydrocarbons as tetrachloroethane, and metallo-organic compounds like sodium methylate and chromium carbonyl are produced by the same plants that make inorganics.

TABLE I

PRODUCTION OF INORGANIC CHEMICALS
IN THE UNITED STATES, 1962

Product	Millions of tons
Sulfuric acid	19.12
Ammonia	5.78
Sodium carbonate (soda ash, including trona)	5.59
Sodium hydroxide (caustic soda)	5.46
Chlorine	5.14
Nitric acid	3.64
Ammonium nitrate	3.45
Phosphoric acid	2.41
Oxygen	1.54
Ammonium sulfate	1.09
Calcium carbide	1.08
Hydrochloric acid	1.06
Carbon dioxide	1.03
Aluminum sulfate	0.92
Nitrogen solutions	0.90
Sodium sulfate	0.88
Sodium tripolyphosphate	0.77
Sodium silicate	0.55
Titanium dioxide	0.52
Phosphorus	0.45
Calcium phosphate	0.25
Hydrofluoric acid	0.13
Sodium bichromate	0.13
Potassium hydroxide	0.12
Sodium metal	0.12
Sodium chlorate	0.11

Taken from Current Industrial Reports, U. S. Dept. of Commerce, "Inorganic Chemicals and Gases," Summary for 1962, March 27, 1963.

The availability of additional raw material over and above that required for a particular product leads to consideration of other products that could be made from the same source. In one plant, a large supply of salt and limestone led to the complex: soda ash, sodium bichromate, and chromic acid from incremental soda ash; cement from additional lime-stone; chlorine and caustic from incremental salt; pure calcium products from soda ash side streams; a variety of chlorinated products from in-cremental chlorine; several sodium silicate compounds from soda ash; and coke with coke by-products from a coke plant to supply the soda ash operation.

RAW MATERIALS

The inorganic chemical industry relies to a great extent on naturally occurring elements and compounds for its raw materials. Salt deposits of high purity are found in numerous locations in the United States. With salt as a starting.material, sodium carbonate is obtained by the ammonia-soda process; sodium hydroxide and chlorine by electrolysis. Salt may be mined by either dry or wet mining; in the latter, water is pumped down into salt deposits of high purity and the concentrated brine forced to the surface. Some salt is made by evaporation of sea water in ponds along the west coast of the United States.

Natural deposits are the main source of sulfur in the United States. In the Frasch process, used to mine sulfur, superheated water pumped into the deposit melts the sulfur, which is then forced to the surface and allowed to solidify. The major portion of sulfuric acid is made with sulfur as a beginning material. Minor portions are produced by recovery or regeneration of spent acids, burning of iron pyrites, roasting of sulfide ores in metallurgical operations, and oxidation of hydrogen sulfide recovered from gas processing. From sulfuric acid, numerous sulfate compounds, both organic and inorganic, are obtained by a variety of processes.

The atmosphere furnishes oxygen and nitrogen by the fractionation of liquid air. Originally used primarily in cutting and welding operations, oxygen is increasingly used in the chemical industry as a tonnage chemi-cal. Oxygen plants located adjacent to chemical plants are common. Nitrogen is used in the catalytic synthesis of ammonia and hence in-directly in the manufacture of numerous ammonium compounds, includ-ing fertilizers. Another major use is in the manufacture of nitric acid by a catalytic vapor phase reaction.

Phosphate rock is obtained from deposits in Florida, Tennessee, and the western states. Appropriate processing yields phosphoric acid and various phosphate compounds. Primary applications are in fertilizers, soaps, and detergents.

Many inorganic chemicals are found in natural deposits, requiring only refining and purification. Trona is a naturally occurring mixture of sodium carbonate and bicarbonate found in California and Wyoming. This mixture is purified and calcined to produce sodium carbonate. Potassium compounds are becoming important commercially because of fertilizer demands. The well-known Searles Lake operation has been a source of potassium chloride for many years; other sources are sylvinite deposits in the southwestern United States and more recently opened deposits in Saskatchewan. Sylvinite (42.7% KCl, 56.6% NaCl) is mined, dissolved, and the KCl separated by fractional crystallization or flotation. From KCl, a number of potassium compounds are made. Production of potassium salts in 1960 amounted to 2,638,000 tons of K_2O equivalent.

WASTE CHARACTERISTICS

An outstanding characteristic of wastes from inorganic chemical manufacture is their variability. As has been pointed out above, a particular product may be manufactured by completely different processes using completely different raw materials. This situation usually gives rise to dissimilar effluents from the manufacturing plants. The dissimilarity involves differences in either waste composition or concentration. Waste components in the industry cover a wide range and normally contain raw materials, intermediates, and products, as well as processing chemicals. Concentrations cover a wide range, from almost zero to saturated solutions, and suspensions or slurries. A large production capacity does not indicate a large waste problem, because many of the tonnage chemicals produced do not have an appreciable liquid waste. On the other hand, tonnage production which does involve a waste problem may give rise to such quantities of waste that the volume itself becomes troublesome, as in the production of soda ash.

BIOLOGICAL INACTIVITY

In general, wastes from inorganic chemical manufacture are themselves inorganic. As such, they are not amenable to biological degradation as a general approach to effluent treatment. Anions such as chlorides, sulfates, and phosphates, together with typical cations such as sodium, potassium, calcium, and magnesium are most often dealt with by chemical rather than biological processes.

ANIONS

Chloride is an example of a troublesome inorganic waste. Sodium chloride, a typical compound, is not biologically degradable, cannot be destroyed by aeration or a combination of aeration and natural processes, does not break down in the stream, and can be precipitated only with a few expensive reagents such as silver and platinum salts. Chlorides are common in the inorganic plant effluent, but are not economical to recover. Sodium chloride can be purchased more cheaply than it can be recovered from even concentrated mixtures, hence recovery is not practiced. The only practical technique for handling chloride effluents is dilution, by impoundment and regulated discharge to the stream. Discharge rate is determined by measurement of stream flow and an agreed-upon maximum chloride concentration in the stream.

In addition to chloride, the sulfate, nitrate, phosphate, carbonate, and hydroxide anions are ordinary components of inorganic effluents. Mixtures are common, and concentrations cover a wide range.

Cations

The most common cations found in inorganic effluents are sodium, calcium, potassium, ammonium, iron, and magnesium. In addition, the presence of chromium, zinc, copper, nickel, cadmium, and other heavy metals is often noted; these cations are discussed in the chapter on Metal Finishing Products. Mixtures and wide concentration ranges may be expected.

Effects on Receiving Stream

The usual sanitary engineering parameters of dissolved oxygen, biochemical oxygen demand, and oxygen depletion in the stream have little or no significance when considering inorganic effluents. Aside from a few oxygen carriers such as nitrates, oxygen levels are not affected directly by inorganics. Occasionally, natural metabolic processes of the stream biota may be halted by inorganics of sufficient concentration, through actual sterilization of the stream. Inorganic effluents must be studied from the standpoint of cationic and anionic constituents, with consideration of the chemical characteristics of each ion.

Some components of the inorganic effluents may be toxic, depending on the material and concentration. Reference to literature data on toxicity and conferences with regulatory agencies are in order when toxicity is suspected. In particular cases, bioassays are necessary to establish toxicity levels. Fortunately, inorganic toxicity has been reasonably well evaluated and the critical materials are fairly well known, although existing data may be contradictory as to concentration levels toxic to aquatic life. A complete discussion of toxicity is beyond the scope of this book, but the waste engineer must recognize a possible problem with some inorganic materials.

Taste and odor comprise another area which must be approached cautiously, especially where a high concentration level or proximity to water treatment plants is involved. Taste is the important aspect; inorganics generally do not present an odor problem. Literature and regulatory agency limitations provide the best guidance. Taste mechanisms are not yet well understood; reactions of individuals vary widely to a given concentration of specific material. Regulatory limits for taste-producing substahces are usually based on an average reaction, with a safety factor sometimes included. Among inorganics, chlorides have been singled out for attention in establishing taste limits. Several agencies have set 250 mg/liter as the maximum stream concentration permissible.

Other effects on receiving streams which must be considered in dealing with a specific inorganic effluent are hardness, concentration, corrosion, chemical reaction, solids, and color. Each effluent must be considered in the light of regulatory requirements, economics, and general feasibility of treatment.

WASTE DISPOSAL TECHNIQUES

Ideally, the problem of waste disposal should be considered an integral part of the manufacturing process. Engineers expend considerable effort on consideration of alternatives in process design in terms of equipment or process steps. As finally evolved, the design should represent the optimum balance between equipment selection and economic process alternatives. Too often, no attention may be given to the problem of waste disposal until this point; or it may even wait until the plant is under construction. Occasionally, the expertly designed plant is found to have resulted in a waste which is either untreatable or treatable only at considerable expense. The burden added by waste treatment then may affect the over-all economics of the process and, in the extreme, may preclude any possible profit from the operation.

Proper consideration should be given to waste disposal during the design phase, in order that the lowest over-all manufacturing cost can be achieved. This can be accomplished primarily by adequate communication between the design engineer and the waste control engineer, from the beginning of the project.

STREAM REQUIREMENTS

The obvious first step in a proper waste control program is to establish the conditions that must be met in the receiving stream. This can be done by conferences with regulatory agency personnel or by reference to published regulations and requirements where these are available. Beyond this, the waste control engineer may aim for concentration levels which his experience indicates are reasonable and practically attainable. In addition to the legal requirements, attention must be given to the moral aspects of waste discharge. These considerations are part of being a "good neighbor" in the community; when properly evaluated and dealt with, good waste control makes future public relations much easier.

Attention should also be given to probable trends in requirements, and allowances made for changes in permissible levels of contaminants in the stream.

Having established the conditions that must be met, the engineer is now ready to consider means of achieving these levels. In the new project design stage, experience and the ability to visualize and solve difficulties are the waste engineer's best assets. In the already existing plant, ingenuity must be exercised to solve problems within the confines of the operating installation.

IN-PLANT PROCEDURES AND CONTROL

Money spent on waste treatment is usually not revenue-producing capital; and the burden imposed, in both investment and operating costs, must be borne by the general process economics. Any reduction in the amount of waste to be treated or in the complexity of the treatment process yields direct benefits in the form of cost reduction, and therefore enhances the over-all profit possibilities of the product.

Reduction in the amount of waste to be treated can be accomplished in several ways. Possibilities range from control of incidental spillage to a major change, such as the addition of a by-product recovery plant. On a new project, proper consideration of waste treatment presumes that the question of by-product recovery has already been answered; in an existing plant such a major change must be evaluated on its economic merits. In evaluation, the feasibility considerations must extend to sales and distribution problems. The new product should be compatible with the company's present line and all costs of by-product utilization compared with all costs of waste treatment. Because of the nature of the inorganic chemical industry, many opportunities exist for alternative processes or raw materials.

Water Reuse. In complex chemical processes, opportunities exist for utilization of slightly contaminated streams in less critical portions of the process. Such reuse decreases the total over-all liquid throughput and hence the volume to be finally treated. Inorganic values in these contaminated process streams may sometimes be utilized. In one plant producing sodium silicate, the entire waste stream was used as process makeup water; this completely eliminated the pollution problem, in addition to recovering all silicate values.

One possibility of water reuse is the application of closed-cycle cooling systems. Cost of the necessary facilities and the effect of concentration buildup through reuse must be balanced against the cost of once-through water. No generalized recommendation can be given; specific circumstances determine the best course for each plant.

Good Housekeeping. A substantial reduction in waste load can be accomplished through the collective contributions of a number of minor improvements in operation. Leaks in equipment, spillage, sewering of residues left in batch equipment, floor washdown, tank overflows, and general sloppy operation of a process can measurably increase the waste load. Elimination of these factors can be accomplished solely by a cooperative attitude on the part of equipment operators and never-ending vigilance on the part of supervision. Proper equipment maintenance, of course, is a necessity, as is proper education of operators. Minor additions, such as drip collectors or float controls for tank levels are helpful.

Waste Segregation. Inorganic pollutants are more easily treated in concentrated solutions. Occasionally, two wastes may be segregated because one is more easily treated than the combination of the two. Where one waste component may be much worse in pollutional characteristics than others, it may be segregated and treated at the source in small volume, rather than attempting treatment of the entire plant waste volume.

Waste Blending. Often, the opposite approach is indicated—blending wastes to take advantage of self-neutralization or to achieve dilution of a troublesome component. Possible synergistic or antagonistic effects of various components must be taken into account in blending. The decision to segregate or to blend is determined by specific waste characteristics. In general, waste streams are initially segregated and kept segregated as long as high concentration and ease of treatment is an advantage. The various waste streams should be blended to achieve dilution when the advantages of segregation have been exhausted.

CHEMICAL TECHNIQUES

After application of proper design and pretreatment techniques have reduced the waste load as much as possible, there remains an irreducible residue which must be treated. As pointed out previously, there is no general approach to treatment in the inorganic chemical industry. The waste engineer has available to him a number of chemical and physical techniques for treatment, reviewed briefly below. Proper utilization of these techniques should result in an acceptable plant effluent.

Neutralization. Regulatory agency requirements for pH normally range between 5.5 and 8.5, with more restrictive limits for particular streams. Many compounds can be used for pH adjustment. Most can be eliminated on the basis of cost or practicality, leaving relatively few in common usage. Selection of an alkali or an acid for pH adjustment is based on cost and availability, reaction rate, sludge production, and ease of application. Where neutralization is accompanied by precipitation, difficulties encountered in separation and disposal of the solids must be considered. Alkalies commonly in use are caustic soda, soda ash, lime, and limestone. Use of each of these must be evaluated in the circumstances of the specific waste.

Similarly, many acids could be used, but the most common are sulfuric and hydrochloric. Carbon dioxide can be used where the pH change required is not too great. As flue gas, this is probably the cheapest acid value available; it is used by bubbling the gas through the solution or by contact in a spray tower.

Where several waste streams varying in pH are concerned, or where the plant effluent swings frequently from acid to alkaline, equalization basins can be used advantageously, thus eliminating some of the chemical cost involved in neutralization.

Precipitation. Inorganic wastes frequently lend themselves to precipitation as a method of treatment. This may be accomplished by appropriate mixing of streams or by selection of a suitable precipitant. The one requirement is that the end product be insoluble or of such limited solubility that the polluting component is sufficiently removed to meet stream requirements. Consideration could be given to recovery of the precipitate as a by-product, but usually the material is not sufficiently valuable to justify separation and recovery. The waste engineer must also recognize the problem involved in solids separation and disposal. Large land areas are required for solids disposal if the precipitate is bulky. Attention should be paid to the residues from the reagents added, as these could be more pollutional in character than the original component. With the numerous relatively insoluble substances found in inorganic chemistry, both precipitation as a method of treatment and specific precipitants for a given component are dictated by the circumstances of each plant.

Oxidation-Reduction. Oxidation and reduction processes are less common in the inorganic chemical manufacturing industry than in other inorganic industries such as metal finishing. However, these processes should not be overlooked where they are applicable. Common oxidizing agents are atmospheric or manufactured oxygen, ozone, chlorine, hypochlorites, and occasionally permanganates, chromates, and nitrates.

Reducing agents are even less commonly used in the inorganic field. One application is the reduction of hexavalent chromium from the manufacture of chromic acid and bichromates. This application is more common in metal finishing, and is discussed in the chapter dealing with that industry.

Miscellaneous. Inactivation of particular waste components by complexation with a chelating agent is possible but is usually considered too expensive as a general means of treatment. Calcium, magnesium, and other multibasic cations can be complexed with certain phosphates and organic sequestering agents. Such agents are expensive and find application only in special situations.

Ion exchange is a possibility where the waste material is fairly valuable and may be recovered. This technique is occasionally practiced on chromates, and copper, nickel, and other metal cations.

PHYSICAL TECHNIQUES

Physical treatment methods are generally less expensive than chemical treatment methods because the equipment is simple and no chemical additives are involved.

Flocculation. Finely divided solid materials are generally removed by flocculation and settling. Precipitates of ferric hydroxide, aluminum hydroxide, and silica have the property of forming large flocs of high surface area. These flocs tend to remove fine suspended particles both by adsorption and by mechanical sweeping action as they move through the solution. The long settling times associated with finely divided solids can be shortened appreciably by flocculation, and flocs may assist in removing colloids that otherwise would not settle at all. Basic requirements are time for floc formation and mild agitation for thorough mixing. Flocculator equipment is common and may be obtained from a number of suppliers.

Settling. Solids separation by settling, with or without flocculation, is common in the industry. Settling tanks are available from suppliers in a variety of designs, shapes, and sizes, or may be built at the site. Frequently, settling basins rather than tanks are used where volumes are large and settling rates low. In soda ash plants, the basins may cover several hundred acres. Sludge from the settling operation can be filtered for further concentration of solids or can be conducted through a shallow lagoon for additional dewatering and ultimate disposal.

Filtration. Filtration is frequently resorted to because of the crystalline nature of the solids encountered. Many types of filters are available; equipment choice is dictated by volume and nature of the solids. Plate-and-frame and leaf filters are commonly used in batch applications. For continuous operation, several types of rotary filters are available, featuring provision for washing, for cake removal by strings or by scraper, and frequently the use of vacuum. For materials difficult to filter, filter aids may be used. Other types of filters include sand filters, hay filters, and plain screens.

Miscellaneous. If a plant effluent contains only few components, evaporation and fractional crystallization are sometimes utilized to recover valuable materials. However, this is not frequent; in fact, economics is usually against this procedure. Even with multiple effects, evaporation is a relatively expensive operation, particularly where dilute concentrations are being handled. Where evaporation is practiced, it is sometimes difficult to distinguish whether it is a by-product recovery process or a waste treatment process.

Solvent extraction is a possible treatment operation, but it is much more frequent in organic manufacture than in inorganic. The cost of solvents other than water usually precludes extensive use of this technique for inorganic wastes.

SOLIDS DISPOSAL

The wastes engineer must give attention to the problem of disposing of solid residues after filtration, settling, or clarification. Where large volumes of bulky solids are involved, solids disposal can be a greater problem in some respects than the original pollution characteristics of the component. A sufficient quantity of land must be available and must be so located that the disposal area does not become an eyesore. The amount of land necessary, of course, varies with the amount and characteristics of the solids. Allowance must be made for foreseeable future operations. Provision must be made for conveying or trucking to the site, unless the material is conveyed as a slurry which can be further dewatered at the site. Occasionally, solids separated during processing are stored; this occurs where the solids contain valuable materials uneconomic to extract by present technology but where a future breakthrough may make recovery attractive.

IMPOUNDMENT AND REGULATED DISCHARGE

Some materials such as chlorides are, by their very nature, not amenable to any practical sort of treatment. The only reasonable technique thus far devised for handling such wastes is impoundment, with regulated discharge to control the concentration in the receiving stream. This fact has been recognized by a number of regulatory agencies, including the Ohio River Valley Water Sanitation Commission (ORSANCO), and is in fact required by some agencies for chloride control. The impoundment basins are ordinarily sized to hold total plant waste output for a period of months. Discharge from these basins is regulated according to flow in the receiving stream. The waste discharge rate is adjusted so that some previously agreed upon concentration in the stream will not be exceeded. This practice not only keeps the concentration below a damaging level but also provides a relatively constant concentration, so downstream users of the stream do not have to cope with wide variations in contaminant level.

DILUTION

A very obvious and important means of disposal is by dilution. Where the receiving stream or body of water is large in relation to the waste flow, dilution of the waste can sometimes be achieved so that waste concentrations are negligible or at least reduced many times. Where untreatable wastes such as chlorides are involved, plant location next to large volumes of dilution water may eliminate an otherwise difficult pollution problem. Occasionally it may be desirable to combine waste flows with such relatively uncontaminated flows as cooling water in order to take advantage of dilution factors available.

DISPOSAL OF WASTES FROM SPECIFIC INDUSTRIES

SULFURIC ACID

From the standpoint of tonnage, sulfuric acid is the leading inorganic chemical. The major portion is made by the contact process, in which sulfur is burned to sulfur dioxide, purified if necessary, and a mixture of dry sulfur dioxide gas and air passed through a preheater and a reactor where it is catalytically oxidized to sulfur trioxide. After cooling, the gas is partially absorbed by oleum and finally scrubbed with a 97% acid. The products are oleum and 98% sulfuric acid. The process is such that no significant liquid wastes are formed and hence no water pollution problem is encountered. Air pollution problems may exist.

AMMONIA

The large production of ammonia results from its demand by the fertilizer industry as a source of fixed nitrogen. Ammonia may be applied to the land directly as liquid, in solution, or as an ammonium compound.

Ammonia is produced by the reaction of nitrogen and hydrogen gases in the presence of a nickel catalyst at high temperature and pressure. The principal sources of nitrogen and hydrogen are air and natural gas, although other raw materials are currently used. Where other special sources of synthesis gas are employed, operating conditions and catalysts are different. No stream pollution problems of any significance are encountered in the manufacture of ammonia.

SODIUM CARBONATE

The basic method used in the manufacture of sodium carbonate or soda ash is the ammonia-soda process perfected by Solvay. This method was first used commercially about 1870 and is still the most economical method of synthesizing the product. The chemistry involved is fairly complex, and is discussed in most elementary chemistry texts as a classic example of inorganic reaction. A detailed discussion of all aspects of the process has been presented by Hou (1). Raw materials for the process are salt, limestone, and coke; products and by-products are sodium carbonate, calcium chloride, and carbon dioxide. Carbon dioxide and ammonia are recycled, with the ammonia entering into a number of intermediate reactions. The process consists of the following chemical reactions:

$$NH_4OH + CO_2 \rightarrow NH_4HCO_3 \qquad (1)$$
$$NH_4HCO_3 + NaCl \rightarrow NaHCO_3 + NH_4Cl \qquad (2)$$
$$2NaHCO_3 \rightarrow Na_2CO_3 + CO_2 + H_2O \qquad (3)$$
$$2NH_4Cl + Ca(OH)_2 \rightarrow 2NH_3 + CaCl_2 + 2H_2O \qquad (4)$$

Initially, a strong sodium chloride solution is purified to remove calcium, magnesium, and other heavy metal ions. The brine is ammoniated and contacted with carbon dioxide in a carbonating tower. In the tower, reactions (1) and (2) occur, producing sodium bicarbonate and ammonium chloride. Because the bicarbonate has limited solubility in this solution, it crystallizes and is separated on vacuum filters. The bicarbonate is calcined in a sealed rotary kiln, where reaction (3) occurs, forming light soda ash which is cooled and stored. Carbon dioxide from the calciner is recycled to the carbonating tower; additional CO_2 is produced by burning lime and by combustion of carbon. The filtrate from bicarbonate separation is treated with lime in a free-ammonia still, causing reaction (4), and the ammonia is returned to the process. The calcium chloride formed and the unreacted sodium chloride and other solids are waste products.

A typical analysis of the waste stream called "distiller's waste" from a soda ash plant has been given by Hou (1):

Component	Concentration, g/liter
CaCl₂	85–95
NaCl	45–50
CaCO₃ *	6–15
CaSO₄ *	3–5
Mg(OH)₂ *	3–10
CaO	2–4
Fe₂O₃ and Al₂O₃ *	1–3
SiO₂ *	1–4
NH₃	0.006–0.012

The components marked by an asterisk are relatively insoluble and are removed from the waste stream before discharge.

Standard practice in the industry is to remove the solids by settling in large lagoons or waste lakes, several hundred acres in extent. Impounding on this large scale is expensive and can be troublesome, especially if land availability at the plant site is limited. During its life, a soda ash plant may require several waste lakes, with new areas opened as old ones are filled. When the solids are settled, the dissolved chloride problem remains. The ammonia-soda process is only about 75% efficient in terms of sodium, and uses none of the chloride present in the original brine. Production of 1 ton of soda ash results in about 1½ tons of soluble chlorides as waste. Typically, this quantity of chloride will be contained in about 2600 gal of liquid.

Since chlorides generally are soluble, do not break down, and are not subject to bacterial degradation, treatment possibilities are few. Part of the calcium chloride can be recovered from the waste by separation from the sodium chloride, although recovery is generally not economical at the low market price. In addition, market demand could absorb only a fraction of the calcium chloride available from soda ash production. The major use of calcium chloride is for ice and dust control on streets and roads; some minor uses have been found, as in concrete, but no processes or industries requiring substantial amounts of chloride have as yet developed. If all calcium chloride were recovered from the waste, one soda ash plant of medium size could supply the entire present demand.

A number of solutions to the soda ash waste problem have been investigated over a period of years. These include recovery of calcium chloride with separation and reuse of the accompanying sodium chloride, separation by means of ionic membranes, and alternative methods of manufacture. Despite years of intensive effort by the industry, none of these possibilities has found widespread use, because of economical or technical reasons. Thus far, the ammonia-soda process has resisted substitute methods of manufacture. Minor improvements in operating conditions and in equipment have been found and adopted, but have not resulted in significant improvement in the waste problem. In summary, there appears to be no alternative process that would produce a smaller volume and concentration of wastes and there appears to be no promising method of treatment of the waste produced.

The present method of handling such waste, practiced by all soda ash producers in the United States, is discharge to surface waters. Many of the plants originally built to produce soda ash were located on inland waters close to raw materials and markets. Later plants were established on or near oceans, where the effects of chloride discharges are negligible. No new plants have been constructed in the United States since 1935. Should further expansion occur, it would undoubtedly be on coastal waters.

The ideal solution to this problem, with present technology, is removal of solids in a waste lake and discharge of the effluent to salt or brackish water. However, discharge of soda ash waste to fresh water is not a major pollution problem where ample dilution water is available. For plants located on the headwaters of an inland river system, detention ponds and regulated discharge to correspond with watershed runoff patterns minimize the pollution effect. Even though this practice does not reduce the total amount of chloride waste reaching the stream, detrimental effects of chloride are reduced because of the lower and more uniform chloride levels achieved. ORSANCO, after thorough study of all factors, formulated a chloride control measure in 1958; this requires impoundment of waste containing significant chloride loads, with regulated discharge under the supervision of the appropriate State water pollution control agency. The regulation recognizes the lack of treatment methods for chloride waste, and utilizes dilution as the only practical course of action available. There is a possibility, however, that future scientific development in waste disposal or in related fields may provide improved methods of handling the industry's waste.

CHLORINE AND SODIUM HYDROXIDE

Chlorine and sodium hydroxide are produced as coproducts by the electrolysis of salt brine; hydrogen is also produced as a by-product Sodium chloride brine is treated to remove magnesium, calcium, heavy metal ions, and sulfate ions. The purified brine is introduced into a diaphragm or a mercury cell, where the decomposition occurs. Chlorine is formed in the anode compartment, and sodium hydroxide and hydrogen at the cathode. The chlorine is collected, dried in sulfuric acid drying towers, and compressed to form liquid chlorine. About half the salt is decomposed, yielding a solution containing 10–12% caustic soda and the undecomposed sodium chloride. This weak caustic solution is concentrated by evaporation to 50% sodium hydroxide, with salt recovery and recycle.

To avoid impurity buildup in the cell anolyte, some bleeding of recycle streams is practiced. Together with wastes from brine treating and cell room operation, these produce waste concentrations of minor significance when mixed with cooling water. Effluent from a high efficiency mercury cell plant will contain 6–12 lb of sodium hydroxide, 12–20 lb of sodium chloride, and 0.03–0.05 lb of mercury, dissolved in about 50,000 gal of water per ton of chlorine produced. With additional dilution in the stream, concentrations are not significant. Chlorine-caustic plants have never been considered to present a stream pollution problem. Occasionally, an impounding basin will be provided to equalize any variation in daily operations.

Nitric Acid

Nitric acid may be prepared by the catalytic oxidation of ammonia or by treating a nitrate salt with sulfuric acid. Most of the nitric acid is produced from ammonia. Anhydrous ammonia is mixed with air, heated, and reacted in the vapor phase in the presence of a platinum-rhodium catalyst under moderately high temperatures and pressures. The nitric oxide formed is cooled and absorbed in water to yield nitric acid. The effluent from the process is primarily cooling water and presents no significant pollution problem.

Phosphoric Acid

Phosphoric acid is made by treating phosphate rock with sulfuric acid or by burning elemental phosphorus produced in an electric or blast furnace. In the "wet process" method of manufacturing phosphoric acid, phosphate rock and sulfuric acid are mixed, and their reaction produces phosphoric acid and calcium sulfate. The calcium sulfate precipitate is filtered and washed to remove as much phosphoric acid as possible, and the filtrate is recycled to the process. The weak acid produced by the process is evaporated to concentrate it to about 50% phosphoric acid. During evaporation, gaseous fluorides are evolved and are collected by water scrubbing. The scrub water is treated with lime to precipitate the fluorides and to raise the pH. This is ordinarily done in combination with similar wastes in an integrated phosphate plant. Patton has reviewed the phosphate industry and discussed the treatment of waste from the manufacture of superphosphate, triple superphosphate, phosphoric acid, and other compounds made in an integrated phosphate complex (2).

AMMONIUM COMPOUNDS

A number of ammonium compounds are produced by treating ammonia with the corresponding acid, such as nitric acid or sulfuric acid to produce ammonium nitrate and ammonium sulfate. Most ammonium sulfate, however, is a by-product recovered from coke oven operations. No significant pollution problems are presented in the manufacture of these compounds *per se*, although problems do arise from other aspects of the operation, particularly in coke ovens.

OXYGEN

Commercial oxygen is produced by the liquefaction and subsequent fractionation of air. Nitrogen is produced as a coproduct and may be recovered or wasted. Additional fractionation and processing yields the rare gases argon, neon, helium, krypton, and xenon. With the low temperatures involved in the production of oxygen, liquid effluents are not a problem.

TRENDS IN THE INORGANIC CHEMICAL INDUSTRY

The inorganic chemical industry is made up of a large number of individual plants manufacturing individual products from specific raw materials, and bearing little relation to each other from the standpoint of waste treatment. In general, the products are made from raw materials that are mined for the purpose or from raw materials which are only one or two chemical steps from a naturally occurring deposit. The processes are old and well understood, and reflect the most economic utilization of materials found in nature. Until cheaper sources of raw materials are found, such as waste from other processes, it is unlikely that any of the present processes will be supplanted.

Growth in the industry generally follows the population increase, influenced by demand from a higher level of industrial development. In fact, the level of industrial development of a country can frequently be indicated by reference to the current per capita consumption of the leading inorganic chemicals. With these considerations, it is reasonable to conclude that the industry will grow slowly but steadily, with occasional spurts of production of a particular product to fill a specific need arising from new technology.

With the economic restrictions imposed on a highly competitive industry operating from naturally occurring raw materials, it is unlikely that any radical changes will occur. It is also unlikely that the characteristics of the waste produced will change, although some change in volume may be brought about by water reuse practices. Should regulatory requirements become more restrictive, the cost of additional treatment may force consideration of more advantageous locations or the substitution of new products. Hopefully, waste treatment research may develop new techniques which are less costly and which can be applied to this industry. In addition, work in other scientific fields may result in future breakthroughs applicable to the inorganic industry.

REFERENCES

1. Hou, T. P., "Manufacture of Soda," 2nd ed. Reinhold, New York, 1942.
2. Patton, V. D., *Ind. Water Wastes* 8, No. 3, 24–33 (May 1963).

Chapter 18

ORGANIC CHEMICALS

by C. FRED GURNHAM

The manufacture of organic chemicals is not a single industry, but a complex of many. In the research laboratories, over 500,000 different organic chemicals have been produced and identified. The number of these produced on an industrial scale, for commercial application, is at least in the hundreds. Obviously, there can be no simple characterization of the industry, nor of its wastewaters and their disposal; there is no such thing as a "typical" plant.

Closely related to organic chemical production is, of course, the inorganic chemical industry. Many companies produce in both areas, often in the same plants. The wastewater problems, however, are enough unlike to justify separate consideration. Raw materials for organic chemical manufacture come from several other industries, each of which has wastewater problems of its own. Of particular interest in this connection are the chapters on Starch and Starch Products, Fermentation Products, Coke and Gas, and Petroleum; other chapters also cover industries that supply raw materials. Products of the organic chemical industry are consumed in practically every type of manufacturing; the most significant end uses are described in this chapter.

THE INDUSTRY

Although the organic chemical industry cannot be characterized or typified, its history and its operations can be described broadly. The manufacture of a few specific organic chemicals is older than recorded history: alcohol, cellulose, sugar, natural dyes, tannins, and other crude or processed natural materials.

Synthetic organic chemicals, developed for chemical or process use rather than for food or clothing, are more recent. The manufacture of coal tar derivatives became a significant industry during the 1880's. During and following World War I, the synthetic organic chemical industry moved forward rapidly in the United States, first in imitation of the industry in Germany, then in a position of leadership.

The introduction of chemicals from petroleum and natural gas, in the 1920's, gave further impetus to the industry. Its growth has generally been continuous since that time. In fact, more than half the organic chemicals produced today were unknown 15 years ago except in the research laboratory.

RAW MATERIALS

Petroleum and natural gas have become the principal sources of raw material for synthetic organics. Crude products used for the production of chemicals (the so-called "petrochemicals") totaled 35.1 billion lb in 1963. Among the major chemicals present in these crudes are ethylene, propylene, butylenes, benzene, and toluene.

Coal tar, a coproduct of coke in the thermal degradation of coal, is second to petroleum but nevertheless a significant material for the manufacture of chemicals. During 1963, 672 million gal was produced. Many chemicals of industrial significance occur in coal tar; benzene, toluene, and naphthalene are probably the most useful. Benzene, for example, is used in the manufacture of mono- and dichlorobenzenes, aniline, maleic acid and anhydride, phenol, styrene, benzene hexachloride, dichloro-diphenyl-trichloro-ethane (DDT), detergents, and almost countless other commercial chemicals.

Some simple organic chemicals, widely used as intermediates for the manufacture of other products, are themselves obtained from basically inorganic sources. The most common example of this is the water gas reaction, in which carbon monoxide and hydrogen are combined to form methanol and smaller amounts of other organic chemicals. Only a few products are made in this manner, but it is a substantial segment of the organic chemical industry.

Considerable use is made of agricultural crops for organic chemical raw materials, but additional agricultural residues of little present value could be exploited further. Most agricultural products, even those of high chemical purity, are used for nonchemical purposes, cellulose as a textile or paper fiber; and fatty oils, starches, and sugar as foods. Chemical uses, however, are also significant: cellulose derivatives in plastics, synthetic fibers, and lacquers; oat hulls and corn cobs for furfural and nylon; and fatty oils for soaps, glycerine, and other derivatives. Many agricultural materials are subjected to fermentation (see the chapter on Fermentation Products), and the substances so obtained then serve as raw materials or intermediates for synthetic organic chemical manufacture.

END USES

Not many synthetic organic chemicals are used in recognizable form by the ultimate consumer. Among the few exceptions are automobile antifreeze and paint thinner. Some chemicals require only blending with other materials and packaging to prepare them for the retail market, such as synthetic detergents, gasoline antiknock compounds, and certain pharmaceuticals. More commonly, however, the chemicals undergo several transformations before they reach the public. In general, chemical manufacture is not a retail consumer industry.

The 1962 production of synthetic organic chemicals was 64.2 billion lb, and the 1963 production approached 70 billion. Among the larger subdivisions of this gross production, in 1962, were:

	billion lb
Intermediates (used in the manufacture of more advanced products)	11.4
Plastic materials and synthetic resins	9.0
Elastomers	3.2
Surface-active agents	1.9
Plasticizers	0.8
Pesticides and other organic agricultural chemicals	0.8

Other major end uses of synthetic organic chemicals include synthetic fibers, medicinal chemicals, antiknock agents, solvents, explosives (military and peacetime), dyes, and lubricating oil additives.

Production plants in organic chemical manufacture are of great diversity. Some producing units cover hundreds of acres and turn out thousands of tons of a single product per month. Others are small, manufacturing a multiplicity of products, but in quantities of only a few tons per year. Of course, many organic chemicals have annual production rates measured in pounds or even grams; these are manufactured in "production laboratories" rather than conventional plants, although some companies make so many such products that they comprise large-scale operations. Few, if any, organic chemical production facilities are alike in the scope and size of their operations and products; and the wastewaters of each plant are apt to be unique.

WASTE CHARACTERISTICS

Wastewaters from the manufacture of organic chemicals cannot be characterized any more than can the industry itself. As in all industries, the wastewaters usually contain trace or larger concentrations of all raw materials used in the plant, all intermediates produced during manufacture, all final products, coproducts, and by-products, and the auxiliary or processing chemicals employed. It is desirable, from the viewpoint of economics, that these substances not be lost, but some losses appear to be unavoidable.

In the study of an individual manufacturing plant, all of these possible pollutants should be known; and analysis of the wastewater should recognize any that may be of pollutional significance. It is not always necessary nor even desirable to evaluate each specific chemical; analytical methods have not been developed for some substances, the wastewater composition is often too complex to permit detailed analysis, and possible synergistic or antagonistic pollutional effects are overlooked in such a procedure. It is usually adequate to analyze the wastewater for broad chemical classes, such as aldehydes or hydrocarbons.

Analysis by compound or class of compound is useful in tracking down sources of pollution and in planning in-plant control of wastewater. However, for over-all pollution control, it is preferable to use the parameters familiar to pollution control agencies. These include the biochemical oxygen demand (BOD), chemical oxygen demand, color, turbidity, suspended solids, and similar tests; plus more specific tests necessitated by the particular waste, for example, toxicity, grease, and foaming characteristics.

It is of interest to compare and contrast wastewaters from the organic chemical industry with their municipal counterpart, sanitary sewage. Many of the pollutional characteristics are similar, including the common factor of volume or flow rate, and the analytical parameters of BOD, volatile solids, and other measures of organic loads. The pathogens and other microorganisms of sewage, however, are not characteristic of organic chemical wastes; and the possible toxic substances, foam producers, and other specific chemical pollutants are not normal constituents of sewage. Organic waste loadings are occasionally expressed in "population equivalents," based on units of 0.17 lb BOD discharged per capita per day; this is an unfortunate concept because it disregards other pollutional aspects and because the analysis for BOD in industrial wastes is not always straightforward.

Solubility. Many organic chemicals have limited solubility in water, and are classified, in the chemical handbooks, as "insoluble." Gross contamination of wastewater by such materials, either solid or liquid, can be removed by settling or floating, sometimes with the aid of coagulants. Many so-called "insoluble" organics, however, have serious pollutional characteristics even in the trace concentrations equivalent to the low solubility. Taste, color, and toxicity are among these objectionable qualities, which may be exhibited at concentrations well below 1 mg/liter.

Volatility. Some organic materials, including many used as solvents, have substantial vapor pressures and are easily volatilized. They may thus escape from the wastewater, reducing its over-all pollution, especially during any treatment involving aeration. Obviously, an air pollution problem may be caused by this practice; a decision must be made as to which form of pollution is less objectionable, or which form is more readily treated further.

ORGANIC LOAD

All organic wastes of course contain compounds of carbon, usually with hydrogen and oxygen, and often with nitrogen, sulfur, chlorine, phosphorus, and, indeed, any of the other chemical elements. Most organic wastes exhibit a significant BOD; noteworthy exceptions being organics that are relatively immune to biological degradation (such as some hydrocarbons and ethers), compounds that resist degradation until the available microorganisms have adapted or become acclimated to them, and toxic compounds that retard or even stop biological activity. Dilution, time, and acclimation of organisms may cause even these resistant or refractory substances to exert an oxygen demand.

The chemical oxygen demand test (COD) is frequently used to measure organic wastes, in place of the BOD, because it is not affected by materials toxic to microorganisms. Some classes of chemicals, however, resist chemical breakdown in the COD test. These are usually not the chemicals that resist the BOD test, and there is no general correlation between the two tests. Valuable empirical relationships can often be established, however, particularly in comparing wastes from a single plant or unit.

All organic compounds are "volatile" in the sense that they are evaporated or oxidized in the conventional muffle furnace test for "volatile materials." Determination of weight loss under 600°C conditions in an air atmosphere may be a useful adjunct to the BOD and COD tests in evaluation of gross organic load in an uncharacterized waste. The test can be applied to total residue on evaporation, to residue from a filtered sample, to suspended matter in the waste, or to any other fraction of significance.

Many organic compounds are soluble in solvents other than water. When they occur in a waterborne waste, either in solution or suspension, they can be extracted or dissolved by such solvents. Hexane and petroleum ether are used in this manner to determine "grease." Not all the materials commonly thought of as grease are completely dissolved, whereas some nongreases are dissolved; nevertheless, the test has a certain empirical value. In the absence of any better test for this general class of materials, which includes fats, oils, waxes, and similar substances and which is significant from a pollutional standpoint, the solvent test is accepted.

Chloroform is often employed as a solvent because of its specific dissolving power. In the carbon-chloroform extract test (CCE), which has value as a research tool, organic materials are adsorbed from the water or wastewater in a bed of carbon, and certain of these are extracted from the carbon by chloroform. Evaporation of the chloroform results in a weighable quantity of the impurity, and can be reported as a measure of the degree of pollution. Uncontrollable variations in carbon properties and in analytical procedure make this test of doubtful reproducibility, however. The material recovered can be subjected to further analysis and characterization by an experienced organic analyst; this is a more significant use of the test technique than is the gross quantity recovered.

Alcohol is a useful solvent for many organics, but because of its complete miscibility with water, it cannot be applied to wastewaters as a selective solvent. It is used, however, to dissolve certain components of the organics adsorbed on carbon. This is the carbon-alcohol extract (CAE) test, and differs from the CCE test in the classes of organic compounds selectively recovered.

As shown above, organic load can be measured by several different methods, no one of which provides a complete description. Each method yields unique information, often of value to the engineer, but none responds to all classes of organic compounds. Furthermore, correlation among the various methods is at best empirical and often nonexistent. It is possible to analyze a sample for its total carbon content, using a combustion technique; this is closest to a true indication of organic loading, but the equipment required is too expensive for most laboratories. The less absolute procedures already described will probably serve for a long time.

OTHER PARAMETERS

Organic loading, measured by the biochemical oxygen demand or other test, is the most frequently used indication of gross pollution. In wastewaters from organic chemical manufacture, other parameters of pollution are often of equal or greater significance.

Toxicity. Chemicals that exhibit toxic effects in the dilutions encountered in the receiving stream must be eliminated from the wastewater or, at least, reduced below a toxic concentration. Wastes from the pesticide industry are conspicuously in this category, which also includes organic cyanides, aldehydes, and many other classes. Toxicity to humans, of course, cannot be tolerated; toxicity to domestic and farm animals may be expensive, as well as improper, if blame for a killing can be established. Toxicity to fish and other aquatic life is of interest to the public, and has been a major factor in the demand for strict antipollution legislation. Many fish kills, even over extensive areas, result from natural causes; many more from municipal or agricultural pollution; however, industry is responsible on some occasions and is blamed by the public for most such occurrences.

Taste and Odor. In receiving streams that are subsequently used for potable water supplies, chemicals that cause taste and odor are highly undesirable. Certain organic chemicals, even in dilutions of several million to one, impart detectable and therefore objectionable tastes. Phenol, diphenyl ether, and certain other phenolic derivatives have long been recognized in this category; there are others less well understood. Synergistic effects on the production of tastes are common, and make the situation worse. Some tastes are readily removed by the usual processes of water purification; others, including phenolics, are destroyed only by special and more expensive treatment.

Froth. Surface-active chemicals discharged to streams result in unsightly froth formation on the water surface. Detergents are most commonly blamed for this pollution; many other chemicals possess the property to some degree. Many natural waters have frothing tendencies, but industrial and domestic wastewaters are frequently at fault if the frothing is excessive.

Refractory Materials. In the synthetic organic chemical industry, many chemicals are produced (and lost in wastewaters) that resist the normal self-purification processes of natural streams. Those processes include microbiological degradation, as the most significant, plus chemical oxidation, precipitation, and adsorption. To the extent that such resistant or refractory substances are also taste-producers, foamers, toxic materials, or other obvious pollutants, they extend the pollutional effect far downstream and sometimes into municipal or other water supplies. There is no universally accepted test or standard of refractoriness, usually considered as biodegradability, but this property must be taken into account in the evaluation of a waste.

General. Pollutional properties not unique to the organic chemical industry are nevertheless significant in this industry and must be provided for. These include high temperature, color, suspended solids, turbidity, oils, and grease (including solvents and other chemicals). The pH factor and its related parameters, acidity or alkalinity, are often significant. Specific inorganic chemicals may be present and important from the viewpoint of pollution; chlorides and compounds of nitrogen, sulfur, and phosphorus are most apt to be troublesome.

EFFECTS IN SEWERS

If municipal sewers and sewage treatment are available, and if the waste is acceptable in the sewerage system, organic chemical manufacturers generally prefer to dispose of their wastewaters in this manner rather than directly to a natural watercourse. Organic chemical wastes are often amenable to sewage treatment processes, and can be handled as part of the municipal wastewater. Major factors to be considered in evaluating this method of disposal are possible physical damage to the sewers or treatment plant, possible interference with the processes of sewage treatment, and possible ineffectiveness of the sewage treatment process in removing the industrial pollution.

Damage to Physical Plant. Wastes from some organic chemical manufacture, because of low pH, may be damaging to concrete and iron structures, including sewer conduits and plant equipment. This can be overcome by pretreatment, but must not be overlooked or neglected. Flammable wastes are a hazard in sewers, particularly insoluble floating liquids such as oils and solvents. These materials should be and usually are banned from municipal sewers. Excessive suspended solids, especially heavy materials such as sand, grit, carbon, and spent catalysts, can be troublesome in stopping sewers, depositing in manholes and wetwells, and overloading plant equipment. Such material can be removed by simple pretreatment.

Interference with Treatment. Effective treatment of municipal sewage can be interfered with by certain organic chemical industry wastes, if they are present in the sewage in excessive amount. High-temperature wastes, unless adequately diluted with sewage, cause convection currents in primary treatment units and reduce the efficiency of removal of sewage solids. Overloads of any kind, but especially high concentrations of organic matter, cause poor operation of secondary treatment units and of sludge digesters. The sewage treatment plant can, of course, be designed to handle heavy organic concentrations in a routine matter, although surges or shock loads are never welcome.

Toxic materials, inorganic or organic, affect the microorganisms that produce secondary treatment and sludge digestion, and may disrupt the entire treatment operation, often for extended periods. Neither the chemical waste nor the sanitary sewage receives proper treatment at such times. An occurrence of this sort, or the fear of one, makes municipal officials reluctant to admit chemical industry wastes to the sewers. Oily wastes, although not directly toxic, have a similar deleterious effect in that they blanket the microorganisms and retard or stop oxygen transfer and organic assimilation.

Refractory Wastes. Certain organic constituents of wastewaters have no effect on the sewage treatment plant or process, neither are they affected by the process. Such materials pass unchanged, except for dilution, through the sewerage system, and pass unchanged into the receiving watercourse. If they are undesirable stream constituents, the sewage treatment has not abated their pollutional effect, and discharge to the municipal sewer has not been a suitable disposal practice. Other chemicals may be partially destroyed by sewage treatment processes, but are still discharged in excessive concentrations in the plant effluent. Responsibility for stream pollution has perhaps been shifted to the municipality, which may, however, require that the manufacturer make more effective provision for destroying these refractory wastes.

WASTE TREATMENT AND DISPOSAL

The production of organic chemicals results in many types of contaminated wastewater, and disposal practices cover the range of known practical techniques. The primary goal is to get rid of these wastewaters, preferably away from the company premises; and to do so without damage to the receiving locale, which may be a natural stream, an underground formation, the ocean, or a municipal sewage treatment system. On occasion, disposal may involve permanent impoundment on company land.

A second goal, significant in the plans of industrial management, though of little importance to some individuals, is to accomplish satisfactory disposal at minimum cost and minimum inconvenience. In our type of civilization, this is a reasonable goal, although secondary to protection of the receiving environment.

The achieving of these goals requires the study, usually, of alternate disposal practices. Organic wastes, by their nature, can be destroyed completely and permanently by incineration; but this is almost never economical or practical for dilute organic wastes, and other, more acceptable methods must be explored.

IN-PLANT CONTROL

The first consideration in wastewater planning for an organic chemical plant, as for any industry, is the possible elimination or control of wastes at the points where they originate. This may be difficult, perhaps impossible; but it should be the first approach investigated.

Material Recovery. Substantially all organic chemical processes involve reactions that reach equilibrium or are otherwise stopped short of completion, leaving unreacted raw materials in the intermediate product. Recovery and reuse of these chemicals may be an operating economy as well as partial relief from the waste burden. As one example, the acylation of cellulose to cellulose acetate yields a waste aqueous solution of acetic acid; it is good chemical engineering economics as well as good wastewater control to concentrate and recover this chemical for reuse.

Organic reactions rarely yield the single, desired product; by-products and coproducts are inevitable, in addition to unreacted raw materials. If these have little value, they enter the plant waste stream and add to the problem of wastewater disposal. To the extent that such secondary products can be salvaged for use or market, the economy is twofold. In most industries, the marketing of by-products is difficult, because the sales area is quite foreign to the company's usual product line. However, this concept is well accepted in the organic chemical industry, where the over-all economy is largely based on the working and reworking of by-products into marketable chemicals.

Other In-plant Practices. The salvage of unreacted chemicals and the recovery of by-products are established practices in organic chemical manufacture. Other possibilities for waste reduction occur within the manufacturing process, many of which are in no way unique to this industry. Multiple reuse of water, control of spills and leaks, and general good housekeeping are widely practiced in the organic chemical industry, though they do require continuous surveillance and improvement.

Changes in manufacturing procedure are frequently possible, but are usually selected for improvement in product quality, increased product yield, or other manufacturing economy, rather than to abate pollution. However, an example of a related change has been the rather spectacular conversion of almost the whole synthetic detergent industry, within about a 2-year period, from the widely used "hard" alkylbenzenesulfonate type of detergent to a linear alkyl type that is biodegradable. Without affecting cleansing properties, adoption of the new compound changes the characteristics of household wastes so they are no longer resistant to sewage treatment processes and the natural processes of stream self-purification. The manufacturing process for the biodegradable detergents is more expensive than the earlier process, and the changeover was made solely to relieve the pollution problem.

PHYSICAL TREATMENT

The principal pollutional characteristics of organic chemical wastes relate to dissolved or colloidal constituents, not removable by simple physical or mechanical treatment. Nevertheless, sedimentation is commonly an early step in treatment in order to remove grit and other suspended solids that are inevitably present.

Floating oils, solvents, and liquid chemicals occur in most organic chemical wastes. They are removed by skimming, in either conventional settling tanks or specially designed equipment such as the oil separators of the petroleum industry. Flotation may be used to hasten the separation of oils and other floatable material. Salvage of the skimmed material may be possible, but usually this is not feasible and it is simply incinerated.

Centrifuging provides an accelerated form of settling, but is generally too expensive for use on raw wastes. It is employed to concentrate organic sludges and to dewater oily skimmings.

CHEMICAL TREATMENT

The wastewater contaminants peculiar to organic chemical manufacture are not, for the most part, amenable to removal by chemical means, in part because of their low concentrations. Chemical treatments are used, however, for the treatment of other, more general, contaminants.

Control of pH is often necessary, either for discharge to a watercourse or in preparation for further treatment such as biological processing. Oxidation, utilizing air, chlorine, ozone, or peroxides, is employed on specific organic wastes, such as phenols and cyanides, but is not of general application. Chemical oxidation, however, shows definite promise as a treatment technique if its cost can be reduced; this is under study.

Chemical coagulation, as a prelude to sedimentation, is used on organic chemical wastes. Colloidal and oily wastes, in particular, are benefited by this treatment. Adsorption, on carbon or cheaper but less effective adsorbents, is currently used for only a few specific wastes. It has greater potential as a water purification operation, but would be interesting in organic chemical waste treatment if it were less costly. Development of cheaper adsorption techniques and materials is under constant study.

Trace concentrations of certain highly pollutional organic wastes, from the detergent, pesticide, dyestuff, and medicinal chemical industries, are removable by adsorption.

BIOLOGICAL TREATMENT

The dominant characteristic of organic chemical industry wastewaters is, of course, their content of organic compounds. As pointed out earlier, these are not particularly amenable to physical and chemical treatments. Most such compounds, however, are metabolizable by microorganisms; hence, biological techniques are commonly used for treatment.

Biodegradability. Amenability to the processes of microorganism metabolism is referred to as biodegradability. This property is not precisely defined, and there is no single standard test for its measurement. Biodegradation is, however, the dominant mechanism in the removal of organic pollutants both in natural stream self-purification processes and in the accelerated processes of biological waste treatment.

In aerobic microorganism metabolism, a portion of the organic food material is oxidized, yielding energy required for growth and reproduction and giving off such nonpollutional end products as CO_2, H_2O, and $NO_3{}^-$ and $SO_4{}^=$ ions. Another portion of the food is converted into protoplasm, causing growth. This fraction is still organic and still presumably pollutional; but it is readily removed from the wastewater as sludge, living or dead. From 80 to 95% of the assimilable organic compounds introduced into a biological treatment unit can thus be removed from the wastewater.

All organic chemicals are not equally acceptable as food for the microorganisms; some are readily assimilated, others are refractory. A mixed culture of organisms, as occurs in sanitary sewage, possesses a remarkable capacity to adapt to strange or different organics and to assimilate and metabolize them. After an initial lag period, which may last for several days or weeks, almost any organic chemical can be consumed by the self-modified culture. For certain compounds, the removal rate may be too slow for practical utilization, but biological treatment is entirely feasible for most organic chemical wastes.

Hydrocarbons, ethers, and some compounds of high molecular weight are among the substances most resistant to biodegradation. Tertiary carbon compounds are resistant, and secondary more so than primary. This led to the detergent industry's substitution of linear or primary alkyl sulfonate structures for the earlier branched or secondary alkyls, making the product much less refractory.

Other correlations of chemical structure and biodegradability have been reported, but there are numerous exceptions and deviations from the rules. Acclimation of the organisms is of primary importance, and environmental parameters such as temperature and size and geometry of the unit also are significant. Until a specific chemical has been investigated experimentally, it is unwise to attempt to predict its biodegradability.

Treatment Techniques. The usual techniques for biological treatment of organic chemical wastewaters are activated sludge, the trickling filter, and lagoons or oxidation ponds. Multiple units or combinations of techniques are often used, especially for difficult wastes or to produce effluents of high quality. Shock loads and sudden changes in the environment are detrimental to any biological process, so waste equalization and temperature control are essential.

Pretreatment and Posttreatment. Biological treatment of organic chemical wastewaters is usually preceded by sedimentation or screening, to remove unnecessary overloads on the process. Chemical treatment is sometimes used for the removal of colloidal matter and for pH control. Equalization is desirable to level out the flow and concentration variations that exist in almost any raw wastewater.

Following biological treatment, final clarification is necessary to remove organic sludge. In the activated sludge process, some sludge is returned to the process, but a substantial quantity of the organic matter is removed from the system by the clarification process. In lagooning, separate sedimentation is not needed because the lagoon or oxidation pond serves for both bio-oxidation and settling.

DISPOSAL

Practically all the wastewaters of civilization, including municipal and industrial, eventually reach a natural watercourse, preferably after some degree of treatment. The logical and generally accepted philosophy of waste discharge has been that streams are the natural and inevitable transport means for waste removal, and that this is a proper use of the stream. It is proper only as long as waste discharge does not interfere with other reasonable stream uses, as by causing pollution. Wastewaters require treatment to the point that their presence, in diluted form, is no detriment to the other uses, most of which are granted a higher priority.

Starting in the early 1960's, the "public conscience" became more outspoken against any waste transport in stream waters. Interpreted literally, this would require absolute purity of all municipal and industrial effluents. The concept is impossible, except as a goal toward which civilization may strive. It is, nevertheless, a trend in public thinking. The organic chemical industry is particularly affected by this philosophy because some of its wastes have strongly pollutional properties, even in minute concentrations.

Regardless of which philosophy of stream use prevails, it is always industry's task to release its wastes with minimum effect on the environment. Contaminating constituents must be destroyed or removed as thoroughly as practical; thereafter, the dilutional value of the stream may, perhaps, be utilized. Treatment of wastewaters produces two materials: the purified water suitable for release, and a concentrate of the contaminants removed. The latter, too, requires disposal.

Effluent Disposal. The final clear water effluent, adequately prepared for release, may be discharged to a surface stream, to a municipal sewerage system, or underground. Discharge to surface waters is most common, and the effluent must then meet standards established by the State or other control agency. The organic chemical manufacturing industry must be particularly alert to possible discharges of excessive organic matter as measured by the BOD test, toxicity of specific chemicals, and other obvious pollutional effects such as color, odor, taste, or foam.

Many wastes from the organic chemical industry are treated jointly with municipal wastes, either by discharge into the city system or by accepting city wastes at the company waste treatment plant. Joint treatment offers advantages to the chemical manufacturer, in equalization and in secondary treatment. Where the municipality accepts the responsibility of treatment, any substantial contribution to the system is usually compensated for by fees or sewer charges. Some organic chemical wastes, such as flammable solvents, are not acceptable in city sewers, and the company must provide pretreatment or separate disposal to produce a satisfactory discharge.

The organic chemical industry is making increasing use of underground disposal systems, but usually only for its strong wastes, as described below.

Concentrate Disposal. In preparing a wastewater for release to the environment, impurities or concentrates are removed which themselves require disposal. These may be sludges, oily liquids, and concentrated liquids that were segregated from the main waste stream. Disposal of these concentrates becomes easier the more they are condensed in volume. Dewatering of sludges and of oily skimmings and evaporation of liquid concentrates are frequently used practices.

Incineration is an obvious concentration technique for organic wastes. Organic chemical waste incinerators must be designed to handle sludges and other solid and semisolid wastes, waste oils and other liquid chemicals, and oil-borne solids. Combustion gases from sulfur or chlorine compounds are often corrosive and may also cause air pollution unless special preventive measures are taken. The incinerators are provided with auxiliary heat, not needed when combustible oily wastes are being burned.

Certain chemical sludges can be partially destroyed and somewhat reduced in volume by anaerobic digestion. This is best accomplished in a mixture with domestic sewage sludge, in a joint treatment system.

After maximum volume reduction has been accomplished, the resulting ash, dewatered sludge, or other residue is usually disposed of on land. It has no value, but may be used as land fill; otherwise it is simply dumped. Nearby streams must be protected from leaching of undesirable residues. Chemical plants located on the coast sometimes barge their wastes and discharge them at sea; concentration is less important in this technique, as it affects only barge capacity.

Clear liquid wastes can be disposed of underground if suitable formations are available. The organic chemical industry is making increasing use of this practice. It is costly, so is used only for strong wastes that are difficult to treat for surface disposal. Strongly toxic wastes, as from pesticide production, are well suited to underground disposal in deep strata, where contamination of potable water aquifers is most unlikely. It should be kept in mind that underground contamination, in contrast to surface water pollution, is not remediable simply by discontinuing the flow of waste, but may require years for complete removal.

TRENDS

It is difficult to predict specific trends in so varied an industry as organic chemical manufacture. The industry is growing, both in total production and in the number of different products. Hundreds of new organic chemicals are put into commercial production each year.

There will probably be no abrupt change in the types of raw materials used for organic chemical manufacture, nor in the basic intermediates produced and used by the industry. Such compounds as methanol, acetaldehyde, phenol, chlorobenzene, and nitrobenzene will continue to be produced in large tonnages and to be consumed in the production of more complex organics.

Methods of recovery of chemicals now lost will continue to improve, with emphasis on salvage of unreacted raw materials and further utilization of by-products and coproducts. It is sound economics to convert such materials into marketable products, rather than to lose them to the waste stream or the incinerator. One such recovery possibility receiving study is the salvage of waste hydrogen chloride, produced in large quantities in chlorination reactions. Because there is little market for HCl as such, it will probably be reoxidized to elemental chlorine. Perhaps improved chlorination methods will be developed to use HCl directly as the chlorinating agent.

The outstanding trend in the organic chemical industry is the continuing introduction of new materials, useful in consumer products. The development of organic plastics and the large-scale substitution of these for other structural materials is one example. With this philosophy, the industry must continue to grow.

Chapter 19

METAL FINISHING PRODUCTS

by D. GARDNER FOULKE

The metal finishing industry is related to many industries; it cuts across and is part of the transportation (especially automotive), the electrical (appliance and electronic), the jewelry, and other industries. However, metal finishing waste treatment is but distantly related to the other industries discussed in this book; at least, the relationship is specific in that several problems may be common to other industries but they may differ greatly in importance with respect to the over-all waste treatment picture of each industry. Iron and steel are faced with the disposal of considerable amounts of pickle liquor containing much iron and acid, whereas metal finishing pickle solution is normally dilute and the rinses contain little acid or metal. Metal mining may have acids and cyanides with which to contend. Wastes from the chemical industry are so diverse that they must be related at times to those from a metal finishing plant, but such instances are rare. In general, metal finishing waste treatment, like most industrial waste treatment, includes precipitation and sedimentation; however, detoxication is a much greater problem and BOD need not be considered.

THE INDUSTRY

The metal finishing industry's rather broad ramifications may be broken down into three categories: cleaning and conversion coatings, organic coatings, and plating and anodizing. These various processes are a part of the production steps required for end products as diverse as satellites, electronic parts, oil well piping, automobile trim, and silverware. Cleaning and conversion coating processes are common pretreatments before the final finish, be it an organic schedule or a final plate.

The over-all industry is not organized into a single trade association because there are thousands of small job shops, a smaller number of large independent shops, and many captive metal finishing facilities oriented toward a specific end product such as the automobile. Consequently, it is difficult to obtain reliable data on the gross product or value added by manufacture. General Motors Corporation, in 1959, spent a billion dollars for metal finishing, cleaning, painting, plating, and related operations. In view of the tremendous increase in precious metal plating in recent years, it is believed that electroplating alone (including cleaning, anodizing, and conversion coating) may now approach a billion dollars per year, and that metal finishing is a multibillion dollar business.

Of the 15,000–20,000 metal finishing facilities in the United States, only a few produce a single finish. In job plating, nickel leads (22,000 tons, 1963), followed by copper (11,000 tons), with zinc, cadmium, silver, lead, and others following. It should be noted that tin led with 65,000 tons in the Free World during 1963, but most tin plating is done at steel mills and the waste becomes part of their problem.

Before the work pieces enter the plating bath, they must be properly cleaned and conditioned with intermediate rinses after each treatment. These rinses are the carriers of waste by "dragout" from the processing tanks as the work pieces are transferred from tank to tank, manually or by conveyor; on racks, in barrels or baskets for smaller parts, or by continuous drawing of wire and strip through cleaning, processing, and rinsing tanks. The organic finishing cycle is less complex, consisting only of cleaning, phosphating, or, less frequently, chromating with intermediate rinsing, drying, and painting.

WASTE CHARACTERISTICS

Metal finishing wastes, except for the organic finishing segment, are characterized by the fact that they have little effect on BOD. On the other hand, many waste materials, even in relatively small quantities, are toxic to aquatic and other life, including sewage treatment plant microorganisms.

Cleaning and conversion coating includes a diverse group of processes, ranging in pH from under 1 to almost 14, and including organism nutrients such as phosphate and toxic materials such as chromate ion and metal cations. At times, these wastes contain compounds of BOD significance, such as ketones, hydrocarbons, chlorinated hydrocarbons, and surfactants. Acid dips and cyanide preplate conditioners (in Europe, cyanide is used also in cleaners) are used in this group of operations.

Plating and anodizing baths may be acid or alkaline in nature, and always contain significant amounts of metal ions. They may contain toxic amounts of cyanide or chromic acid, small amounts of these being transferred to the rinsewaters as the work proceeds to its next processing step.

Organic finishing wastes consist of oils, thinners, and pigments that escape the area from water-wash spray booths and spillage.

Metal finishing wastes discharged to sewers may be harmful to sewer structure, hazardous to sanitary department employees, and toxic to treatment plant organisms. For these reasons stringent regulations have been set in Europe and are becoming more prevalent in the United States.

Sewer structures of concrete, steel, and even cast iron are attacked by acid wastes. Even neutral wastes high in sulfate content and less concentrated with respect to chelating agents may corrode concrete structures. Emulsified oils from cleaners may be released as free oils in sewers, and the scum formed builds up on the sewer walls, restricting flow.

The release of explosive solvents creates hazards for sanitary department employees. The presence of simple cyanides is always a danger but, fortunately, there have been relatively few fatalities from this cause.

The toxic effects of metal finishing wastes upon biological organisms responsible for the breakdown of organic materials contained in sewage, by both biological oxidation (aerobic) and sludge digestion (anaerobic), are well known. Cyanides in small amounts are toxic to aerobic organisms, although aerobic bacteria can be acclimated to cyanide and thereafter will feed upon it. However, slug amounts of cyanide are not tolerated, nor can the effect of associated metal ions be clearly predicted.

The information established by a number of workers, including the British Water Pollution Research Laboratories, the Benjamin Franklin Institute, and Michigan State University, indicating that aerobic bacteria can feed upon cyanide, is real but, in view of the many variables affecting sewage treatment, is no justification for the metal finisher to depend upon biological destruction of cyanide in his effluent.

The literature is controversial regarding the effect of chromate and heavy metals on biological treatment, but the fact remains that these compounds can be toxic. Consequently, close cooperation with engineers of the local sanitary district is necessary so that neither the metal finishing facility nor the sewage treatment plant is unduly imposed upon.

WASTE DISPOSAL

In-plant Waste Control

The metal finishing industry requires a plentiful supply of water because thorough rinsing between processing steps is essential. Dilute rinsewaters make up the bulk of metal finishing wastes. Serious domestic animal and fish kills have, however, resulted from accidental spillage or uncontrolled dumping of concentrated solutions. Concentrated solution treatment is only infrequently required and is not discussed here except for the statement that such solutions should be hauled away or specifically treated batchwise by processes adapted from the treatments used for rinse solution wastes.

Because rinse solutions contain relatively small amounts of harmful impurities, they are particularly amenable to treatment for reuse. That little progress has been made in this direction by the metal finishing industry is not an indictment of the industry; it simply indicates that the waste problem of the metal finishing industry, in common with all industry, is economic. As long as water is cheap, excessive water use will continue. On the other hand, the reluctance in some quarters to adopt good housekeeping practices and water conservation policies serves to increase the general waste load, although this load can be reduced at no increase in processing cost.

The day-to-day waste load consists of dragout from processing tanks into the rinsewaters. In many plating shops, spillage and leaks add appreciably to the waste load. Regular dumping of spent process tanks containing alkaline cleaners and acid dips constitutes another source of wastes. Acids and alkalies are generally emptied at the same time to provide mutual neutralization. Plating baths are rarely discarded; instead, they are rejuvenated by standard methods (carbon, chemical, and electrolytic treatment), although it is not uncommon to drain off a portion of an anodizing tank (chromic or sulfuric acid), an aluminum etch tank, or an electroless nickel tank, to reduce the buildup of undesirable bath impurities.

Economics dictates the solution of metal finishing wastewater problems to be threefold. Dilution by high water flow is applicable to fewer areas as each year passes; consequently it is not considered to merit discussion. Closed cycle operation is presently economical only in high-cost water regions and in areas controlled by strong legal restrictions. Batch or continuous treatment of wastes is the most common solution to the problem. Integrated treatment, wherein rinses are treated in the process line, is often economical but does not provide protection against accidental or intentional dumping of concentrated solutions.

Table I indicates the common types of metal finishing wastes. There are many others that are specific to a particular processing sequence, but they are so infrequent that their treatment must be engineered for the particular installation.

Regardless of the approach to the problem and the type of waste involved, good housekeeping practices, combined with enlightened engineering, results in saving of money and reduction of the waste load which must be handled by sewage treatment plants, and streams, lakes, and oceans.

Good Housekeeping and Engineering Practices. Each metal finishing shop should approach its waste disposal problem with two objectives in

TABLE I

CLASSIFICATION OF METAL FINISHING WASTES

Process	Impurities	Origin	Treatment
Cleaning and conversion coatings	Oil and grease	Cleaning	Grease separation
	Chlorinated solvents	Degreasing	Oil separation
	Hydrocarbon solvents	Diphase and other cleaning	Oil separation
	Alkalies: caustics, carbonates, silicates, and phosphates[a]	Cleaning and phosphating	Neutralization
	Acids: HCl, H_2SO_4, HNO_3, HF, H_3PO_4, and HOAc	Acid dips	Neutralization
	Sludge	Metal hydroxides, metal particles, and buffing compound residues	Sedimentation, filtration
	Chromates	Chromating solutions	Reduction, ion exchange
Organic finishing	Solvents	Lacquering	Oil separation
	Oils	Painting	Oil separation
	Sludge	Pigments	Sedimentation
Plating and anodizing	Metal ions: Cu, Ni, Zn, Cd, precious metals, etc.	Plating and anodizing	Precipitation and sedimentation, ion exchange
	Simple and complex cyanides	Plating solutions	Destruction by oxidation
	Chromates	Plating and anodizing	Reduction and precipitation, ion exchange

[a] Phosphates of iron, manganese, and zinc.

mind: conservation of water and elimination of all unnecessary waste. By these means, the third and primary objective, that the effluents meet local requirements, may be accomplished as economically as possible. Good housekeeping and conservation practice must be adhered to.

Rinse Tank Design. The rinse tank should be provided with a dam overflow at its entrance end, and the water should not enter at the top of the tank. Best design calls for water entering under pressure from a manifold at the bottom of the entrance side, or near the middle of long tanks; air may be added at the bottom of the exit end to give good mixing and to permit counterflow rinsing. Entrance and exit ends of the tank refer to the straight-through conveyor plating, i.e., to work travel rather than to water flow (Fig. 1.). The system must be properly designed so rinsewater will not be siphoned into the water mains should a drop in pressure occur.

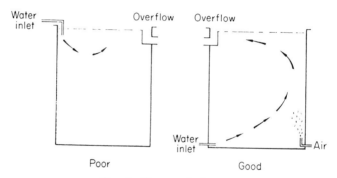

FIG. 1. Rinse tank design.

Reduction of Dragout. Work should be drained for a sufficient time before rinsing, either over the plating tank or in a separate dry reclaim tank. Synchronized fog or spray rinse nozzles should be installed at the exit of each plating tank and over the plating tank itself, so concentrated rinse drains back into the tank. This is particularly useful where plating tanks are operating at high temperature with substantial water loss by evaporation. Drip pans should be placed between tanks in such a way that solution draining from the work runs back into the tank from which the work emerged. Air blowoff is often additionally useful.

Reclaim Rinses. The first rinse, immediately after the plating tank, is finding increasing use as a reclaim rinse. This is a nonflowing or stagnant solution and is fed back into the plating tank from time to time. Such a system is most useful following heated processing tanks. Under certain conditions, as when process tanks are not heated, these solutions are sent to special reclaim units.

Design for Good Housekeeping. Piping and auxiliary equipment leaks should be controlled. Free-running hoses for rinsing should be eliminated by installing spring-actuated faucets at the working end. Racks should be well designed and maintained, and the work should be designed and racked so it will drain satisfactorily. This is a feature that is frequently overlooked by the plater, under the misapprehension that he is not to be concerned with design problems. The stylist must, of course, have a free hand in deciding how the part will look on the finished product. Construction of the part, however, is a problem that should be solved by joint efforts of the design engineer, tool engineer, and plater. Apart from the difficulty in plating certain contours produced by fabrication practices that fail to consider plating difficulties, design of the work is an additional way in which the plater can save money for his organization: for example, by advising a design that will help him rack the parts more efficiently to assure quality plating and satisfactory drainage of parts being plated.

Multiple Rinses. Multiple rinses should be used where possible. A 3-stage rinse can reduce water consumption greatly, and the use of parallel flow rinses (Fig. 2) can reduce water use considerably. Experiments carried out in 20-gal rinse tanks showed that the concentration curve for a single rinse tank (flow at 4.5 gpm) crossed a corresponding curve for the third tank of a 3-tank (0.03 gpm each) parallel rinse system after 6

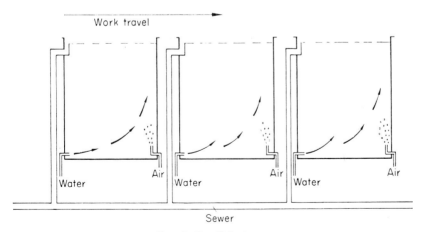

Fig. 2. Parallel rinses.

days. After providing a substantial margin of safety, by dumping each rinse tank every other day instead of after 5 or 6 days, the resulting saving was 2087 gal per day. A plant using 500,000 gal per day with a single rinse tank after each operation can operate on 17,000 gal per day with the 3-tank parallel rinse, and the waste can be handled by a smaller system whether the method be recovery or treatment. Water flow through parallel rinses depends upon the amount of dragout, which varies with concentration of constituents in the plating tank, size, shape, and number of parts processed per hour, and standards set for the effluent. N. Hanson, in a talk before the Chicago Electro-Platers' Institute in 1961, said that where a rack carrying 100 sq ft of work was rinsed each minute, the dragout would be 0.5 gpm. If the bath was a 13 oz/gal cyanide solution and the concentration of cyanide salt must be held below 0.005 oz/gal (39 mg/liter) in the rinse, 189 gpm of water would be needed for a single rinse, 3.7 gpm for a 2-rinse system, and only 1 gpm for a 3-tank rinse arrangement after the cyanide plating bath.

Where recovery of water and chemicals is planned, multiple countercurrent rinsing (Fig. 3) should be used, whereby rinse tank No. 3 flows into No. 2 and No. 2 into No. 1. The No. 1 tank may then be treated by ion exchange or by evaporation, and the purified water returned to the third rinse. A practice that is finding increased acceptance in the industry is control of the amount of water flowing into a rinse tank by determining the conductivity of the used rinsewater leaving the tank. When the concentration of plating solution that has been rinsed off rises to a predetermined level in the rinse tank, a conductivity cell in the effluent line causes the water supply valve to open, thus adding more fresh rinsewater. A typical plant that installed conductivity controllers for rinses

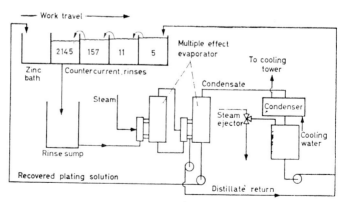

Fig. 3. Countercurrent rinses and multiple effect evaporation. Numerical values indicate cyanide content, expressed as mg/liter.

following gold, silver, cadmium, copper, and nickel plating and aluminum chromate conversion coatings on electronic parts reduced its plating room water consumption from 1,108,500 gal in a 3-month period to 733,-000 gal, representing a 34% water saving.

Leak Control. Every step possible should be taken to detect leaks from plating tanks and auxiliary equipment. In some installations, this is accomplished by elevating the tanks above floor level so leaks from the bottom of the tanks can be observed readily. In most modern plating plants, provision is made to place walls or curbs around the plating systems so accidental losses or leaks from the tanks or from the equipment are retained within the curbed area. This area may be drained to emergency storage tanks, but should never have drains connected directly to sewer systems. Leaks can occur into the plating tanks as well as out of them. Cooling coil leaks may provide an unsuspected cause for loss of concentrated plating solutions from the tank.

Heat Exchangers. The amount of cooling water circulated through heat exchangers should be maintained at a minimum by periodic cleaning of the heat exchanger, or by chemical water conditioning in a recycle water system. As far as possible, water used as a cooling medium through heat exchangers should be conserved for reuse, either as a cooling medium or as rinsewater in other portions of the plating system. The heat exchanger may be a source of leakage, either into or out of the plating system, depending on the cooling water pressure.

Steam Condensate. Steam condensate from heating plating systems should be considered as a source of pure water for solution makeup and rinsing. Sometimes it will be found, however, that contamination of steam used for power generation makes the water unfit for use because of its oil content. In many older installations, where boilers are operated considerably beyond capacity, it may be found that boiler water carry-over introduces chemicals into the condensate. These should be evaluated as to whether they have detrimental effect on the system.

WASTE TREATMENT

Cleaning is a necessary preliminary step to organic finishing or plating and to the application of conversion coatings. Conversion coatings often directly precede painting and sometimes precede plating when they are used as a pretreatment before fabrication, e.g., phosphate coating as a drawing lubricant. Many of these baths are alkaline in nature, which is one reason they have been grouped together.

Cleaning and Conversion Coatings. Cleaning solutions are used to emulsify fats and oils, to float off dirt, and, in general, to provide a chemically clean surface to which a final coating will adhere. Alkalies of many types are used, depending upon the basis metal being treated. Emulsion and two-phase cleaners, formulated with hydrocarbon solvents, are also used. Chlorinated solvents usually cause air pollution rather than water problems. Alkaline cleaning wastes are commonly segregated from acid wastes for piping reasons. They are mixed with other alkaline wastes, detoxicated if necessary, then blended with acid wastes for mutual neutralization.

Usually the alkaline cleaning operation is followed by an acid dip. Rinses following this step are mixed in the "acid sewer" with other acid wastes. In most plants, acid rinses exceed alkaline rinses in number; the dragout from each processing tank is roughly equal, hence acid wastes are in excess after self-neutralization. An inexpensive lime treatment can be used for final conditioning. Where only alkaline wastes are encountered, as in cleaning and etching aluminum, or when the alkali is in excess, wastes must be neutralized with acid, sulfuric acid being the cheapest.

Conversion treatment by the chromate process utilizes an acid bath, and the wastes join other acid wastes. Redox treatment is required as described under chromium plating. When the basis metal is entirely brass and heavy bright dipping is practiced, specific treatments of the spent baths may be advisable, as described in the chapter on Nonferrous Metals. When copper is removed or stripped in large amounts, as in the production of printed circuit boards, the rinses ordinarily join the acid waste system; the baths themselves should be regenerated and the copper removed.

Plating and Anodizing. Although the alkaline and acid wastes from cleaning rinse operations may almost neutralize each other, subsequent plating and anodizing processes add a considerable waste load of metallic compounds, toxic materials, and additional acids and alkalies. These acid and alkaline wastes should be segregated until their toxic constituents are transformed to a nontoxic form; then they can be brought together for mutual neutralization as far as possible.

Cyanide Plating. A number of methods for treating cyanide wastes have been proposed, but oxidation by alkaline hypochlorite or chlorine is the generally accepted procedure. This oxidation may be carried only to cyanate, or further to carbon dioxide and nitrogen, depending upon the requirements for discharge.

The chemical reactions of cyanide chlorination are as follows, the first showing oxidation to cyanate, the second complete destruction:

$$NaCN + 2NaOH + Cl_2 \rightarrow NaCNO + 2NaCl + H_2O \qquad (1)$$
$$2NaCNO + 4NaOH + 3Cl_2 \rightarrow 6NaCl + 2CO_2 + N_2 + 2H_2O \qquad (2)$$

The first reaction is rapid, being 80–90% complete in 2 minutes. By weight, 2.7 lb of chlorine and 3.1 lb of sodium hydroxide are theoretically required for each pound of cyanide as CN. The second reaction is slower, and an hour is usually allowed. The total chemicals theoretically required for the combined reactions are 6.8 lb of chlorine and 7.3 lb of sodium hydroxide per pound of cyanide. In practice it has been found that 8 lb of chlorine is required for each pound of cyanide.

In a typical automatic system, the pH is reduced to 5 and chlorine is injected, then the pH is raised to about 11.5 and another chlorine injection is made, which lowers the pH below 10. In such a sequence, all cyanogen chloride and cyanate are oxidized to nitrogen and carbon dioxide. In batch operation, if cyanates can be tolerated in the discharge, the pH is usually raised above 10 and chlorine is added. If cyanates must be destroyed, the pH is adjusted to 8.5 and a reaction time of at least an hour is provided with a 10% excess of oxidant present.

Ozonation. Ozone is a suitable oxidant for cyanide, the final product being substantially cyanate. The reaction is usually written as:

$$CN^- + O_3 \rightarrow CNO^- + O_2 \qquad (3)$$

The theoretical ozone requirement is 1.84 lb/lb of CN^-, but the actual consumption is only about 1.5 lb, implying some auto-oxidation. The following equation probably applies also to some degree:

$$3CN^- + O_3 \rightarrow 3CNO^- \qquad (4)$$

The theoretical ratio is 0.615 lb O_3/lb CN^-. Economic studies have shown that ozonation costs are apt to exceed chlorination costs. The cost of producing the ozone is an important factor; as this is reduced, ozonation becomes attractive. This method has been used by a number of plants and has the advantage of not building up chloride in the effluent waters.

Volatilization of hydrogen cyanide is not often used even though the molecular weight of HCN, 27, is approximately the same as that of air, 29, making for rapid dissipation of gaseous HCN. The pH of the waste is lowered to about 4.0, and a current of air or acid gases is injected into the solution. Where this method has been used for any considerable amount of cyanide, the exhaust gases have usually been blown into the atmosphere through a high stack; in some plants, they have been recovered by absorption in caustic soda solution.

Conversion of cyanide has been effected by the addition of ferrous pickling waste. However, this method is not satisfactory for dilute effluents, and the ferriferrocyanide or Prussian Blue finally formed must be completely precipitated because of the danger of releasing cyanide to the stream in sunlight and because of the intense color of the colloid which is objectionable in the stream. Calcium polysulfide reacts with cyanide to form thiocyanate of low toxicity, but the polysulfide reagent must not in itself be in excess. Because control is not easy, this method is rarely used.

Electrolytic oxidation of cyanides has been suggested, but is of more theoretical than practical interest. Electrolytic treatment in the presence of chloride is claimed to be effective. Cyanide sludges and concentrated cyanide wastes have been burned in incinerators, using waste oil as fuel.

Chromium Plating. Hexavalent chromium, as chromic acid or chromates, occurs in wastes from chromium plating. In the hexavalent form, chromium is not precipitated or removed by simple treatment with alkali and increase in pH. The chromate ion must therefore be reduced to chromic ion (Cr^{3+}), which is amenable to precipitation by lime. Reducing agents commonly used are sulfur dioxide, soluble sulfites, or ferrous sulfate. The last adds to the sludge problem, and is used only if the plant has a plentiful supply of waste ferrous sulfate pickle liquor available. The more common procedure is to adjust the effluent pH to below 3 and to add gaseous sulfur dioxide, metered from steel cylinders or tank cars, or a solution of sodium sulfite or bisulfite of 50–100 gm/liter concentration, fed by gravity or a proportioning pump.

Typical equations for chromic acid reduction are:

$$2CrO_3 + 3Na_2SO_3 + 3H_2SO_4 \rightarrow Cr_2(SO_4)_3 + 3Na_2SO_4 + 3H_2O \qquad (5)$$
$$2CrO_3 + 3SO_2 \rightarrow Cr_2(SO_4)_3 \qquad (6)$$
$$2CrO_3 + 6FeSO_4 + 6H_2SO_4 \rightarrow Cr_2(SO_4)_3 + 3Fe_2(SO_4)_3 + 6H_2O \qquad (7)$$

Thus 1 lb of chromic acid (CrO_3) requires about 1.9 lb of sodium sulfite, almost 1 lb of SO_2, or 8.5 lb of ferrous sulfate as the heptahydrate. The actual requirement of reducing agent is as much as 25% greater than the theoretical, and a considerable quantity of sulfuric acid must be provided to maintain the pH below 3.

At one automobile trim and accessory plant, large quantities of chromic acid are reduced daily by use of flue gases containing sulfur dioxide, from the burning of soft coal. Electrolytic reduction has been studied but has not been used commercially.

The waste stream carrying reduced chromium normally contains acid dip effluents also, including H_2SO_4, HCl, or HNO_3, with small quantities of iron, zinc, or copper. This mixture is blended with the alkaline effluents, and the pH is adjusted to between 8 and 9 with lime, as required for neutralization and precipitation.

The batch treatment for cyanide and chromic acid must be controlled. This implies that laboratory analytical determinations should be made so the reagent can be fed accurately; or instrumentation should be installed to determine the condition of the effluents so the treatment chemicals can be fed automatically. The final effluent must be monitored so that it meets local regulations.

Integrated Waste Treatment. Toxic wastes, primarily chromic acid and cyanide, are the effluents most troublesome to the metal finisher. In many instances they can be handled at the source by integrating the waste treatment into the rinse system. This is done* by making the first rinse after the chromic acid or cyanide tank, or after a dragout rinse tank, serve as a treatment tank for destroying the cyanide or chromic acid. Advantages of this method are that the impurities are destroyed at the point of highest concentration, undiluted by other rinses, and that it is not necessary to control the amount of reagent carefully because any excess is eventually consumed and not wasted to the waterway. A disadvantage is that no provision is made for the treatment of concentrated solutions or accidental spills or leakages. This method is not satisfactory for chromate control when chromate conversions are needed subsequent to zinc and cadmium plating. Precipitation occurs in the reservoir tank, and sludge must be removed periodically.

Sludge. Coarse solids in the effluent steam from metal finishing shops, such as metal slivers, sand, and other polishing media, may be separated without difficulty. Sludges formed in the treatment process, on the other hand, are troublesome and need special attention. These are chemical precipitates and consist largely of hydrous oxides and salts of metal from iron acid dips, nickel plating baths, copper bright acid dips, aluminum etching and anodizing baths, chromium plating and anodizing baths, and copper, zinc, cadmium, and other metallic acid and treated cyanide baths. These so-called hydroxides exist in differing degrees of hydration, being highly hydrated and voluminous when freshly formed, but decreasing 75–80% in volume as they age under water.

The settling of sludge may sometimes be improved by coprecipitation of other sludges. Iron salts have been used for this purpose. At times, rel-

* U. S. Patent 2,725,314 (1955).

atively minor changes in operation conditions accelerate the settling of sludge, but such data must be obtained experimentally. Flocculating agents, including organic compounds of high molecular weight, are helpful in that sludge settling time is reduced although sludge volume remains about the same.

The settling of sludge is conducted in conventional sedimentation tanks of various designs, and the settled sludge is removed at an appropriate point, sometimes as a fairly compact material, but more often as a watery sludge. It is then usually deposited in sludge drying basins to dehydrate further, with ultimate disposal as a solid material into sinkholes, abandoned mine shafts, the ocean, or as land fill where this is permitted. It is seldom economically possible to recover metallic values in sludges. The handling and disposal of sludge is a major problem, which can be minimized by observing good housekeeping and engineering practices.

Water Reuse. The common goal in rinsewater reuse is to treat and recycle rinses carrying toxic materials, thus eliminating the need to discharge them to the sewer or waterway. Such installations are usually of the semiclosed circuit variety. Rinsewaters in certain instances have been made a part of the cooling water circulation system to provide a closed system; in other instances they have been fully treated by evaporation or ion exchange to provide a closed circuit system. With few exceptions, these methods of closed circuit operation have been used only for wastes requiring extensive treatment facilities, such as cyanides and chromic acid. Rinses from supporting process steps, as pickles and cleaners, have generally continued on an open circuit basis.

Where recycled plating rinses represent a considerable portion of the in-plant water use, it is necessary to treat these wastes before reuse. In a typical example of this approach, all wastes are segregated into separate sewers or waste lines:

Dilute acids with hexavalent chromium
Dilute alkalies with cyanide
Cooling water discharges, and dilute acids and alkalies without hexavalent chromium or cyanides
Concentrated acids with and without hexavalent chromium
Concentrated alkalies without cyanide
Concentrated alkalies with cyanide

The three concentrated waste streams are held in storage tanks and bled slowly into the corresponding dilute streams for treatment. Dilute cyanide and hexavalent chromium wastes are conducted to separate surge tanks to equalize the concentration and flow. Cyanide wastes are pumped through a chlorine injector to oxidation tanks. Combined chromate wastes are treated with sulfur dioxide, then flow by gravity to join the cooling waters and general wastes in a large neutralization basin. After adjustment of pH to the optimum for coagulation, the solutions flow to primary and then secondary clarification and finally to a reclaimed water sump. This water is returned to the plant through gravel pressure filters and zeolite softeners, via a proportional blending system that achieves any degree of softness desired. City water is demineralized for plating and phosphating solutions and final rinses.

Capital investment in one particular plant using the above water treatment facility was about $750,000; this plant now reuses over 70% of the water. In 1957, chemicals were used to treat dilute and concentrated wastes totaling almost 336 million gal, and to demineralize 7 million gal. The daily saving of city water in painting, porcelain, enameling, and plating departments under this system amounts to almost 750,000 gal. The decrease in city water consumption represents a saving of about $30,000 per year, after taking into account the cost of softening, filtering, chlorinating, and pumping the water back into the plant, approximately 5 cents per 1000 gal. The cost of city water is 21 cents per 1000 gal, which is relatively high.

The reclaimed water has the advantage of being softer (59 mg/liter $CaCO_3$) than the city water (395), but the total dissolved solids are about 1200 mg/liter, compared with 450 for the city water. The effect of higher total solids on end use and equipment is not fully known, but trouble attributable to reclaimed water has been slight. Bacterial growth encountered in the circulating systems is removed by chlorination. High pH of the circulated water caused several conversion coating problems, which were overcome by changing the treatment to yield a water of lower pH, in the range of 7.8 to 8.4.

Where water recovery is practiced, it is important that the proper sequence be used, such as the countercurrent system shown in Fig. 3. This method provides sufficiently clean water for the final rinse; and the first rinse after plating is high enough in metal values that recovery is economical. In one such installation, the 1–1½ gpm of water that flows through the 4-tank countercurrent rinse system is about 10 times the volume of plating solution (zinc cyanide) dragged out of the plating tank on the work. Cyanide analyses for each tank are shown in Fig. 3, and it is evident that a considerable concentration of zinc and cyanide occurs in the first rinse. The amount of water required for rinsing is less than 10% of that normally used, and amounts to only 0.05 gal of rinsewater per 8-hour shift per gal of plating solution. In another plant, in which a 4-tank countercurrent rinse system was substituted for a reclaim and two following rinses, water consumption was reduced from 900 to 75 gal per hour, a 95% saving.

Evaporation. Single stage and multistage evaporation have been used to recover process water and plating chemicals. Because of the high cost of equipment, this method is not normally applied to all rinsing operations. A schematic drawing of such an installation is shown in Fig. 3. In one plant, the overflow from a 4-compartment rinse tank goes to a holding tank and is fed into a double effect evaporator through a preheater. Condensate is returned to the rinse tanks. This provides a totally enclosed system for the rinsing operation after zinc plating. However, rinsewater following alkaline cleaners and acid pickles is not reused.

Ion Exchange. A typical application of ion exchange to the recovery of water and chemicals is used by an aircraft instrument manufacturer whose metal finishing operations include cadmium, chromium, copper, gold, nickel, silver, tin, and zinc plating; chromic and sulfuric anodizing; and surface treatments including chromate coating, phosphating, and blackening. Rinses following the cyanide plating tanks are treated to remove cyanide by oxidation; noncyanide alkaline rinses, acid rinses, and heavy metal rinses are neutralized, settled, and sent to the sewer. On the other hand, rinses containing chromic acid and chromates (anodizing, magnesium and aluminum chromating, chromium plating, bright dipping, and copper stripping baths) are countercurrent and the most concentrated tank of each series is conserved. The rinses are passed through a cation exchange resin, primarily to remove sodium ions but also to take out aluminum, magnesium, and copper. Chromate ion is then removed by two anion exchangers. The demineralized effluents are joined and returned to the rinse tanks for reuse. A third anion exchange column is used to treat well water for makeup to prevent buildup of sulfates and chlorides, which are detrimental to the chromium recovery system. The two anion resin beds are regenerated about every 10 weeks on a staggered schedule, and the chromic acid is reused in the chromic acid pickle. This provides a closed system for the rinsewaters that contain chromates only. The cation exchange resin column, if also used for chromic acid anodizing solutions, builds up in aluminum and other cations. These are normally reduced by bleeding off part of the bath to the sewer or treatment system.

Ion exchange treatment has been employed to provide closed circuit rinsing. A plant producing electronic parts, faced with the lack of a receiving stream, found it necessary to adopt what is essentially a closed system. In this plant, any effluent from the waste treatment process would have to be disposed of on land and would, therefore, drain into the underlying aquifer. Consequently, all toxic ions, including heavy metals, had to be reduced to a minimum. Originally, a demineralization system was set up to treat the raw well water which contained traces of H_2S (removed by chlorination) and 200 mg/liter of cations as $CaCO_3$, and all rinse waters. At present however, evaporation and other losses are made up by feed from a shallow well, containing only 17 mg/liter of cations. The plating operation includes nickel, copper, silver, gold, rhodium, and palladium. A 50 gpm demineralization plant removes all heavy metals by a cation exchange resin and cyanides and other anions are removed by anion exchange resin, yielding a rinsewater of excellent quality. Regeneration of the cation exchanger yields an acid solution of the metallic ions, which is delivered to a waste acid holding tank.

Early attempts to use ion exchange resins for removal of cyanides from effluents failed because of regeneration problems and fouling of the resin by hydroxides. Recently, in Europe, progress has been made by using two anion and one cation exchange columns in series. An effluent containing potassium copper cyanide passes first through an alkali resistant cation exchange resin which removes the cations, including some potassium and copper from $K_2Cu(CN)_3$, and forms free HCN. Some copper cyanide is precipitated in the resin bed. The effluent continues through a weakly basic anion resin which absorbs the remaining copper cyanide complex. The third column contains a strongly basic resin which removes the HCN. In regeneration, caustic solution is passed through column 3 and then through column 1, so the sodium cyanide formed removes the precipitated $Cu_2(CN)_2$. Ion exchange resins are also being used widely to recover soluble gold cyanides. This, of course, is much more attractive economically than the recovery of copper cyanides.

TRENDS

The direction metal finishing wastewater control will take in the near future will be dictated by economics, influenced by legal pressures. It has been suggested for a number of years that noncyanide solutions would do much toward solving the plating wastewater problem. The cost of substitute complexing materials and technical process problems have militated against rapid progress in this direction, but the trend is growing in strength.

The increase in chemical reduction, or electroless, plating has resulted in hardly a ripple as far as the plating industry is concerned, nor has this trend changed the general waste characteristics except to contribute to the BOD load slightly. Vacuum deposition has not yet become practical, and when it does, BOD and air pollution may become more significant for the industry.

The trend toward microminiaturization in electronics will minimize the wastewater control problem, but its effect upon the metal finishing industry, geared to about 22,000 tons of nickel compared to only 30 tons of gold (mostly electronic applications) will not be very significant.

The strongest pressure for change will be the result of the water supply problem as affected by the population and concomitant industrial explosion. As water becomes scarcer, there will be an increasing trend toward reuse of water by established or improved methods and procedures, because it will become possible to write off capital and operating expenses on the bases of reduction of water cost and chemical recovery. This trend has already begun in the plating industry for special cases, in that fully closed systems are now in operation on an economic basis. This points up that the real problem in the electroplating industry is economic rather than technical. It is heartening to note that industry is recognizing that pollution abatement is a necessary expense, and is moving in that direction which will preserve and protect our greatest of natural resources.

Chapter 20

PULP AND PAPER

by HARRY W. GEHM

The manufacture of pulp, paper, and paperboard, now the fifth largest industry in this country, has enjoyed a growth rate of about 35% over the last 10 years. Growth is now continuing at the rate of 5% annually. In 1962, more than 27 million tons of pulp and 37 million tons of paper and paperboard products were produced. At present, there are 851 mills in production, ranging in capacity from 5 tons to over 2000 tons daily, and well spread throughout the country. The southeastern and Gulf coast states account for the bulk of production because of the number of large pulp mills, but concentrations of the industry also exist in the northwest, central, north central, and New England states. A complete list of operating units can be found in "Lockwood's Directory of the Paper and Allied Trades" (2). Research and development in the fields of stream pollution control, waste treatment, and by-product production are carried on by the National Council for Stream Improvement, the Sulphite Pulp Manufacturers Research League, the University of Washington and other colleges, and individual companies.

The development of many new uses and products made from paper has been responsible for the rapid growth of the industry. New pulping and bleaching processes, as well as new adaptations of older ones, have contributed to filling increasing demands. This is particularly true of processes permitting the use of previously undesirable species of wood.

The most common types of pulp produced are kraft, sulfite, neutral sulfite, semichemical, and groundwood. In addition, soda, cold soda, chemi-groundwood, and other special pulps are made in limited quantities. Some textile fiber pulps such as flax, cotton, rag, and jute are made in relatively small quantities for use in specialty papers, and some paper is made from straw and bagasse. Most types of pulp produced can be bleached to various degrees of brightness for different uses. Kraft and sulfite pulps are bleached to a high degree to produce chemical cellulose, which consists almost entirely of alpha-cellulose.

Paper products can generally be classified under one of four major categories: fine papers, coarse papers, tissues, and specialties. Examples of fine papers are bond, book, mimeo, printing, writing, and white papers in general. Coarse papers include newsprint, common wrapping, and container boards, as well as building products. Tissues include most of the widely used thin papers such as utility tissues, glassine, and special wrapping papers. A few of the almost innumerable specialty papers are electrical insulating, cigarette, photographic, card stocks, and monetary papers.

EFFECT OF EFFLUENTS ON SURFACE WATERS

The major stream pollution problems arising from the discharge of spent process waters from pulp and paper making are caused by suspended matter and dissolved organic substances. The former are detrimental in that they can form bottom deposits in receiving streams; these are inimical to aquatic life, unsightly, and, on decomposition, odoriferous. Such deposits can also exert an appreciable demand for the dissolved oxygen contained in the overlying water. The discharge of highly dispersed solids such as fiber debris, filler, and coating materials can render a stream opalescent. Such opalescence, in addition to being unsightly, retards self-purification by limiting light penetration.

Dissolved solids such as are found in spent pulping liquors can have a variety of effects on streams. Some, such as wood sugars, deplete the dissolved oxygen and stimulate the growth of slime organisms, causing biological unbalance to occur. Others, such as lignins and tannins, cause discoloration; and some, such as resin acid soaps and mercaptans, in high concentration, are toxic to aquatic life. A critical review of the literature relating to the effect of pulp and papermill effluents on the aquatic environment was published by the National Council for Stream Improvement (3). Problems resulting from the normal discharge of inorganic compounds such as acids and alkalies are at present minor. Because the major difficulties resulting from the discharge of pulp and papermill wastewaters arise from organic matter, these effluents are generally classified as organic wastes.

EFFLUENT VOLUMES

Large quantities of water are employed in the production of pulp and paper products. Water is needed for grinding wood and as a carrying agent in chemical pulping and bleaching, as well as to bring chemicals and heat into contact with the raw material. It is employed as a pulp washing agent and as a "furnish" carrier in the paper machine system. In wood preparation it is employed as a conveying and washing agent and for hydraulic debarking. The quantity of water employed varies with the physical equipment of a particular mill, the processes employed, the product produced, and its availability. It is estimated that about 1800 billion gal. are used annually by the industry in the United States. Both surface water and groundwater supplies are employed, and most of the used water is returned to surface streams since loss through evaporation is generally less than 5% of the volume handled. Examples of the volume of effluent produced in relation to product manufactured are presented in Table I.

TABLE I

EFFLUENT VOLUMES FROM THE MANUFACTURE OF PULP
AND PAPER PRODUCTS

Process	Gal per ton
Pulp manufacture	
Kraft and soda pulps	15,000–35,000
Sulfite pulp	40,000–60,000
Semichemical pulp	30,000–40,000
Groundwood pulp	4,000–10,000
Deinked pulp	20,000–35,000
Pulp bleaching	
Kraft and soda pulp	15,000–60,000
Sulfite pulp	30,000–50,000
Neutral sulfite pulp	40,000–60,000
Paper manufacture	
White papers	20,000–40,000
Tissues	8,000–35,000
Kraft papers	2,000–10,000
Paperboard	2,000–15,000
Specialty papers	20,000–100,000

Distinct benefits are derived from reuse and for this reason it is widely practiced. These advantages are savings in heat, fiber, chemicals, and in water requirement itself. Where process water is treated to a high degree, the latter saving can be substantial. Resulting reduction in effluent volume can reduce substantially the size of effluent treatment structures required. Reuse, however, can reach the point where further recycling leads to detrimental conditions in the mill and its operation. Examples of such difficulties are increased rates of corrosion, foaming, freeness and sheet formation troubles, felt plugging, and product quality deterioration. Hence the necessity for and the values accruing from water reuse are dependent on many variables that must be carefully weighed. In most instances the practicability of any specific reuse can be determined only by trial and error.

CHARACTER OF EFFLUENTS

Wood Preparation Effluents. These waters result from transporting, washing, and debarking wood, and contain both coarse and fine particles of bark, wood slivers, and silt. In addition, some dissolved solids are contained in them from sap washed from the wood. The concentration of these solids depends largely on the season in which the wood was cut and on the degree of water recirculation practiced.

Screening and Pulp Cleaning Waters. These contain wood debris, pulp, fines, and grit.

Mechanical Pulping Effluents. These waters result from the production of groundwood and defibrinated wood. They contain both fine and coarse wood debris, and solubles released on grinding or milling of the wood.

Mechanical-Chemical Pulping Effluents. These are similar to the effluents produced by mechanical pulping, with the addition of spent chemicals and added solubles released by treatment of the wood with caustic soda or sodium bisulfite prior to mechanical pulping. Cold soda and chemi-groundwood are examples of these pulps.

Chemical Pulping Wastes. Produced by the preparation of kraft, soda, sulfite, or semichemical pulps, these contain the spent liquor itself, with the exceptions of kraft and soda pulp production where the spent liquor is invariably recovered, and some other types of pulp production where heavy spent liquor is segregated for recovery, by-product production, or separate disposal. All such effluents are relatively low in suspended solids, the bulk of the impurities being in solution in the form of lignins, tannins, carbohydrates, salts of fatty acids, and other organics, as well as wood ash constituents and spent cooking chemical.

Textile Fiber Pulping Effluents. These consist of drainings and washwaters obtained from the cooking and washing of jute, rags, flax, cotton linters, rope, and similar materials. The cooking chemical is generally caustic in nature, and in some instances a scouring step employing detergents precedes cooking. The effluents produced contain impurities present in the raw materials, cooking chemicals, and products of cellulose hydrolysis.

Deinking Wastes. Deinked pulp is produced from used papers, which are cooked in caustic solutions containing dispersing agents, and are washed to remove inks, filler, and coating materials prior to bleaching. Filler and coating materials, inks, sizing, fine fibers, and hydrolysis products are contained in the effluent from such processes.

Paperboard Effluents. Some paperboards, insulating boards, and roofing felts are produced from used papers, pulp made by defibrinating wood in an attrition mill, or a combination of the two materials together with some virgin fiber. In most of these processes, the bulk of the losses is contained in the machine water, although in some the furnish is washed and thickened prior to delivery to the paper machine. Fillers, fine fibers, sizing, and coating materials are contained in the wastewaters from the used paper processes, and wood juices in those obtained from defibrinating wood.

Machine Waters. In general these contain mainly fiber fines and fillers, but may also contain a considerable amount of dissolved solids from sizing materials and special additives of both organic and inorganic materials. When operating on furnishes of pulps that have not been previously thoroughly washed, the machine water can contain a considerable amount of solubles carried with them from the pulping process.

Bleaching Wastes. All types of pulp can be bleached to improve brightness. Most of the bleaching chemicals employed are oxidizing agents, including chlorine, chlorine dioxide, hypochlorites, peroxides, and hydrosulfites. In bleaching most alkaline wood pulps, caustic soda is used to remove materials rendered extractable by the oxidizing agents. Each bleaching stage is followed by a washing step to remove extracted materials and spent chemicals. Bleaching washwaters are generally colored by the presence of lignins and tannins removed from the pulp; in addition, they contain a small amount of fiber fines and hydrolysis products. Type of pulp bleached, degree of bleaching, and process employed determine the pollution load carried by these effluents.

POLLUTION LOADS

Table II gives the pollution load carried by effluents from typical pulp and paper producing processes. Variations from mill to mill and even within the same mill can be considerable for a number of reasons. For example, wood harvested during different seasons contains variable amounts of solubles and the degree of cooking varies for the various grades of pulp produced. When fiber is reclaimed from salvaged materials, the effluent character depends to a large degree on the type of materials employed. The BOD produced varies almost directly with the pulp yield obtained from wood, as can be seen from Fig. 1, in which the total BOD appearing in the effluents is plotted against pulp yield without recovery of the spent pulping liquors. Efficient heat and chemical recovery systems, as employed in chemical pulp mills, can reduce these losses as much as 95%.

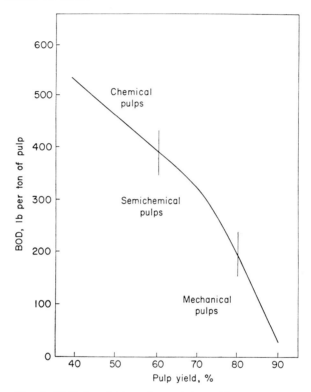

FIG. 1. BOD in solution after pulping without recovery.

SUSPENDED SOLIDS REDUCTION

The suspended matter present in pulp and paper mill wastes consists mainly of fiber, fiber debris, and filling and coating materials such as clays, calcium carbonate, and titanium dioxide. In most mills the bulk of these materials are captured from the machine waters by means of savealls and are returned to the system for reuse. Savealls are generally screening, filtration, settling, or flotation devices. Their efficiency depends upon the process employed and the nature of the solids they are expected to retain. Under some conditions, highly efficient devices of this kind can retain a sufficient quantity of the suspended solids content

TABLE II

EFFLUENT LOADS FROM PULP AND PAPER MANUFACTURE

	lb per ton of product	
Effluent	Suspended solids	5-day BOD
Kraft and soda pulp	20–30	25–50
Groundwood pulp	40–80	15–25
Sulfite pulp (no liquor recovery)	20–40	400–600
Neutral sulfite semichemical pulp	100–180	250–450
Textile fiber pulps	300–500	200–300
Straw pulp	400–500	400–500
Bleaching	6–35	12–200
Deinked pulp	500–800	100–130
Fine papers		
Tissue	50–100	15–30
Bond, mimeo, and printing	50–100	20–40
Glassine	10–15	15–25
Coarse papers		
Boxboard	50–70	20–40
Corrugating board	50–70	25–60
Kraft wrapping	15–25	5–15
Newsprint	20–60	10–20
Specialty papers		
Fiber	200–300	140–170
Asbestos	300–400	20–40
Roofing felt	50–100	40–60
Insulating board	50–100	150–250

of the effluents so that further removal is not necessary. However, in many other instances, further treatment is necessary and the solids so collected are not suitable for reuse but must be disposed of. This is particularly true for mills that reclaim the fiber from used paper, as only a part of such stock is reclaimable by deinking processes. In these the fiber is freed of ink, filler, sizing materials, and fiber fines, all of which are not reclaimable.

The most common means for treating solids-bearing wastes in the paper industry is sedimentation, although in some plants flotation and filtration are used. Circular mechanically cleaned clarifiers predominate as the type of settling unit employed, followed by reactor-type clarifiers, rectangular mechanically cleaned basins, and conical tanks without collector mechanisms. Some of these are equipped with influent deaerating devices to prevent floating fiber from accumulating on the surface. Most of them have skimmers and some have integral mechanical flocculators. A few mills employ earth-embanked alternating basins to remove suspended solids from their effluents. In instances where a greater fraction of the total suspended solids must be removed than will settle normally, coagulants such as alum, activated silica, and polyelectrolytes are used to render the nonsettleable solids settleable.

In general, sedimentation without the addition of coagulants removes 70–80% of the total suspended solids from paper mill effluents. This percentage can be lower when highly efficient savealls are employed in the mill or when dispersing agents are present. The percentage may be higher when sizing materials such as alum, which tend to coagulate the solids, are used in the papermaking process. Coagulants can produce a total suspended solids reduction in excess of 90% when interfering substances such as those contained in cooking liquors are absent. Effluent quality produced from paper machine waters by plain sedimentation generally ranges from 1 to 2 lb per 1000 gal and, if coagulants are employed, from ¼ to 1 lb per 1000 gal of effluent.

SLUDGE DEWATERING AND DISPOSAL

The underflow from clarifiers treating pulp and paper mill effluents ranges in consistency from 2 to 12% solids depending on the nature of the solids settled out and the clarifier operation. It can be generally stated that the greater the percentage of inert suspended matter present, the thicker the underflow. However, the length, type, concentration, and degree of hydration of fiber present in the waste treated can all influence the density of the underflow. Some effluents, such as those containing groundwood fines or highly hydrated glassine fiber, produce very thin underflows that are difficult to thicken and to remove from the clarifier in a concentration suitable for further dewatering and disposal. An active research program is being carried on by the industry to find means for dewatering these sludges. In some instances, flotation is employed to separate the more hydrous solids, since this process can generally produce thicker slurries.

Underflows of under 5% solids concentration are generally moved by positive displacement or centrifugal pumps, and thicker flows are handled by screw impeller pumps. Secondary thickening is sometimes used where further dewatering prior to disposal is practiced.

Some papermill sludges such as deinking sludge can be dewatered by vacuum filtration; others, such as most boardmill sludges, are resistant to filtration. Recently, horizontal conveyor-type centrifuges have come into use for dewatering some of the more difficult sludges, such as the sludge produced by clarification of fine papermill and boardmill effluents. Vacuum filtration produces cakes varying between 20 and 30% solids at rates from 5 to 20 dry lb/sq ft/hour. Horizontal conveyor-type centrifugals can produce cakes up to 40% solids at feed rates as high as 4000 gal/hour with a recovery of 85% of the feed solids. In most plants, conditioning agents are not used, because most of the common ones are not effective in promoting dewatering. Recently there has been interest in the use of polyelectrolytes for this purpose. Drying beds are used by some mills to dewater sludge. Some of these have underdrains while others are simply impoundments in which water separating from the solids is decanted and natural drying is allowed to take place. When the sludge becomes sufficiently dense, it is dug out mechanically and transported to a disposal area. Such basins are generally built in multiple so that cleaned sections will be available at all times.

Land disposal is almost universally used for final disposition of paper mill sludges. In some instances the sludge is mixed with other materials for use as fill. If the concentration of nitrogenous sizing materials is low and the sludge is sufficiently dry, this practice does not give rise to an odor problem. Experiments with incineration and wet combustion have indicated that, for sludges high in ash, these methods are unsatisfactory and are excessive in cost because of the difficulty of dewatering to a sufficiently high degree to support combustion. Also, the quantity of sludge to be disposed of by many mills is too small to justify the high capital cost of incineration equipment and its operation.

BOD REDUCTION METHODS

STABILIZATION BASINS

Stabilization basins are the most widely used units for biological oxidation at pulp and paper mills. Most of these are located at southern mills, where large areas of suitable land are available and the high ambient temperature is favorable to high microbial metabolic rates. Two types are presently in use, the natural reaeration variety and the mechanically aerated type. The natural reaeration basin is normally shallow and can be irregular in depth, since its design is based essentially on air-exposed water surface, particularly when a high degree of BOD reduction is required. To produce a 90% BOD reduction, BOD loading is maintained below 50 lb per acre per day. It has been established that a reaeration coefficient, k_2, of 0.15 is suitable for basins with an average depth of 5 ft. In some instances, because of natural terrain and the fact that either long storage is available or a high percentage of BOD reduction is not necessary, deep stabilization basins have been constructed. Some of these serve a dual purpose, providing storage for discharge regulation in proportion to flow in the receiving stream. Performance figures for several such basins are presented in Table III.

TABLE III

PERFORMANCE OF STABILIZATION PONDS IN REDUCING BOD

Mill product	Type of treatment system	Pond area, acres	Maximum retention, days	BOD Influent, mg/liter	BOD Effluent, mg/liter	BOD Removal, %
Newsprint	Multiple plus flowage	100	20	200	40	80
Bleached kraft	Single	215	30	299	157	48
Newsprint	Single	140	15	180	110	39
Unbleached kraft	Multiple plus flowage	350	82	200	20	90
Bleached kraft	Single	175	35	108	36	67
	Single plus flowage	4480	180	130	10	92
	Single	300	40	150	45	70

Mechanically aerated basins have come into use in recent years for the purpose of raising oxidation rates and hence shortening the storage period required. Diffused air, low head recirculating pumps, and low dam and riffle systems have been tried, but the most common aeration device employed is the mechanical surface aerator. When adequately aerated, an oxidation rate of $k = 0.1$ at 20°C and $k = 0.16$ at 30°C is observed. Under these conditions, about 75% BOD reduction can be expected in 4 days detention and 90% in 7 days. Loadings can be carried as high as 400 lb per acre per day, and are dependent on waste strength and the degree of aeration applied. If the nutrient elements, nitrogen and phosphorus, are in short supply in a specific waste, these reductions may be diminished somewhat, but it is doubtful that addition of these elements is justified as it is with the activated sludge process.

Allowable BOD loadings for aerated basins have been found to be as follows, at summer temperatures, and producing an 85% BOD reduction:

Influent BOD, mg/liter	Loading, lb per acre-ft
400	217
200	108
100	54

Requirements for successful design and operation together with the advantages and disadvantages of stabilization basins can be summarized as follows. These basins must receive a waste substantially free from settleable solids because, if allowed to accumulate, these liquefy on decomposition and add to the BOD loading. For this reason, it is prudent to build a small entrance basin, that can be cleaned periodically, between the effluent clarification system and the major stabilizing system, to trap suspended matter overflowing the clarifier during periods of upset. The stabilization basins themselves are best built in multiple to prevent short circuiting. At least two separate basins should be used, or one or more dividing walls provided if a single basin is employed. All dikes should be built properly on the basis of soil conditions and provided with core walls where necessary. Basins should be cleared of stumps, and the bottom should be compacted or sealed if this appears necessary. Inlet and outlet structures should be designed to provide for varying the water level for mosquito control. Stabilization basins have distinct advantages over mechanical oxidation systems in that they are not subject to process upset, can absorb variations in loading, require little attention, and involve little operating cost. The greatest shortcomings are the high land requirement, particularly with nonaerated basins, and the fact that color is not removed from pulping effluents. Odor, from either aerated or nonaerated stabilization basins, is no problem when kraft mill effluents are treated. However, when certain other effluents such as boardmill waste are treated, a high degree of aeration must be provided to prevent formation of odorous gases.

TRICKLING FILTERS

Many attempts have been made to apply trickling filters to the treatment of pulp and paper mill wastes. Experiments have indicated that filters using stone media are costly and are not satisfactory for general application in that they cannot provide a high degree of purification at high loading rates and they are subject to clogging with fiber. To date, stone trickling filters are employed in this country by only two small mills.

TABLE IV

BOD LOADING VERSUS BOD REDUCTION, FOR PLASTIC MEDIA TRICKLING FILTERS

Applied	Removed
200	100
300	130
400	175
500	220
600	270
700	310
800	370

Values indicate BOD, lb/1000 cu ft of media per day.

Plastic media have been employed in trickling filters providing partial purification of pulp mill effluents (40–60% BOD reduction) since they largely eliminate the media-clogging problem and can be operated at high hydraulic loadings. Two large installations are now operating at southern kraft mills. There is also interest in filters using these media for pretreatment and cooling of hot effluents, prior to the application of other methods of oxidation.

Performance tests with the plastic media indicated that, at loadings of 100–800 lb/1000 cu ft, the BOD reduction averaged about 45% and remained constant irrespective of loading when treating unbleached kraft mill effluent having an initial BOD between 250 and 400 mg/liter. Removals as high as 370 lb of BOD/1000 cu ft were observed at hydraulic loadings of 175 mgd/acre. An example of the relationship of BOD loading to reduction is shown in Table IV.

From these data, the ability of the filter to remove a large quantity of

BOD at high application rates is obvious. Hence, it appears that the future application of such filters lies in the area of "roughing" treatment and waste precooling. The operating cost is somewhat lower than for activated sludge treatment since less power is generally required for waste recycle than for aeration. Nutrient addition is necessary for good filter performance.

ACTIVATED SLUDGE TREATMENT

In 1948, experimentation was started to determine if the activated sludge process could be applied for reduction of BOD of kraft pulping effluents. Laboratory trials indicated that these effluents could be oxidized to a high degree by the process if good internal mill control of waste strength and alkalinity was practiced, and nutrients in the form of ammonia and phosphates were added. Two exhaustive pilot plant studies followed, one dealing with unbleached kraft effluent and the other with bleached. The conclusions arrived at were similar to the laboratory findings; shortly thereafter, a large unit was built at a southern mill where the process worked successfully, producing BOD reductions of 80–90% and about a 30% color reduction. Bioassay tests indicated that the effluent produced was not toxic to fish life. Oxidation rates in excess of 100 lb of BOD/1000 cu ft of aerator capacity could be obtained due to the relatively high temperature of the effluents and the ready availability of wood hydrolysis products present in the waste as microbial food.

Following the adaptation of this process to kraft effluents, pilot studies with other wastes from the production of pulp and paper products were conducted by the industry. These included paperboard, roofing felt, neutral sulfite pulping, and deinking effluents. When the same conditions established for the treatment of kraft effluent were met, these wastes could also be oxidized to a high degree. To date, 12 full-scale plants have been put into operation at mills. Six of these treat kraft effluent, 4 board-mill, 1 deinking, and 1 roofing felt waste, amounting to a total of over 100 mgd. Another 10–20 mgd is treated in municipal activated sludge plants in combination with sanitary sewage.

Two modifications of the basic activated sludge flowsheet are in use. In the contact stabilization system, aeration periods employed for the mixed liquor are shorter than normal and the return sludge is aerated for a substantial period. It is claimed that capital cost can be somewhat reduced by this modification and that a reservoir of active sludge is maintained against possible damage to the mixed liquor sludge by shock loads. The other modification is the so-called "dynamic" system in which aeration, sludge separation, and sludge return are incorporated in a single unit. This arrangement promotes improved conditions, since the return sludge does not have to be pumped and is returned in fresh condition to the waste undergoing treatment. Because there is a greater degree of sensitivity inherent to this arrangement than to the conventional process, hydraulic design capacity, particularly of the settling sections of such units, should be conservative.

The activated sludge process is generally applied where sufficient and suitable land is not available for stabilization basins and where the degree of oxidation of the waste needs to be high. The waste to be treated must be free from mineral acidity or caustic alkalinity, the temperature should preferably be below 110°C, and the volatile suspended solids content should average no higher than 1 lb/1000 gal. Requirements for added nutrient are generally somewhat less than the theoretical optimum of 1 mg/liter of nitrogen to 20 mg/liter of BOD and 1 mg/liter of phosphorus to 60 mg/liter of BOD, because of the presence of traces of these elements in most effluents.

Although successful in treating most pulp and paper mill effluents and combinations thereof, the activated sludge process has some serious shortcomings. The capital cost is high, ranging from $80,000 to $100,000 per mgd of capacity, depending on size, and exclusive of pretreatment for reduction of the suspended solids content of the waste. Removal of color, while generally measurable, is not effected to a high degree when treating pulping and bleaching wastes. The waste activated sludge produced compacts poorly and is extremely resistant to dewatering; hence, it presents a difficult disposal problem. At present, it is vacuum filtered where a large quantity of primary sludge is available to absorb it. In other cases it is disposed of on the land together with fly ash. Another shortcoming to the use of this process is that wastes having a BOD approaching 3000 mg/liter cannot be treated because of the oxygen exchange limitation. There is also the fact that its sensitivity to surges in waste load requires careful control and frequently considerable in-mill sewer rearrangement for the process to operate satisfactorily. Experimental work now in progress indicates that partial pretreatment in a roughing filter containing plastic media may do much to stabilize the process reaction to surges in loading. Experimental evidence has also been obtained indicating that treatment of a fraction of the total effluent by this process, followed by recombination with the remaining waste flow, stimulates further oxidation of the total waste in stabilization basins and thus shortens the storage period required for a given degree of oxidation.

LAND DISPOSAL BY IRRIGATION AND SEEPAGE

A recent survey of the pulp and paper industry revealed that 26 mills are experimenting with or are practicing effluent disposal by irrigation or soil seepage. Seventeen of these are full-scale operations, of which 9 are spray units, 1 is flood irrigation, and the remainder are either seepage ponds or ditch-type irrigation. Three are hardboard mills, 2 boxboard mills, 2 kraft pulp mills, 1 semichemical pulp mill, 1 sulfite pulp mill, and 1 fine paper mill.

The majority of these systems are seasonal operations tailored to cope with low stream flow conditions occurring during the warm weather period. The exceptions are one spray system and two seepage basins which are operated the year around. The recent trend has been toward the disposal of weak wastes by irrigation, rather than the disposal of strong wastes by soil seepage. All of the 6 most recent full-scale installations are designed for irrigation, 5 being by spray application and the remaining 1 by ridge-and-furrow distribution. Several factors have contributed to this trend toward accepting the principles of irrigation in contrast to depending upon seepage through porous soils. Foremost is the general scarcity of soils suitable for high rate seepage installations at most mills. Unless an extremely porous soil is available, the land requirement becomes large and the distribution problem serious and costly. Vegetation, by increasing soil porosity and evaporating considerable water through transpiration, reduces greatly the land area requirement.

Like all methods of effluent disposal, irrigation has both advantages and disadvantages. At best, land requirements are high, since for most soils 40–50 acres are required per mgd of effluent. This, however, is of no disadvantage for certain mills located in agricultural areas where the effluent is used to supplement existing irrigation water. The limitation does restrict use of irrigation either to relatively small mills or for disposal of specific effluents of relatively low volume. BOD loading generally must be maintained below 200 lb per acre per day to maintain the soil in aerobic condition. The pH should not be below 6.0 or above 9.0, and the sodium adsorption ratio should be less than 8.0. There is no evidence that the disposition of salt-bearing effluents from pulp and paper making operations differs substantially from irrigation with water of like salt content.

Isolated cases of groundwater contamination have occurred in areas where pulping liquors were applied to the soil. In all known cases the soil was highly porous sand, allowing rapid transit of effluent to the water table and creating a high concentration of effluent in a localized area. Since the potential for groundwater contamination does exist when highly colored effluents are applied to the soil, individual site evaluation for soil type, direction of groundwater movement, and location of existing wells must be made. It does not appear, from present knowledge, that problems of groundwater contamination are likely to occur in land disposal operations related to irrigation on moderate and heavy textured soils employing effluents other than pulping liquors. With pulping liquors, hydraulic loadings are limited and the dilution afforded upon reaching the groundwater table is substantially greater than the dilution that occurs in high-rate percolation through porous soil.

As many mills are located on streams which exhibit a well defined low-flow pattern of short duration, the effluent disposal problem is seasonal. Except for some streams in the Rocky Mountain area fed by melting snow, this low-flow period coincides with seasonal demands for irrigation water and is generally of short duration. Hence, there is a potential for tailoring a waste disposal program either to the increased demands for irrigation water during this period or to disposal on the land when evaporation and evapotranspiration rates are greatest.

Although well suited to reasonably level land and warm weather application, irrigation disposal exhibits some disadvantages in hilly terrain or where effluent treatment is required the year around in freezing climates. In hilly terrain the potential for runoff at high hydraulic loadings exists, which may increase the land requirements; and freezing temperatures may include excessive ice buildup in the sprayed area or other problems attendant with handling liquids in lines that are taken out of operation during periods of freezing temperatures.

The operating cost of land disposal compares favorably with other methods of secondary treatment and may represent a substantial saving in capital investment. Added advantages over other methods are that BOD reduction may approach 100% and performance is uniform. The pumping cost for spray irrigation systems is generally less than the power requirement of biological treatment processes.

Land disposal does not have the potential of wholesale application as a treatment method in the industry. In some instances, however, it does offer an economically attractive means of solving some of the waste disposal problems of the industry where small waste volumes are involved. The land requirements for disposal of the total mill effluent from pulp mills are great enough that integration of waste disposal with a productive agricultural program is indicated.

BY-PRODUCTS FROM SPENT PULPING LIQUORS

Although the trend for large sulfite mills is toward the application of recovery systems to dispose of spent liquor, some small mills manufacture by-products from it. These consist mainly of liquor concentrates, lignin sulfonates, acetic and formic acids, torula yeast, and ethanol. The last two are produced through fermentation of wood sugars contained in the liquor. Markets for these products are at present limited, so this means of reducing the pollution load of spent sulfite liquor is restricted. At present, about 10 mills in this country produce by-products, utilizing 10–15% of the total amount of liquor produced. An excellent capitulation of the status of by-product production from spent sulfite liquor was reported in *Chemical and Engineering News* (*1*), and a paper by Wiley and Holderby covers by-products from all sources (*4*).

In general, the disposal of spent sulfite liquor is a declining problem in this country, due to the demise of old mills, installation of recovery systems, substitution of kraft pulping with its inherent recovery system, as well as increasing by-product developments and markets.

REFERENCES

1. "Chemicals From the Other Half of the Tree," *Chem. Eng. News* **41**, No. 6, 83–89 (Feb. 11, 1963).
2. "Lockwood's Directory of the Paper and Allied Trades," Lockwood Trade Journal Co., New York; annual.
3. National Council for Stream Improvement, Tech. Bull. No. 148, "Aquatic Biology and the Pulp & Paper Industry," 1961.
4. Wiley, A. J., and Holderby, J. M., *Pulp Paper Mag. Can.* **61**, T212–T217 (1960).

Chapter 21

TEXTILES

by R. HOBART SOUTHER

Textile manufacturing operations are among the major industrial water users; in many areas, this industry has the wastes most difficult to treat satisfactorily. Textile wastes are variable in character, and this makes their treatment a complex problem.

In a modern textile mill, many compounds produced by other industries are used. Synthetic yarns, dyes, and finishes from the chemical industries and sizes from the food-producing industries are among these substances. Some of these compounds are added onto the basic fiber, then partially or wholly washed off as pollutional material. These compounds may be organic or inorganic in nature; either can cause a pollution problem. Inorganic materials may render water unsuitable for use because of excess concentrations of soluble salts, and because insoluble salts precipitate and deposit on stream bottoms, blanketing aquatic life and even clogging streams.

The organic compounds may undergo a gradual chemical or biological change which removes oxygen from the water, resulting in a septic condition characterized by odors, gases, floating solids, and a generally disagreeable appearance. Metal salts may be toxic to animals, fish, and other aquatic life. Each of these types of pollution is a special waste treatment problem.

THE TEXTILE INDUSTRY

All fibers used in the textile industry fall into one of two main groups: natural or manufactured. The natural fibers can be further divided into animal and vegetable fibers, and the manufactured fibers are divided into regenerated and synthetic fibers. The principal fibers of commercial significance are shown in the accompanying tabulation.

Natural		Manufactured	
Animal	Vegetable	Regenerated	Synthetic
Wool	Cotton	Rayon	Polyamide
Silk	Flax	Soybean	Polyacrylic
Hair	Hemp	Casein	Polyester

ANIMAL FIBERS

Of the various animal fibers known to man, wool is the oldest and best known. Wool as obtained from the sheep's back contains large quantities of dirt, grass, burrs, dried sheep perspiration or "suint," and wool grease discharged from glands to protect the fiber during growth of the animal. In extreme cases, wool may contain as little as 30% fiber, with 70% foreign matter, and may be as high as 45% grease. Wastes from the manufacture of wool are contributed by the scouring, carbonizing, bleaching, dyeing, and finishing operations. All may come from the same manufacturer, or scouring and carbonizing may be done in one plant and other operations in another.

The removal of foreign matter may be accomplished by scouring in warm water with soap and alkali. Under these conditions, of course, the BOD of the waste is increased by the amount of soap present. Currently, soap is rarely used; it has been replaced by synthetic detergent with an extremely low BOD. Consequently, BOD of the discharge can be attributed almost exclusively to the raw wool itself. Alkali is rarely used in modern wool scouring, so is no longer a problem in the waste discharge.

It is customary in many mills to open and "dust" the wool, thereby removing much of the solid impurities before wet operations begin. The dusted wool is then sent to a scouring machine, and is conveyed through 2–6 bowls of a solution of nonionic detergent at about 140°F. It was formerly a common procedure to run the first bowl at a low temperature, in order to remove only suint, but little is gained by this unless the wool grease is recovered. With the use of synthetic detergents, the old method of acid cracking to remove wool grease is not efficient, so the separation is best accomplished by means of a centrifuge.

As the wool passes through the scouring machine, it is squeezed by rolls to remove the liquor and a part of the dirt at the end of each bowl. Scouring is generally done in a counterflow operation; the finishing water from bowl flows back to the other bowls in the scouring train. Hoppers in each bowl collect insoluble dirt that settles from the wool; this can be removed from the liquor by centrifuging if necessary.

The volume of waste discharged varies from 500 to 2000 gal or more per 1000 lb of wool scoured; the smaller quantity is more common. The BOD of these wastes ranges from 2000 to more than 6000 mg/liter, and the grease content may be as high as 2½%.

Wool scouring wastes would interfere with any municipal sewage treatment system because of their grease content and the broken fibers they carry. When soap and soda ash were used as the detergent materials, the liquors were treated with concentrated sulfuric acid to separate the grease. This was drawn off and purified for other uses. With synthetic detergents, this method is not always feasible; the centrifuge is frequently used to remove fibers and excess grease. Centrifuging generally produces a better quality of grease, suitable for use in cosmetics, but the recovery is appreciably lower, being in the neighborhood of one-third of the grease present, whereas the acid-cracking method gave recoveries only slightly less than quantitative.

The use of chlorine for cracking wool scouring waste has been suggested but has never been used commercially, possibly because of cost. Solvent methods of grease recovery from spent scouring liquor have been considered and may yet come into use, but in the past they have been too expensive for commercial application.

Wool grease has been recovered by treating waste liquor with calcium hypochlorite, reducing the pH to about 7.5, discarding the clear liquors, and treating the scum and sludge with sulfuric acid. A proposed similar process uses calcium chloride, but the sludge volume is so large that the process has not been used on a commercial scale.

Solvent scouring of wool has been introduced, with the object of recovering the grease and therefore reducing the pollution load on the stream. Although this is successful technically, it has not proved economical.

Scoured wool may be dyed as raw stock, tops, or after spinning and weaving. Wastes from a dyeing and finishing process are contributed by the spent liquors and by subsequent washing of the wool after bleaching, dyeing, or other finishing. It is usually not practical to separate rinsewaters from the stronger wastes. These wastes vary greatly in strength, not only because of the amount of water used but also because of the various types of dyes and other chemicals.

Waste from wool dyeing and finishing has been treated by chemical precipitation with iron or aluminum salts. Usually, however, it is better to use biological treatment, with either the trickling filter or an aeration process.

Wool production for 1961 was 291 million linear yards, which is 66% less than for 1947. In 1961, there were 15,490 broad looms in place—a decrease of 43% since 1947. In 1961, there were 1.17 million spindles in place, a drop of 36% from 1947. Silk and hair production in the United States is small compared with wool, so is not discussed here.

VEGETABLE FIBERS

Cotton has been the mainstay of the vegetable fiber industries, but there has been a large drop in cotton production during the 10-year period 1953–1961. In 1953 there were 11,332,562,000 square yards produced; this decreased to 10,824,130,000 by 1961. The 1961 value was approximately $6 billion of which about 40% was value added by manufacture. The industry employs about 1,100,000 workers. The various operations which cotton fiber goes through in its conversion to finished fabric are outlined in Fig. 1, a flow diagram of a typical integrated cotton textile mill. Many of these processes are dry, producing no liquid wastes.

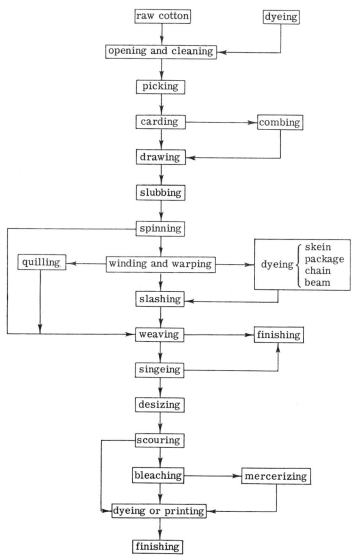

Fɪɢ. 1.   Flow diagram: raw cotton to finished cloth.

Wet Processing Operations. Composite wastes from an integrated cotton textile plant may contain any or all of the chemicals mentioned below. The pH varies between 6.5 and 11. The waste has high turbidity and color, and a solids content of 1000–1600 mg/liter, BOD of 200–600 mg/liter, total alkalinity of 300–900 mg/liter, suspended solids of 30–50 mg/liter, and chromium up to 3 and occasionally 25 mg/liter. Volume ranges from 30 to 100 gal of waste per lb of goods produced. Vegetable fibers other than cotton have generally similar wastes.

(1) *Slashing.* Before yarn can be woven into fabric, it must be strengthened by loading it with starch or other sizing substances. This operation is called "slashing," and little liquid waste results. The cloth at this stage is "creige," and may be sold as such. Subsequent operations are considered as finishing but include preparatory treatments. Substitution of sizes with low BOD values, such as carboxymethyl cellulose in place of starch, reduces BOD in the final effluent.

(2) *Scouring and desizing.* It is necessary to remove certain natural ingredients and the sizing materials from slashing operations to prepare cloth for dyeing and finishing. This may contribute about 50% of the total pollution load in textile processing. Acids and enzymes are used to hydrolyze the starch. Caustic soda, soda ash, chlorine, peroxides, silicates, sodium bisulfite, acids, detergents, and penetrants are used in scouring to prepare a clean, white cloth for finishing. Scouring may contribute up to 30% of the total waste load. Natural impurities in cotton contribute about 3% of the total BOD in the final waste.

(3) *Bleaching.* Bleaching operations use chlorine or peroxide to remove natural coloring matters. About 10% of the pollution load is contributed by this operation.

(4) *Mercerizing.* Mercerizing consists of passing cloth through 20% caustic soda solution. The process contributes negligible BOD, but a high degree of alkalinity.

(5) *Dyeing.* Dyeing is done in a great variety of ways, and new dyes and auxiliary chemicals add to the complexity of the operation. The pollution load may be 20–40%, but volume is large, and there is a high degree of color.

Vat dyes are fast dyes, applied by reducing the dyestuff to soluble form with caustic soda and sodium hydrosulfite, then oxidizing on the fiber with peroxide, chromate, or other oxidizing agent.

Developing dyes are applied by diazotizing the dye with acid and sodium nitrite, and subsequently treating with a developer.

Naphthol dyes are naphthols applied to the fabric, dried, then passed through a developer for chemical coupling to produce the dye.

Sulfur dyes are reduced with sodium sulfide, applied to the fabric, and oxidized, usually with chromate. These dye wastes are difficult to treat in biological processes because of high air requirements to oxidize the sulfur dye molecule, and because of the toxicity of chromate. Chromium recovery is recommended for this operation, to reduce chromium content below 3 mg/liter in the waste going to conventional biotreatment plants and below 10 mg/liter in that going to bioaeration lagoons or prolonged activated sludge treatment processes.

Basic dyes usually require acetic and tannic acid and tartar emetic. Direct dyes are applied from water solutions, with or without penetrants. Indigo dyes are similar to vat dyes, applied cold, with air oxidation. Pigment "dyes" are resin-bonded to the fabric by curing. A small amount of BOD is contributed by resins in the waste.

(6) *Finishing.* Finishing operations impart the desired "hand," or feel and appearance, and better wear properties such as softness, stiffness, smoothness, slickness, and luster. Chemicals used are varied, and include starches and dextrins, natural and synthetic waxes, synthetic resins, ammonium and zinc chlorides, softening agents, penetrants, and various special chemicals to improve service and wash-wear qualities or impart rainproofing, mildewproofing, oil and soil repellency, and fireproofing. The waste is low in volume, with some BOD contribution from starch, gums, waxes, and resins.

REGENERATED FIBERS

Viscose Rayon. Viscose rayon is a manufactured textile fiber, filament, yarn, thread, or fabric, composed of regenerated cellulose. It is made by the viscose, cupra-ammonium, or nitrocellulose process. Natural impurities in regenerated fibers are negligible, because the manufacturer wants his product to be as pure as possible. Rayon should not be confused with acetate rayon.

Viscose rayon is highly absorbent, and takes up water readily. The presence of water increases the penetration of reagents into the cellulose, increases the electrical conductivity, and reduces the breaking strength. Oils also readily wet the cellulose.

Viscose and other regenerated rayons dye readily with most of the dyestuffs used on cotton. Rayon is not as resistant to chemicals as is cotton; hence, drastic treatments must be avoided. High temperatures decrease its resistance to acids and oxidizing bleaches.

Acetate Rayon. Acetate rayon is a cellulose acetate fiber rather than a regenerated cellulose. It is not as absorbent as other rayons, and is more resistant to staining than regular rayon. Acetate does not usually require bleaching; but if bleaching is necessary, only mild oxidizing agents can be used.

SYNTHETIC FIBERS

Polyamides. Nylon includes any long chain synthetic polymeric amide which has recurring amide groups as an integral part of the main polymer chain. This covers a vast group of chemically related products with widely varying properties. Nylon 66 is a combination of hexamethylene diamine and adipic acid. Nylon is a resistant material. It is not affected by heat or cold, is resistant to many chemicals, has high abrasion resistance, and is more resistant to burning than cotton, wool, rayon, or silk. It is resistant to insects, mildew, mold, and fungi.

Acrylics (Polyacrylates). The acrylics are synthetic, molecularly oriented fibers from polymers that contain a preponderance of acrylic units in the polymer chain. They are resistant to sunlight, weathering, industrial fumes, chemicals, insects, and bacteria. This resistance makes it more difficult to dye these fibers.

Polyesters. The polyester fibers are manufactured from ethylene glycol and terephthalic acid. They have remarkable resistance to heat, low flammability, good shape and crease retention, and are readily processed, although dyeing requires a carrier or pressure technique.

The manufacture of synthetic fiber in its raw form is properly a part of the organic chemical industry. Typical steps in the further processing, from fiber to finished product, are shown in the flowsheet of Fig. 2.

TEXTILE WASTE CHARACTERISTICS

The pollutional features of textile wastes differ widely among various segments of the industry, and each type of waste presents a special treatment problem.

Organic substances such as dyes, starches, and detergents in textile waste undergo chemical and biological changes which consume dissolved oxygen from the receiving stream and so destroy fish life. Such organics should be removed to prevent septic conditions and obnoxious odors, and to avoid rendering the stream waters unsuitable for municipal, industrial, agricultural, and residential use.

High concentrations of soluble inorganic salts may make the stream unsuitable for industrial and municipal use, and may have a corrosive effect on boats and other structures. Metals such as chromium and zinc are toxic to aquatic life, and should be removed before discharge.

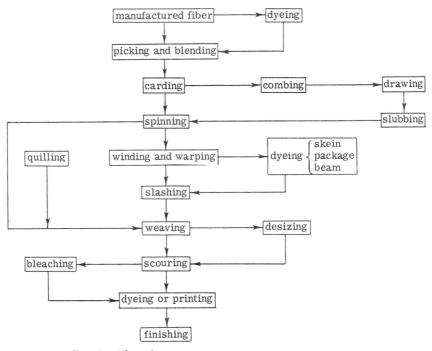

Fig. 2.   Flow diagram: synthetic fiber to finished cloth.

Colors from dyes vary and, although not toxic, are esthetically objectionable, particularly in drinking and recreational waters. Certain carrier chemicals used in dyeing, such as phenols, may add tastes and odors.

A composite waste from an integrated cotton textile plant consists of the following materials: starches, dextrins, gums, glucose, waxes, pectins, alcohols, fatty acids, acetic acid, soaps, detergents, sodium hydroxide, carbonates, sulfides, sulfates, chlorides, dyes and pigments, carboxymethyl cellulose, gelatine, dye carriers (phenols and benzoic acid), peroxides, and chlorine bleach compounds. The pH varies between 4 and 12, and the color is that of the predominant dye used. Other ranges are: total solids, 1000–1600 mg/liter; BOD, 200–1800 mg/liter; total alkalinity, 300–900 mg/liter; suspended solids, 30–300 mg/liter; and chromium, 0–25 mg/liter. The volume of waste per 1000 lb of finished goods ranges from 20,000 to 100,000 gal.

Table I is a compilation of waste characteristics from a cotton textile plant. Table II shows the properties of wastes from various types of synthetic textile processing. Table III shows the pollutional effect of industrial processes in woolen mills.

TEXTILE WASTEWATER PROBLEMS

RECOVERY AND REUSE

Waste reduction, prevention, and utilization practices may provide several dividends ·in addition to reducing the quantity of materials wasted. The savings in materials may be enough to pay for the cost of treatment of the remaining waste. Some of these in-plant measures and ways in which waste costs may be reduced are given below.

Reduction of Waste Volume. Strong rinsewaters from dye operations may be reused to make up new baths. Weak rinses may be recycled through in-plant water treatment units. In a counterflow system, rinsewaters are circulated in the opposite direction to movement of the cloth.

Reduction of Process Chemicals. Chemicals may be reduced to a minimum by proper control of cloth processing, as by the use of redox potential to control hydrosulfite in vat dyeing.

Recovery and Reuse of Chemicals. Caustic soda can be recovered from mercerizing liquors and reused, as can sodium bichromate from dyeing operations.

Process Modification. Dye from the first rinse may be employed to make up the next standing bath. Modification of processing chemicals is sometimes possible.

Substitution of Chemicals. It is desirable to substitute chemicals with low pollutional effects for those that are more pollutional. Examples of such substitution include: carboxymethyl cellulose for starch in slashing; mineral acid for acetic acid, which has a significant BOD; nonbiodegradable synthetic detergents for soap, unless detergents are a problem; and polyvinyl alcohol and polystyrenes for starch in finishing.

Good Housekeeping. Waste control by good housekeeping requires close control of all operations to avoid spillage and wasting of materials

TABLE I

COTTON PROCESSING WASTE CHARACTERISTICS

Process	Concentrations			Total quantities			
	pH	BOD, mg/liter	Total solids, mg/liter	Flow, gal/1000 lb	BOD, lb/1000 lb	Total solids, lb/1000 lb	Population equivalents, per 1000 lb
Slashing and sizing	7.0–9.5	620–2500	8,500–22,600	60–940	0.5–5.0	47–67	2–30
Desizing	—	1700–5200	16,000–32,000	300–1,100	14.8–16.1	66–70	90–100
Kiering	10–13	680–2900	7,600–17,400	310–1,700	1.5–17.5	19–47	10–105
Scouring	—	50–110	—	2,300–5,100	1.36–3.02	—	8–18
Bleaching	8.5–9.6	90–1700	2,300–14,400	300–14,900	5.0–14.8	38–290	30–90
Mercerizing	5.5–9.5	45–65	600–1,900	27,900–36,950	10.5–13.5	185–450	60–80
Dyeing:							
Aniline black	—	40–55	600–1,200	15,000–23,000	5–10	100–200	40–60
Basic	6–7.5	100–200	500–800	18,000–36,000	15–50	150–250	100–400
Developed colors	5–10	75–200	2,900–8,200	8,900–25,000	15–20	325–650	90–120
Direct	6.5–7.6	220–600	2,200–14,000	1,700–6,400	1.3–11.7	25–250	25–75
Indigo	5–10	90–1700	1,100–9,500	600–6,000	1.8–9.5	21–63	10–60
Naphthol	5–10	15–675	4,500–10,700	2,300–16,800	2–15	200–650	13–80
Sulfur	8–10	11–1800	4,200–14,100	2,900–25,600	2–250	300–1200	14–1500
Vats	5–10	125–1500	1,700–7,400	1,000–20,000	12–30	150–250	75–175

Taken from Reference (*4*).

to the drain. It is essential to avoid preparing too large batches of solutions that spoil and must be thrown away at the end of a run.

WATER CONSERVATION

The textile industry, like other industries, recognizes its responsibility in the conservation of water; that is, to use it and return it to the stream for others to use. Economy in the use of water has resulted from the ever increasing cost of water as well as awareness of an impending scarcity

TABLE II

SYNTHETIC TEXTILE WASTE CHARACTERISTICS

Fibers and operations	BOD			Solids	
	mg/liter	lb/1000 lb fabric	pH	Suspended, lb/1000 lb	Dissolved, lb/1000 lb
Acrylics					
Scouring	350	5.2	8.8	3.4	15.6
Softening	13	0.2	7.4	0.6	1.4
Dyeing, basic	208	3.1	8.3	0.5	6.0
Dyeing, acid	610	8.5	4.2	1.6	9.2
Rayon					
Boiling off	240	2.0	3.9	1.5	32.2
Dyeing	50	0.7	7.1	2.7	150
Rayon-Nylon (50–50 blend)					
Scouring	585	8.7	8.2	74.0	306
Dyeing	123	1.8	3.5	1.4	89.0
Fixing	112	1.7	7.0	16.9	83.3
Nylon					
Scouring	2260	34.0	—	—	—
Dyeing	675	10.0	7.6	0.1	26.6
Acetates					
Over-all	665	50.0	—	—	—

Data by courtesy of Chatham Manufacturing Company.

in the foreseeable future. It is estimated that the textile industry has reduced its consumption per unit product by 20–40% since 1954. More stringent regulatory requirements have helped in reducing water consumption in an effort to abate pollution. Sometimes the water volume remains the same, but the concentration of pollution increases. This points to the fact that the textile industry will conserve water, and use far less per unit in processing, in the future.

TREATMENT OF WASTES

After every effort has been made to reduce waste strength and volume by conservation and good housekeeping, there still remains the

TABLE III

WOOL PROCESSING WASTE CHARACTERISTICS

(Based on Annual Production at a Typical Mill)

	Weight of cloth processed		BOD		Alkalinity		Acidity		Volume	
	1000 lb per year	% of total plant production	lb per 1000 lb	% of total	lb per 1000 lb	% of total	lb per 1000 lb	% of total	gal per 1000 lb	% of total
Scouring for grease removal	473	59	104.5	42	109.3	58	0	0	3,689	7
Stock dyeing	700	88	34.3	14	12.8	7	0	0	1,876	3
Washing after fulling	800	100	94.0	37	38.2	20	0	0	32,800	59
Return fulling	176	22	15.0	6	13.9	8	0	0	4,564	8
Neutralization after carbonizing	800	100	1.7	0.7	12.7	7	40.5	100	12,528	22
Optical bleach	100	13	1.4	0.5	1.1	0.6	0	0	268	0.5
Total	800	—	250.9	—	188.0	—	40.5	—	55,725	—

Adapted from "Pollution Sources in Wool Scouring and Finishing Mills," New England Interstate Water Pollution Control Commission, 1954.

A composite of all wastes would contain 432 mg/liter BOD and 237 mg/liter alkalinity.

problem of disposing of the remaining pollution in wastewater without adverse effect on the receiving stream. The wastes may be treated in various ways, and the best combination of methods differs from plant to plant. Each plant must evaluate possible treatment procedures according to existing treatment, type of waste, and degree of treatment needed.

Segregation. The separation of wastes for separate and special treatment may depend on: the character of individual wastes and the stream requirements, the cost of in-plant changes such as piping and sewers, the benefits gained if weak effluent can be discharged untreated to the stream, and the cost of workmen of higher skills to avoid human errors in controlling valves.

Lagooning and Storage. Equalization is an aid to eliminate variation in flows and pollution load, and is accomplished by storage, as in a lagoon. Proper maintenance of lagoons is necessary to avoid odors; aeration helps to reduce odors and other pollutional characteristics. Lagooning with aeration after other biotreatment processes serves as a polishing treatment, and accomplishes maximum pollution removal, usually above 95%.

Oxidation ponds, with and without aeration, are the most effective type of lagoon. Without air, the usual loading is 50 lb of BOD per acre, but may be up to 90 lb or more in polishing or post-treatment operations. With air, 3–10 days retention is required, depending on the amount of oxygen applied.

Screening. Bar screens and rotating screens are used to remove objectionable coarse solids from certain textile wastes containing fibers and trash.

Mechanical Filtration. Coke, ash, coal, rock, and sand filters are frequently used on highly polluted wastes as a secondary treatment, to polish the effluent to a high degree of clarity and usually to a BOD below 10 mg/liter.

Preaeration and Postaeration. Physical and chemical aeration by diffusion, spraying, or cascading provides oxygen and prevents anaerobic decomposition, to control malodorous gases or to polish the effluent.

Neutralization. Neutralization of wastewater is required to adjust it to pH limits required for the receiving streams, or to adjust the waste to pH less than 10.0 for biological treatment in conventional processes. Neutralization is not needed in new techniques of bioaeration lagoon treatment; wastewaters at pH 12, and containing 900–1800 mg/liter BOD and 25 mg/liter of trivalent chromium have little effect on the process, and an equalization pond is not necessary.

Chemical Precipitation. Good results are obtained from chemical precipitation in combination with lagooning, or as the only treatment. The costs are higher than with biological methods.

Chemical Oxidation. Certain wastewaters, containing dyes and auxiliary chemicals, are reducing in character; these should be segregated and oxidized with air or chlorine before they are mixed with other plant wastes for further treatment. Chlorine oxidizes reducing compounds, and is also used in final treatment to reduce the bacteria'count. Chlorine, by destroying microorganisms, retards biological oxidation and should be used sparingly where further reduction in pollution is desired in stream assimilation processes.

Biological Oxidation. Biological methods of removing pollutants from waste utilize natural processes, involving bacteria and other microorganisms, for oxidation of the organic wastes to produce a satisfactory effluent. Sewage is easy to treat biologically, but certain textile wastes free from toxic substances treat as easily as sewage because of their high nutrient content of nitrogen and phosphorus. As nutrients, one part of nitrogen is considered necessary for 20 parts of BOD, and one part of phosphorus for 100 parts of BOD.

(1) *The trickling filter process.* The trickling filter simulates stream flow by spraying wastewater over a broken medium, such as stone or plastic. The medium serves as a base for biological growths which, in the presence of air drawn through the filter, attack the organic matter of the waste and use it for food. This removes a large part of the organic pollution, and the effluent can usually be discharged to a stream after final settling. Failures with older conventional systems were largely caused by a lack of knowledge of waste characteristics and optimum recirculation efficiency. Recent advances have made this method of treatment obsolete, in favor of the prolonged bioaeration treatment, which gives efficiencies up to 99% at much lower costs.

A new approach for treating textile wastes more economically is the use of plastic media in the filters, followed by oxidation ponds for polishing. An example is a trickling filter plant designed with plastic media to remove 50% of the organic pollution, which is the degree of treatment required by the stream. Space for an oxidation pond is reserved for future use, if a treatment efficiency above 90% is ever required.

Trickling filter treatment of sewage and textile waste averages about 75% removal of BOD. More efficient operation can be obtained by recirculation of part of the treated effluent or by treating through 2 stages of filters in series. Trickling filters may also be used in a unique method to reduce the high alkali content of textile wastes of pH 12 or above, prior to activated sludge treatment (2). Wastewater flows of up to 30 mgd can be treated in a filter space of 1 acre. Sludge from settled effluent is disposed of in digesters in the usual sludge disposal procedures.

(2) *The activated sludge process.* In the conventional activated sludge process, the wastewater, after primary settling, flows into a tank of size to retain about 6 hours flow. The microorganisms in activated sludge are suspended in the waste as gelatinous aggregates, which are flocculent and settle rapidly. The mixed sludge and waste is kept in suspension by compressed air or mechanical mixing, either of which also supplies the oxygen necessary for biological activity. The aerated waste is continuously withdrawn and settled, and a portion of the biologically active sludge is returned to the influent. This treatment is very efficient and removes up to 95% of the BOD, resulting in a clear, stable effluent from normal wastes (4). The activated sludge process is more sensitive than trickling filters to changes in pH and to shock loads. It costs less to construct and requires little space. Sludge disposal must be provided.

The biosorption, contact aeration, step aeration, and other modified activated sludge processes have been found to be less subject to upsets, more economical, and equally efficient for treating sewage or mixtures of sewage with textile waste. Less tank space is required, and the primary settling tank is optional.

Total oxidation, extended aeration, prolonged aeration, endogenous respiration, and other activated sludge variations with greatly increased aeration periods are being used more extensively in treating textile waste because of their simplicity and low construction and operating costs. The process involves aerating seeded wastes from 12 to 72 hours, until the organic matter is nearly or totally oxidized, then discharging to the stream. Primary settling and sludge digestion and disposal may be eliminated. The effluent is usually settled, however, and the sludge returned to the aeration tank for further oxidation. An equalizing pond is advantageous if the detention period is less than 1 day. Equalization is not necessary for detention periods from 1 to 3 days. The method of aeration is optional, and either mechanical agitation or diffused air can be used advantageously to obtain efficiency and economy. Excellent results have been obtained with this process, which is rapidly gaining favor for both performance and low cost. One of the first plants of this type has obtained, without pretreatment, remarkable results in the treatment of a mixture of 7% municipal sewage and 93% strong mill waste including sulfur dye waste. A typical influent shows a BOD of 1400 mg/liter, pH 12.0, and hexavalent chromium of 25 mg/liter. The effluent BOD may be as low as 11 mg/liter. Efficiencies range from 93% to 97%, in treatment of a waste that would completely upset conventional trickling filter or activated sludge plants. No equalization, primary treatment, or sludge digestion is needed to obtain high efficiencies (1). This method, followed by oxidation ponding, can be used to obtain any degree of treatment, at low cost. The waste flow is shown in Fig. 3.

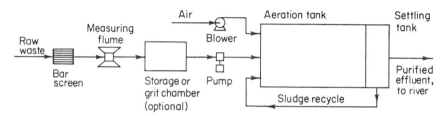

Fig. 3.   Prolonged bioaeration   process.

(3) *Oxidation ponding.* Treatment by oxidation pond is perhaps the cheapest method for reducing the pollution load in textile waste, if land is available. Wastewater flows through a shallow pond, usually about 4 feet deep if colorless, and 3 feet deep if dye wastes are present, with up to 30 days retention time and a BOD loading of about 50 lb/acre/day. BOD loadings can range up to 90 or more if the waste has been biologically pretreated and seeded. Oxygen from air and from algae production feeds the active organisms which stabilize the organic matter. Recirculation may be used to prevent anaerobic conditions. Economy in treatment by this method consists in low construction and low maintenance costs, because of simplicity of operations. Disadvantages are the usual scarcity of land located at least $\frac{1}{5}$ mile from all residences, and the problem of controlling insects.

INDUSTRIAL TRENDS

GROWTH PATTERNS

The textile industry is entering a new phase of industrial growth, through application of research to improve manufacturing machinery and to develop new chemicals and processes for improving wear and esthetic properties of fabrics. This trend may have some effect on pollutional characteristics of wastes, but the over-all problem of waste treatment will not be significantly changed.

Increased production is expected to follow population growth, as in other industries, resulting in greater pollution loads in textile waste effluents even though the pollution per unit of production may be lower. Cotton, once king, is giving way to fabrics made of synthetic fibers and blends of cotton. The consumption of cotton and of textiles in general is expected to remain nearly constant, with less wool but considerably more synthetic and man-made fibers used to supply the population growth in the future.

MANUFACTURING AND CONSUMER CHANGES

New machinery may reduce the amount of pollution in certain operations by requiring less processing. In other cases, water consumption may be decreased but the concentration of pollution increased.

New chemicals are constantly being developed to improve the usefulness and esthetic appeal of textile products offered to please the real and fancied needs of demanding and fastidious consumers. Properties imparted to fabrics by chemicals, which then require disposal, are brilliant shades and hues of color, wash and wear finishes, water and oil repellency, fire retardation, luster, "hand" or feel, nonshrinkage, and stretch. The never-ending cycle of style changes increases the demand for more appealing and exciting properties in fabrics. New dyes and finishing agents are constantly being developed. Chemical manufacturers are striving to develop textile finishing chemicals with lower pollution loads; for example, there is an outstanding need to develop improved low pollutional carriers or dyeing assistants for Dacron fabrics, which may now be as high as 8000 mg/liter BOD in typical scouring baths. No adverse effect on waste treatment is expected from new dyes or finishes, but selection based on pollutional effects should be considered.

RESEARCH NEEDS

Research needs and solutions to problems are based principally on economy. It is generally accepted that research is needed to abate pollution more effectively and at lower cost. Each plant problem may be considered a special research project, with the following procedure of study suggested.

In evaluation of the problem, all textile wastes may be considered to have similar characteristics, but each plant should make a study of its own waste as a special problem. Data must be obtained on the magnitude of the problem, the volume of flows, strength, characteristics, and toxicity of individual and combined wastes.

Reduction of chemicals and conservation of processing water may be brought about by in-plant changes such as improved process control; reduced concentrations of chemicals in sizing, bleaching, and dyeing; substitution of chemicals with low pollutional characteristics for those with high BOD; recovery and reuse of chemicals such as scour and bleach solutions, chromates, and caustic soda; solvent recovery of dye carriers; modification of processes to reduce waste flow; and adoption of good housekeeping methods, to stop spillage or other loss of chemicals to drains.

Stream assimilation studies are necessary to determine maximum permissible waste load and the degree of treatment needed after in-plant changes. Studies on joint treatment of wastes with municipal sewage involve determination of compatibility, and economic evaluation to avoid unnecessary expenditures.

Each plant must study its own possible treatment methods to obtain the best treatment at the lowest cost. This involves a search of the literature, or the setting up of a pilot plant, preferably with the aid of an experienced consultant who is scientifically trained in wastewater problems. It is desirable to consider all of the treatment methods mentioned above, particularly prolonged bioaeration and oxidation ponding processes. One State regulatory agency reports that 80% of all plants currently being constructed are based on aeration methods, because of higher efficiency and economy. Trickling filters, especially the plastic type followed by polishing in oxidation ponds, should also be considered.

SUMMARY

A vast amount of research has been contributed by the cotton, synthetics, and wool segments of the textile industry in striving for newer and better ways to clean up streams. The Textile Foundation, the New England Interstate Water Pollution Control Commission, and the American Association of Textile Chemists and Colorists have made outstanding contributions in both research and data. Wastes formerly considered untreatable by conventional methods are now being treated by processes developed through research. The textile industry recognizes its obligation in conserving water, using it, treating it, and returning it to the stream for others to use. The industry is constantly changing as new fibers and new processes are developed by expanded research programs. Technological advances in improved waste treatment methods can be expected to ensure an even more concentrated effort in accelerating studies to provide clean streams. Awareness by the textile industry of its obligations assures emphasis on continued research in all phases of water conservation.

REFERENCES

1. Ridgway, F., *Chem. Eng.* **70**, No. 1, 40–42 (Jan. 7, 1963).
2. Souther, R. H., and Alspaugh, T. A., *Am. Dyestuff Rptr.* **44**, 390–395 (1955).
3. Souther, R. H., and Alspaugh, T. A., *Sewage Ind. Wastes* **30**, 992–1011 (1958).
4. U.S. Public Health Service, "An Industrial Waste Guide to the Cotton Textile Industry," 1959.

Chapter 22

LEATHER

by FRED O'FLAHERTY[*]

Basic raw materials for leather manufacture are the hides of cattle and the skins of certain other animals. To some extent, these are coproducts or by-products in the preparation of edible meats. The initial stages of manufacture, including animal handling, slaughtering, and skinning, are covered in the chapter on Meat; the present chapter begins with receipt of the hides, fresh or preserved, at the tannery. From certain types of animal, the skin is the only material of value; but waste problems of the preliminary operations may be deduced from the more common products and practices.

THE LEATHER INDUSTRY

The leather industry is one of man's oldest manufacturing industries, as the making of leather began in antiquity among the most primitive men. Skins from animals which furnished food were used as protective shelters and clothing. Through empiric processes, a technical industry has developed with units in many states.

Early tanneries were located on streams, as these provided transportation for hides, chemicals, and tanning materials to the tannery and for finished leather to the manufacturer of leather goods. These same streams provided process water and served as channels for the disposition of waste by-products and effluents of the tanneries.

At the turn of the century there were nearly 1000 tanneries in the United States; many were small and rudimentary in their structure. In the past 60 years the number has been reduced until today there are only a few hundred, and most of these are sizable firms with more than one unit.

The leather industry is really many industries, as each type of leather constitutes a different process with little standardization. Basically there are only three or four types of tannage, but the finishing processes are more numerous. This allows only generalization in discussing waste disposal. Tannery processes are shown in the flow sheets of Figs. 1 and 2.

[*] With the technical counsel and assistance of J. D. Eye, Associate Professor of Civil Engineering, and W. T. Roddy, Director of the Tanners' Council Laboratory, both of the University of Cincinnati.

Sole, belting, and saddlery leathers are tanned with infusions of barks, wood, nuts, and leaves; this is the vegetable tanning process. Shoe upper leathers may be made from calf, goat, horse, or cattle hides tanned with mineral salts, which constitutes the chrome tanning process. Some leathers are tanned by a combination of vegetable and chrome or in combination with the newer synthetic tanning materials.

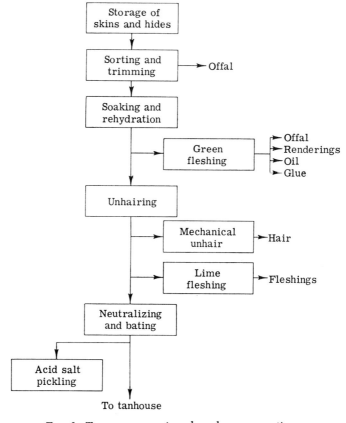

FIG. 1. Tannery processing: beamhouse operations.

In recent years substitute tannages have been developed, such as the syntans and synthetic tans. Some leathers are tanned with formaldehyde, and white leathers are tanned with zirconium salts in a process similar to chrome tanning.

All skins and hides are voided of hair and extraneous tissues before being tanned. This is accomplished by steeping the hides in a saturated lime solution fortified with sodium sulfide or similar materials. The skins and hides are subjected to enzyme treatment to remove the final hair debris and to control swelling.

In all the processes, water is an essential factor. Chemical composition of the water used is considered most important to obtaining desired quality in the leather produced. A tanner with two plants in different locations within the same state may find it difficult to make the same quality leather in both tanneries. The only standard recognized is that distilled

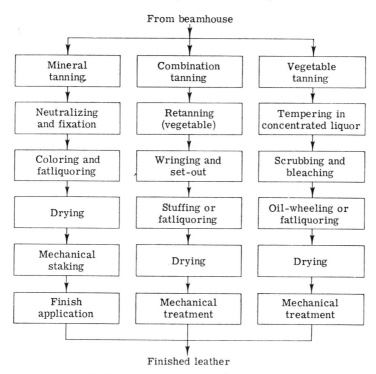

FIG. 2. Tannery processing: tanhouse operations.

water is best but, by treatment, the hardness and other qualities of natural waters are controlled and the water made satisfactory.

Microbiological standards are equally important, but can be controlled by the use of disinfectants. Tanners derive their water supply from many sources or combinations of sources: rivers, lakes, creeks, wells, and municipal supplies. There is practially no reusage of water by the tanning industry. There has been a constant increase in the ratio of water to leather produced; this accounts for better control and shorter time uses of water. In place of using a single soak water, the trend is to change the water 2 or 3 times for an operation.

There is continual change taking place in the chemicals used; therefore, the effluent is not constant from year to year. New developments in the leather industry promise to change the situation still further. The application of enzyme preparations for loosening of the hair will reduce the use of lime suspensions and the difficultly disposable sulfides.

Trimming and fleshing of hides at the packing house or hide processing establishment has eliminated coarse solids and reduced the quantity of smaller solids in tannery effluent.

Another development just past the pilot plant stage is the use of organic solvents in place of water in the processing of vegetable tanned and mineral or chrome tanned leathers. Wide adoption of this practice will materially change the tannery waste material. In the process of leather finishing, solvent-dispersed pigments are gradually replacing the aqueous-type finishes. Many of these newer innovations are still in an early stage of adoption. It is, however, conceivable that the next decade will see a large change in tannery procedures.

Data on the volume of skins and hides processed in the United States is available for the year 1961. Because sole leathers are sold by the pound and most other leathers by the square foot, production comparisons are difficult. The following data are presented as numbers of skins or hides.

Cattle hides, from which shoe upper leather, shoe sole leathers, patent leather, upholstery leather, luggage leather, harness, and miscellaneous items are made, amount to more than 25 million hides, all of domestic slaughter. Kips are skins of a weight group between calves and cattle; they represent a fully developed calfskin or an immature cattle hide. This group, used mainly for men's shoe upper leather, comprised a domestic slaughter of 1,860,000 pieces in 1961. Calfskins, used mainly for shoe upper leather, included 7,370,000 skins of domestic slaughter and a 1961 import of more than 2½ million skins.

Goat and kid skins are mainly imported, as the domestic slaughter is low. The total of such skins processed into leather in 1961 was about 13,761,000 pieces. Goat and kid skins are used in shoe uppers and in leather linings for shoes. Cabretta and hair sheepskins are used in the manufacture of gloves and garments. The total production is imported and amounted to 2,500,000 in 1961. Sheepskins, which are made into shoe linings, gloves, and some garments, were mostly imported in 1961, with a total of 29,959,000 skins. Shearlings are sheep skins which are processed with the wool left on after shearing or clipping. In 1961 these amounted to 2,250,000 pieces.

Horse hides, used for aprons, gloves, garments, and cordovan shoes, are in ever diminishing supply which amounted to 260,000 pieces in 1961. There are also miscellaneous animal skins used to produce leathers, such as kangaroo, crocodile, and seal. No data on quantity are available.

The United States is now considered an export nation for cattle hides. We do not use all the domestic production and, while we do import certain types of cattle hides, the balance is in the direction of export.

In 1962 the total shoe production was more than 600 million pairs. The leather industry furnishes sole material for about 28% of this production; the shoe upper, insole, and lining business represents approximately 85% of the total leather production.

TANNERY WASTE CHARACTERISTICS

Tannery waste is mainly waterborne, and has all of the undesirable characteristics which make for pollution: high BOD, high solids, suspended solids, soluble materials, color, and odor. The discharge is highly putrefactive and its foul appearance and odor draw much attention by the agencies whose responsibility it is to control stream pollution. The industry has been referred to as one of the Four Horsemen of Pollution. This has served as a stimulus for research to find acceptable methods of treating tannery effluents.

For the period 1850 to about 1900, the Massachusetts State Board of Health was very active because of the concentration of tanneries in that state. As legislation was effected in other states, there has been a continuous program of research seeking the most effective and yet economic methods of tannery effluent treatment. Some of the large and more progressive tanners established departments of sanitary engineering where research was undertaken. Typical of this was the work sponsored by the U. S. Leather Company, of Ridgway, Pennsylvania, in cooperation with the state. The Tanners' Council of America, in addition to its support of basic research at the University of Cincinnati, published an educational bulletin, "What the Tanner Should Know About Sewage Disposal." Application of the basic principles established was slow to occur, because of lack of standardization in process and the circumstances and locations of the tanneries.

Continuous operations and intermittent discharges in the tannery cause the waste material to vary considerably in volume and concentrations. For a true evaluation of the industry's waste disposal situation it is necessary to consider many individual plants, each constituting a separate problem. Most of the operations concerned with processing animal skins into leather, from the first soaking and washing to the application of finishes, are not clearly understood technically. The chemical reactions in this conversion process are many and varied, and each adds some different material to the effluent in varying quantities.

In a tannery effluent we may encounter small bits of skin tissue, soluble proteins, hair, blood, dirt or filth, manure, earth, salts of many kinds, and much lime, all mixed with sulfides, sulfhydrates, amines, chrome and vegetable tanning agents, sugars, starches, oils and fats, acids, alkalies, dyes, and pigments. The quantity and concentration of the contaminants preclude the possibility of direct discharge into a receiving stream without at least primary treatment. Today no commercial tannery in the United States discharges its waste without at least primary treatment, and many have secondary or even tertiary treatment systems.

Tannery wastes are evaluated for their pollutional potential by such tests as BOD; total, dissolved, settleable, and suspended solids; pH, causticity, and free mineral acidity; color and turbidity; chlorides; sulfides; Kjeldahl nitrogen; lipids; and taste and odor. Biological oxygen demand, which is an accepted criterion of effluent pollution, is used extensively in evaluation of tannery waste discharge, and is usually very high in comparison with domestic sewage. The BOD of mixed wastes from the beamhouse and bleach house has been reported by McKee and Camp (2) as being from 500 to 2000 mg/liter, and as high as 45,000 mg/liter from spent vegetable tan liquors. In instances where effluents of various parts of the tannery can be combined, mixed, and discharged at a uniform rate over a 24-hour period, the BOD can be reduced to 1000 mg/liter or lower by this treatment alone.

It is estimated that the BOD of the average tannery will amount to 7 or 8 lb for each 100 lb of hide made into leather. Another figure which has been developed is that each pound of hide processed per day is equivalent in oxygen demand to one-half person. This means that a 100-lb hide is the equivalent per day of 50 persons, in the BOD of tannery waste compared with domestic sewage. When we consider that a 1000 hide per day tannery is average, the magnitude of the BOD loading can be realized. For this reason, sanitarians are seriously concerned with BOD reduction and control. In the report of studies conducted by the Tannery Waste Disposal Committee of Pennsylvania, Howalt and Cavett (1) reported that 6% of the waste discharged was responsbile for 50% of the total oxygen demand. They also showed that intermittent flow discharge was accountable for as much as 75% of the oxygen demand, whereas when the discharge was blended and discharged at a regular rate the BOD was greatly reduced. The ratio of gallons of water to pounds of hide processed varies greatly from plant to plant, even among those that make the same type of leather. The lower this ratio, the greater the concentration of contaminants and the higher the BOD.

The chief source of BOD in a tannery effluent is the beamhouse, where hide trimming, soaking, washing, liming, and bating take place. Other areas contribute lesser amounts. In a brochure on tannery wastes published and distributed by the New England Interstate Water Pollution Control Commission (4), much data is given; the following tables are adapted from this publication. Tables I and II show the average composition of effluents from a cattleskin and a pigskin tannery, listing the various processes and their contributions to BOD and other pollutants.

In studies made by Maskey (3) at the Tanners' Council Research Laboratory, data were collected on a sole leather tannery. He reported the BOD and other pollutional parameters as listed in Table III. The solids in tannery waste are mainly the extraneous matters listed above and the soluble proteins of the hide. A hide as removed from the animal will have about 65% moisture content; it will produce a leather with about 12% moisture with a yield of about 70 lb of leather for each 100 lb of hide. The total solids of a typical vegetable tannery (where sole, belting strap, case, and upholstery leathers are processed) may be as high as 7000 mg/liter. About half of this will be organic which, being putrescible, accounts for the malodors associated with such tannery effluent.

The average present-day tannery has 2000–3000 mg/liter of suspended solids before treatment. This consists of shreds of skin tissue, hair, and excess lime, as well as chemical precipitates. Where poorly treated effluents have been discharged with high suspended solids present, they have caused sludge deposits in the receiving stream or sewer. In time these deposits may become considerable, requiring dredging or sewer cleaning. In untreated tannery discharge, the settleable solids vary from 7 to 12%. Their removal is an essential operation in the treatment of tannery wastes.

Because the chemical reactions in the process of leather making vary from high acidity to high alkalinity, the pH of a tannery waste varies also. In those plants where mixing is practiced, the acid is neutralized by the alkali which is usually in excess, and the resultant pH is alkaline in the range from 8 to 11. The pickle liquors (sulfuric acid and sodium chloride) have a pH of 2 or less. Chrome liquors are 3–5 pH, vegetable liquors vary from 3 to 6, and the lime liquors which contain sulfides and amines may be as high as 13 pH. It is evident that mixing of all tannery discharges into a single system is the most practical and economic method for control of BOD, solids, and pH.

Turbidity in tannery waste is caused by many of the constituents in the effluent and is directly associated with the color, which varies from a dirty brown to greens, blues, and a milky appearance. The vegetable tans are reddish tan but when the tans come into contact with iron salts an inky black or intermediate shades result. The wastes also contain dyes and pigments, but the latter are usually in such small quantities that they

TABLE I

Cattleskin Tannery Survey (Average Composition of Strong Liquors)

Process	Volume, gal per day	Biochemical oxygen demand		lb per 1000 lb of hide	Sodium chloride, mg per liter	Total hardness, mg per liter	Protein, mg per liter	Total solids, mg per liter	Volatile solids, mg per liter
		mg per liter	lb per day						
Soak	73,100	2,200	1340	15[a]	20,000	670	1,900	30,000	3,600
Unhair	27,200	15,500	3520	40[a]	18,000	25,000	22,700	78,000	18,000
Relime	27,200	650	150	2[a]	3,500	25,000	–	20,300	2,500
Delime and bate	17,600	6,000	880	10[b]	<10	4,100	4,300	15,000	8,800
Pickle	9,800	2,900	240	3[b]	47,000	2,400	–	79,000	7,200
Chrome tan	8,500	6,500[c]	460	8[b]	26,000	1,800	–	93,000	13,000
Color and fat liquor									
First dump	5,100	2,000	85	3[a]	–	–	–	16,000	8,000
Second dump	5,100	2,200	95	3[a]	250	2,600	–	9,500	4,900
Total	173,600	–	6770	–	–	–	–	–	–

Taken from Masselli et al. (4) with slight modifications.

[a] Based on wet salted hide.
[b] Based on fleshed split hide after relime.
[c] Estimated at 50% of volatile solids concentration.
[d] Based on chrome tanned leather.

TABLE II

PIGSKIN TANNERY SURVEY (AVERAGE COMPOSITION OF STRONG LIQUORS)

Process	Volume, gal per day	Biochemical oxygen demand mg per liter	lb per day	lb per 1000 lb of hide	Sodium chloride, mg per liter	Total hardness, mg per liter	Protein, mg per liter	Total solids, mg per liter	Volatile solids, mg per liter
Soak	3,000	2,400	60	17[a]	35,000	—	—	28,000	2,300
Unhair	4,000	14,000	467	70[b]	5,700	38,000	18,400	55,000	12,900
Delime and bate	4,000	4,400	147	23[b]	640	4,200	1,600	14,000	7,400
Pickle	700	4,200	25	9[b]	80,000	—	—	98,000	12,000
Degrease									
Kerosene layer	340	—	(1210)[c]	435+[a]	—	—	—	—	—
Brine layer	800	2,600	17	7	100,000	—	—	110,000	2,300
Vegetable tan	30	24,000	6	2[d]	—	—	—	93,000	25,000
Chrome tan	600	2,300[e]	12	5[d]	51,000	—	—	80,000	4,600
Color and fat liquor									
First dump	1,000	490	4	1[f]	410	—	—	3,950	890
Second dump	1,000	3,950	33	8[f]	135	—	—	3,980	3,030
Total	15,470	—	771	—	—	—	—	—	—

Taken from Masselli et al. (4) with slight modifications.

[a] Based on wet salted hide.

[b] Based on fleshed hide after soaking (30% flesh removed).

[c] Calculated from kerosene (53% BOD) only. Not included in total.

[d] Based on pickled hide.

[e] Estimated at 50% of volatile solids concentration.

[f] Based on leather.

TABLE III
Effluent from a Sole Leather Tannery

Waste	BOD			Sulfides			Dissolved solids			Total organic N			Sulfates		
	Max	Min	Avg	Max	Min	Avg	Max	Min	Avg	Max	Min	Avg	Max	Min	Avg
Slush wheel	2375	530	1272	50.0	17.8	34.5	12,608	4,560	8,295	74.2	44.8	60.6	269	230	248
16-hr Soak	400	125	332	16.3	13.4	14.6	16,109	2,707	9,912	34.3	26.6	30.1	250	230	238
6-hr Soak	400	110	243	12.4	2.4	8.7	7,455	2,080	3,857	53.2	40.6	44.3	257	222	240
Lime	3975	2225	3201	121.4	84.1	97.1	25,026	14,820	20,618	218.4	163.8	188.7	308	273	292
Wash wheel	700	335	475	—	—	—	1,333	1,021	1,186	92.4	65.8	78.4	240	222	230
Bate	185	130	151	—	—	—	1,212	1,150	1,174	226.9	196.0	210.0	230	212	222

All units in milligrams per liter.
Taken from Maskey (3).

influence the total color only to a minor degree. The most serious aspect of turbidity is its blocking out of sunlight and its effect on aquatic life.

The toxicity of tannery waste is of minor consideration, but such materials as arsenic, chromium, high acidity or alkalinity, and sulfides are present and can be objectionable if they are in high enough concentration. The salts and chemicals in a tannery effluent are many, including sodium chloride, soda ash, sulfides with their reducing action, and amines. Some of these can be toxic to aquatic life and can cause malodors. The total malodors are also contributed to by organic matter when it decomposes and by hydrogen sulfide formed from contact of sulfides with acids.

When hides or skins are soaked and washed in water, depilated in saturated lime which may contain as much as 15% undissolved lime, and bated in an enzyme liquor, there is removed from the hide a quantity of nonfibrous proteins. These are albumins, globulins, mucoids, and mucopolysaccharides, commonly referred to in tannery parlance as the cement substances, and constituting the soluble proteins. These globular proteins are in various stages of denaturization. It is not known just what role these materials play in the final leathers, but from each of the beamhouse processes they contribute to the total nitrogen found in the effluent. All skin proteins are capable of chemical breakdown in the waste and are contributors to the turbidity, malodors, and BOD of the effluent.

In all skins and hides there is a certain amount of lipid material. Waxy fats come from the sebaceous glands, phospholipids from the body of the hide, and the neutral fats, mainly triglycerides, occur as extraneous tissue beneath the hide. The fleshy fatty tissue is removed mechanically but fragments get into the tannery waste. Sebaceous fats are mostly removed by the depilation process; neutral fats are partially removed as soaps in the lime bath and these soaps and fatty acids contribute to the effluent. When present in large quantities as in the hide of force-fed cattle, the amount of fat is so great it interferes with the tanning process. It is common practice to remove or to redistribute such collections of fats by solvent extraction.

After the skin or hide has been tanned it must be lubricated; for this a bath of sulfated and raw oils is applied to the still wet leather. The partially exhausted fat liquors become a part of the total effluent. The adverse influence of fats on biological treatment of industrial waste is well known, so the tanner in his treatment systems uses all means of reducing it to a minimum. With the use of solvents and surface-active agents in the various processes, some fatty material does get into the effluent.

A list of the more common chemicals used in tanneries is given in Table IV, with their BOD values where these are significant.

TABLE IV

CONSUMPTION OF PROCESS CHEMICALS IN UNITED STATES CATTLESKIN TANNERIES

Chemical	Annual consumption, lb	Biochemical oxygen demand	
		per cent of chemical	mg per liter in waste
Sodium chloride (used in pickling)	1,368,000	–	684
Sodium chloride (used in curing)	4,408,000	–	2200
Lime	2,470,000	–	1235
Sodium sulfide (62% Na₂S, 25% S⁻⁻)	981,000	40	490
Sulfuric acid	350,000	–	175
Soda ash	161,000	–	80
Oropon [95% (NH₄)₂SO₄]	144,000	5	72
Calcium formate	88,000	12	44
Lactic acid (30%)	77,000	32	38
Sodium formate	56,000	2	28
Sterizol	42,000	–	20
Ammonium chloride	20,000	–	10
Chemicals absorbed by the hides[a]			
Tanolin R (basic chromium sulfate, 16% Cr)	1,670,000	–	626[b]
Tamol L (naphthalene sulfonic acid–formaldehyde resin)	729,000	–	36
D-1 oil	37,000	83	2
Other oils	650,000	80	33
Quebracho (tannin)	146,000	5	7
Soya-rich flour	100,000	–	5
Tanbark H	88,000	11	4
Titanium dioxide	88,000	–	4
Ade 11 tan	38,000	–	2
Gambade	156,000	4	8
Maratan B	136,000	–	7
Methocel	20,000	6	1
Orotan TV	30,000	5	2
Semi-sol glue	37,000	–	2
Upper tan	28,000	–	1

[a] Absorption estimated at 90% with 10% discharged to waste. Milligrams per liter in waste is based on 10% of the pounds used.

[b] Based on 75% discharged to waste.

TANNERY WASTE DISPOSAL

The ideal method of waste disposal is the removal of contaminants before discharge or their recovery for reuse. This must be considered in the light of economics. The tannery industry is a low profit investment and the large volume of effluent tends to defeat any economic recovery process. Leather processes in general are the result of centuries of operating empirically, with a lack of detailed technical understanding of how each step in the total process is accomplished. This has resulted in a reluctance to change, and even a step like reuse of materials is generally avoided.

Modifications such as change in materials used, proper maintenance of equipment, improved good housekeeping, automation to eliminate human errors, recovery and separate disposal of materials which are pollutants, and the installation of more efficient treatment systems are all significant. In considering process changes we must realize that there are many different processes for each type of leather and each type of tannage. Even when two tanneries are producing the same type of leather, there will be radical differences. This means that no standard modification can be recommended or adopted. The problem is individual at each facility. There is, however, a constant series of changes in process occurring as further research in the technology of tanning is completed and as new methods are developed. The selection of new materials is done on an economic basis in most instances, but more recently there are many changes being made with pollution reduction as the stimulus.

In the late 1920's it was discovered that mellow lime unhairing systems could be developed by the use of primary amines. The amines replaced the mixture of amines and their associated by-products formed at the expense of the skin or hide protein substance while being unhaired. This discovery of the use of amines lacked commercial adoption until the 1960's when, because of objections to high sulfide content of tannery effluents, the sulfides and sulfhydrates were replaced by such materials as dimethylamine sulfate (DMA). This substance is now being used in the absence of lime. Use of DMA has been more acceptable because the amine odor is absent until the DMA is placed in the unhairing bath. The absence of lime also makes for a more desirable effluent.

Another change in materials presently being adopted by many tanners is the use of proteolytic enzymes for loosening the hair. This too eliminates the use of lime in the unhairing system. In both of these changes, there is a reduction of solids in the tannery effluent. The influence of these newer unhairing processes on BOD has not been fully established.

Equipment changes in the tannery are seldom made with effluent improvement in mind; yet in some instances such changes have been effective in reducing pollution. Paddle wheel pits for agitation of the stock during unhairing and bating are being replaced in most tanneries by drums; this allows for a nearly continuous process, without dumping of the stock after each process step, and results in a one-time use of water, which has less pollutants when discharged.

One of the most effective improvements in tannery effluent has resulted from better housekeeping. Most pollution is developed in the beamhouse. This is one place in a tannery where it has been difficult to get reliable workers, because in the past it involved wet and dirty work in a malodorous atmosphere. Today, with tanners situated in urban locations, any odor has become objectionable. In consequence, the modern tanner keeps such places clean by daily washes. This has eliminated the accumulation of decaying scraps and has resulted in a more dilute total effluent.

In a tannery there is little opportunity at the present time for true automation, but advances have been made in control systems and have resulted in more uniform processing and a more uniform effluent. The character of skins and hides is such, however, that tanning is still a single piece system where much human judgment is required.

Many attempts have been made to recover chemicals from the discharges of the several processes. A typical example is the recovery of chromium tanning chemicals. In no case has an economic method been discovered. Because the leather industry is a relatively low profit industry, such methods of recovery are measured in dollars, and to date none have been adopted. The uneconomic recovery of chrome has brought to light the possibility of reuse of spent chrome liquor through replenishing its concentration by adding strong solution. This has permitted reuse for as many as 15 times, with no adverse results.

One of the undesirable pollutants in tannery effluents has been the spent vegetable tan liquors. These liquors, in the past, were produced by leaching various woods, barks, leaves, and nuts, with accompanying weak runoff liquors. With the United States no longer having appropriate chestnut or oak trees, the tanner purchases his vegetable tanning extracts from foreign sources. Because almost all sole leather or vegetable tanning is done in plants located in or near rural areas, the use of lagoons is common and the discharged tanning material is no great problem. Synthetic tanning materials are used in combination with natural and mineral tanning materials. The synthetic materials are expensive and are used only in small quantities; most of them are absorbed by the hide and remain as part of the leather.

Although most of the existing tanneries are quite old, occasionally new plants are being built. All such new plants are located so that tannery wastes are conveniently discharged into municipal sewerage systems, or a disposal system has been planned in keeping with the location selected.

Primary treatment is by screening, settling basins, and lagoons. Some tanners have secondary treatment plants. Prior to 1915, there were practically no treatment facilities at any tannery. This was possible because most tanneries were small and were located on large streams or lakes. In the early years of the 1900's it became evident that this discharge of raw waste material could not continue. By 1910 many studies had begun; although no sensational disposal methods were developed, it was found that many of the methods used in other industries were applicable to tannery waste disposal.

Today each tannery uses the system that is best, depending upon its location and the volume of its effluent. Lagoon and reservoir systems, with controlled volume discharge, are used by many large tanneries. A recent development is the industry-supported research in biological methods, which should have application in the future. Because a tannery has many departments producing discharges, it has been well established that combining of all discharges into a holding tank, where mixing is accomplished, constitutes the best first step. This may be followed by screening, precipitation, and filtration. The disposal of tannery waste has been a changing matter through the centuries and all indications are that it will continue so.

INDUSTRY TRENDS

The leather industry is constantly undergoing changes. In a decade there has been more than a 50% reduction in the number of tanneries; most of those discontinuing were small, although some of the largest sole leather tanneries also were closed. This has resulted in a smaller total number of tanneries, but most of those remaining are large. Only two new tanneries were established during the 1950's, and their locations were determined by the waste disposal situation among other factors. Present-day large tanneries all have technical personnel; although only one or two have sanitary engineers, the others depend upon sanitary engineering firms to provide equivalent services.

In the leather industry it is the rule rather than the exception that a period of 10 years or more will lapse between research and its development and application. This was true in the adoption of amines to replace sulfides, and may also occur for the adoption of enzyme unhairing. During the early 1960's there was completed a fundamental study of the use of enzymes for unhairing hides. Pilot-scale operations have demonstrated the practicability of this process, and some trial experiments have been conducted in tanneries, though full adoption will require many years. This process would entirely eliminate the use of lime and sulfides, which are among the major contaminants in tannery waste.

Another equally revolutionary process, which had its beginning as far back as 1912 and was completed through pilot-scale demonstrations in

1961, is the use of organic solvents in place of salt cure preservation of skins and hides and in place of water in vegetable tanning liquors. Both of these developments could greatly reduce tannery effluent pollution, by elimination of waste salt at the packing plant, the hide dealer, and the tannery. It would also reduce the volume of liquid waste, as the solvents are economically recoverable. The main drawback to adoption is the cost of new plants in which solvents could be safely handled.

Another important factor which militates against revolutionary changes is the ever increasing development of substitutes to replace leather. In 20 years the use of leather soles in shoes decreased from 95 to 28%. The balance, better than 600 million pairs of shoes, have soles of synthetic material. Materials are also being developed to replace the leather in shoe uppers.

A new process, still in the experimental stage, is the production of reconstituted leather. This involves reduction of the proteins of animal skin to a homogeneous mass and their re-formation into a fabric. This product could be used in any place where natural leather is used, and its development could have far reaching effect. If the less desirable areas of a hide could be economically used to make reconstituted leather, rectangular pattern pieces could be produced from the hide minus shanks, belly, and head areas. This in turn would permit a greater degree of mechanization in the tannery, produce a more uniform leather, and eliminate much waste.

In two decades there has been a material reduction in upholstery, harness, and mechanical leathers. This trend will continue and add to the shrinkage of the industry. Of more immediate interest is the present transition to resin finishes from aqueous pigment finishes. The leather industry, the oldest manufacturing industry of man, though thousands of centuries old, is ever changing. There is no question about its continuing; it has met competition in the past and will do so in the future. The problems of leather industry waste disposal will be met through research and development.

REFERENCES

1. Howalt, W., and Cavett, E. S., *Proc. Am. Soc. Civil Engrs.* **53**, 1675–1712 (1927).
2. McKee, J. E., and Camp, T. R., *Sewage Ind. Wastes* **22**, 803–806 (1950).
3. Maskey, D. F., *J. Am. Leather Chemists' Assoc.* **36**, 121–141 (1941).
4. Masselli, J. W., Masselli, N. W., and Burford, M. G. (Hall Laboratory of Chemistry, Wesleyan University, Middletown, Conn.), "Tannery Wastes: Pollution Sources and Methods of Treatment." New England Interstate Water Pollution Control Commission, 1958.
5. Sutherland, R., *Ind. Eng. Chem.* **39**, 628–631 (1947).

General Industries

Chapter 23

POWER
_____

by L. W. CADWALLADER

This chapter covers the electric power industry, which is the principal source of power in the United States, and applies generally to investor-owned utilities, rural electric cooperatives, and governmental agencies engaged in the production of electricity. Not included are captive industrial power facilities which are an integral part of industrial manufacturing processes.

Although it is beyond the scope of this book, progress has been made in research laboratories in connection with the direct conversion of either chemical or heat energy into electric energy. Among the methods studied, 5 may have potential as power generators in the future. They are the thermoelectric generator, the thermionic converter, the fuel cell, the magnetohydrodynamic (MHD) generator, and the fusion reactor. The current stage of development of these concepts ranges from laboratory experimentation to operating prototypes. The most promising appears to be the magnetohydrodynamic process, which utilizes high-temperature high-velocity ionized gas to produce electricity. The only reason for mentioning these exotic energy conversion concepts is to recognize the existence of such research work. No further reference is made to them in this chapter.

This chapter considers the types of equipment commonly used for generating electric power, and the thermal and chemical wastes associated therewith. Reference is made to hydroelectric power plants, conventional fossil fuel plants burning coal, oil, or gas, and atomic or nuclear power plants. Although atomic or nuclear energy is still not a significant source of electricity in the United States, its use is constantly expanding and the outlook is optimistic. The thermal and chemical wastes of an atomic power plant are not different from those of conventional fossil fuel plants. The problem of radioactive wastes from atomic installations is covered in the chapter on Atomic Energy.

Hydroelectric or water power accounted for almost 20% of the electric power generated in this country in 1962. This was a decrease from 27% in 1951, and the percentage is expected to continue decreasing with time.

Hydroelectric power has no wastes, and until recently was considered to have only a beneficial effect on the water. However, in recent years, a new concept has developed concerning river and stream pollution connected with high dams with large, deep impoundment reservoirs. In earlier developments of river impoundments for power production, water storage, flood control, and irrigation, consideration was not given to such river regulation as a contributor to stream pollution. In the past, most large power dams were built in remote areas where river pollution was not a problem. At present, however, and in some areas, attention is being given to the pollution factor related to storage of water in large, deep impoundments. Changes in water quality may occur during storage, and these may constitute a problem which, in some respects, is similar to the pollution effect resulting from sanitary and industrial wastes.

Recent investigations have revealed that the storage of water in deep reservoirs for long periods results in reduction in dissolved oxygen concentration and, under some conditions, may cause an increase in the organic and inorganic content of the water at certain seasons of the year. These conditions are brought about by stratification of the reservoir water due to density differences related to temperature. During seasonal overturn of stratified reservoirs, the degraded bottom water may be devoid of oxygen, and downstream water supplies may be adversely affected by taste- and odor-producing substances and other undesirable contaminants.

Because of this problem, several hydroelectric power developments in the southeastern United States have been provided with a submerged secondary dam or weir designed to direct surface water of high oxygen content into the water wheel intakes, thereby providing good quality water for aquatic life downstream.

No segment of the electric power industry was specifically associated with problems relating to the use and pollution of the nation's water resources until after the termination of World War II. Prior to that time, the yardsticks for measuring water pollution were related to chemical and bacteriological standards, and the majority of laws and regulations governing water quality were based upon such standards.

In the years since World War II, there has developed in this country a growing realization that excessive increases in the temperature of a body of water can have deleterious effects. Fish, shellfish, and other aquatic life are adversely affected by excessively high temperature. In addition, increased water temperature reduces the level of dissolved oxygen concentration and hence produces the same effect as BOD pollution. Increased water temperature, often combined with lowered dissolved oxygen concentration, may have adverse effects on the life cycle of fish and other aquatic animals, and may increase the toxicity effects of other pollutants on aquatic life. Raising the temperature of water by sunlight or by artificial means such as industrial or power plant activities causes complex chemical reactions that influence, for good or bad, the biological life of the nation's watercourses.

This new concept is referred to as "thermal pollution." The power industry, as well as other industries, is concerned with this form of pollution, resulting from the addition of heat to natural waters. Thermal pollution is of particular concern to the electric power industry because approximately 80% of the total electricity produced is generated in steam-electric plants requiring large quantities of water for cooling purposes. Atomic power plants have a similar cooling water requirement.

In addition to the problem of heated water discharges, technological developments in power production have resulted in the creation of occasional chemical wastes not hitherto present.

THE INDUSTRY

The use of electricity has become so essential in the home, on the farm, and in all commerce and industry that the total amount of electricity generated is a good index of over-all industrial and economic potential and prosperity. With only 6% of the world's population, the United States leads in the production of electricity, generating 37% of all the electricity produced in the world in the year 1962. A total of 860 billion kilowatt-hours was generated in the United States (not including Alaska and Hawaii) in 1962 by the electric utility industry, including all plants contributing to the public supply. This was almost as much as the combined output of Russia, the United Kingdom, Japan, Western Germany, Canada, and France.

Of this total of 860 billion kilowatt-hours, 651 billion or 75.7% was generated by investor-owned companies, 6 billion or 0.7% by rural electric cooperatives, 195 billion or 22.7% by all types of governmental agencies, and 8 billion or 0.9% came from other sources. In addition to the above, industrial plants produced 84 billion kilowatt-hours for their own use in their manufacturing processes.

As stated previously, almost 80% of the total electricity now produced in this country is generated in steam power plants, and almost 20% in hydroelectric plants. The remaining fraction of 1% is produced by internal combustion engines.

Of particular significance, from the standpoint of industrial wastewater control, is the upward trend in the percentage of power generated in thermal power plants and the downward trend in the percentage of hydroelectric power. For instance, since 1951 the percentage of steam power has increased from 72% to almost 80% and the percentage of hydroelectric power has decreased from 27% to less than 20%. This trend may well continue in the future, and will be implemented by the advent of economical atomic power.

Based on past experience and predictions for the future, the electric utility industry can expect its load to double approximately every 10 years. The true significance of this rate of growth is apparent when it is projected for a substantial period of time—say, 30 years. Thus, in the year 1970 the nation's electrical requirements can be expected to be twice its 1960 requirements, its 1980 requirements four times its 1960 requirements, its 1990 requirements eight times its 1960 requirements. This forecast brings into focus the magnitude of the problem facing the power industry. Figure 1 shows the actual growth of the electric power

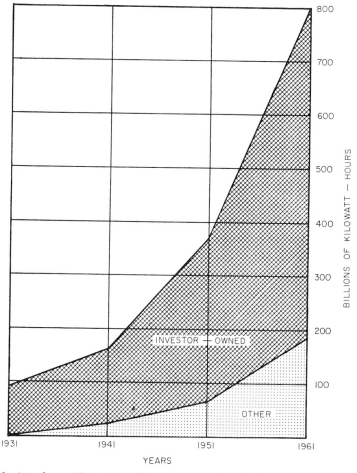

Fig. 1. Actual growth in kilowatt-hour output of total electric utility industry.

industry in 10-year periods from 1931 through 1961. It may be noted that, for the 30-year period covered by this graph, there was an eightfold increase in the production of electricity. It is anticipated that this rate of growth will continue for the foreseeable future.

This growth in electric utility systems requires a huge annual capital investment for additions to generating facilities and for expansion of transmission and distribution systems. The annual investment of the electric utility industry in new facilities is larger than that of any other industry. New construction expenditures of the investor-owned power industry have exceeded $3 billion each year since 1957, and are expected to reach a spending rate of $4 billion annually by 1965. Based on a stable economy, it is forecast that this rate of expenditure will approximately triple to $12 billion annually by 1980.

There are two essential ingredients in the production of electricity: water and fuel. While the type of fuel can vary, water is a common necessity to the generation of electricity in any significant quantity. It is of such importance as to cause the Generating Stations Special Technical Committee of the National Power Survey being conducted by the Federal Power Commission to make the following statement in its April 1963 report:

> Many of the factors which will determine future maximum plant size require difficult extensions to present engineering knowledge and experience. It can be concluded, however, that no single factor enumerated in the foregoing discussion (National Power Survey Advisory Committee Report No. 7), other than restricted circulating water supply, would likely limit station sizes up to 5,000 megawatts.

(One megawatt = 1000 kilowatts.)

While adequate water is essential to the production of electricity, the power industry is not a significant consumer of water. Water requirements of the power industry represent principally a water usage for cooling purposes, and the water is returned to its source unchanged except for an increase in temperature. The quantity of water actually consumed by the industry is generally considered to be negligible.

Certain areas of the United States, such as the coastal regions and the Great Lakes, have an abundance of cooling water the year round. Other areas of the country are not so favorably situated insofar as cooling water availability is concerned.

Restrictions on the total increase in water temperature permitted, or an upper limit on the temperature of the water returned to the river, can impose limitations on the generating capacity installed at a given site. Such limitations can be reduced or entirely eliminated by the installation of cooling towers or cooling ponds to provide supplementary cooling for additional generating capacity.

In general, many regions in which our major coal reserves are located do not have adequate river water supplies for large generating stations. Consequently, plants to be located in the coal mining regions must make careful provision to ensure adequate cooling water.

THERMAL WASTES

Rivers, lakes, and estuaries have a natural temperature pattern which, in the absence of industry and population, varies with atmospheric and weather conditions. In the past, many such bodies of water in this country have frozen over in the winter and have reached a natural summer temperature of 85°F or even higher under adverse conditions of minimum water flow accompanied by high air temperature and humidity. This is to say that, in most instances, nature alone produces severe temperature variations between summer and winter water temperatures.

The biological significance of temperature has been recognized by students of the natural sciences as one of the most important characteristics of the aquatic environment. One of the dominant forces in bringing about evolution through the geological ages has been variation in temperature. Geographical areas of the earth are characterized primarily by their temperature characteristics. Thus, we recognize the Arctic and Antarctic zones, the temperate zones, and the tropical zone. Even within a specific zone, there are seasonal temperature variations that greatly influence the aquatic environment and the type of aquatic community which is found in the various bodies of water. On a smaller scale, we recognize changes in day and night temperatures.

Because these various temperature cycles are so basic, the physiological changes and over-all behavior of aquatic organisms, as influenced by temperature, have been studied for many years. Aside from the recognized importance of temperature on the aquatic organisms, the ease of measuring this environmental characteristic has influenced the amount of research performed. It would not be surprising if temperature effects have been studied as much as any other single environmental factor.

Although temperature effects have been intensely studied, specific information needed to evaluate the effects of heated discharges on receiving waters is meager. This situation exists because most of the studies were performed in laboratories, using a single type of organism or a group of organisms with a limited diversity of species. In a natural aquatic environment, a great diversity of aquatic life is present. This is not simply an uncoordinated mass of living things; rather, the aquatic life exists in an intricately balanced system, often referred to as the biody-namic cycle. Within this system are found a host of organisms, ranging from bacteria and algae through the higher forms such as fish and shell-fish.

This biodynamic cycle is competitive, and may be thought of as a food chain between the lower and higher forms of aquatic life. Actually, the food chain does not consist of a single series of links, but rather of a series of chains that are sometimes interlinked. Conditions which break one series of links do not necessarily destroy the over-all cycle. When conditions become severe, as with extreme pollution, the cycle may be-come broken and the higher forms of aquatic life eliminated. In studying the effects of changing the aquatic environment, we must be concerned with the whole pattern of life, rather than with just one group. Because the largest part of the research background has not been oriented to show the effects of temperature on species competing under natural con-ditions, we lack much of the information needed to evaluate the effects of heated discharges.

This lack of understanding of the relationship between laboratory re-search and natural environmental conditions has resulted in laws and ordinances, relating to temperature restrictions, which have no basis of reliable substantiating data on the ultimate effect of elevation of tem-perature on the biology of the receiving bodies of water.

Temperature surveys conducted in the field under normal conditions of heated water discharges have indicated that fish concentrate in warm water discharges in winter and spring. This concentration is sufficient in magnitude to greatly improve fishing during these seasons of the year.

Nevertheless, the addition of heat and temperature, by population and industry, to the nation's waters has come to be known as "thermal pollu-tion" because it elevates the temperature of the water above its natural temperature. Natural temperature is defined as the water temperature that would exist in a natural environment without population and industry.

The problem of temperature elevation of cooling water and hence po-tential thermal pollution of the receiving bodies of water is inherent with all steam-electric generating stations. This is true whether the steam is furnished from a conventional steam boiler or from an atomic reactor. In fact, thermal pollution is aggravated by the atomic reactor plants presently in operation because their over-all thermal efficiency is approx-imately 8% lower than the most efficient conventional plants burning coal, oil, or gas. Also, the nuclear plant has no heat loss to the atmosphere comparable to the stack gas loss of a conventional fossil fuel-fired boiler, from which about 10% of the heat energy in the fuel is rejected to the atmosphere. Hence the nuclear plant, in its present stage of technology, rejects substantially more heat to the cooling water per kilowatt-hour of electricity generated. This situation will improve as new and more efficient reactor concepts are developed.

Each steam-electric generating unit, whether fossil fuel or nuclear, must be served by a surface condenser to receive the exhaust steam from the turbine and to cool it sufficiently to condense it to water. The cooling of this exhaust steam requires large quantities of cooling water circulating through the unit condenser and returning to the stream at a temperature ranging normally from 11° to 16°F higher than the temperature of the water taken from the river, lake, or estuary.

Under average conditions, two-pass condensers are used, with a temperature rise of about 16°F. Under special conditions, this temperature rise may increase considerably. Where an ample cooling water supply is available and where potential thermal pollution is a problem, single-pass condensers with a temperature rise limited to 11°F may be used. Sometimes, the final decision as to condenser design is dependent on the quantity of cooling water available and the permissible temperature of water returning to the watercourse. The latter, in turn, is related to the temperature restrictions imposed by governmental agencies. Perhaps the states of Maryland and Pennsylvania have the most restrictive temperature regulations at the present time. The Maryland law requires that the temperature of the warm water discharge "must be below 100°F in the stream within 50 feet from waste outlet." The Pennsylvania law specifies that "the heat content of discharges shall be limited to an amount that could not raise the temperature of the entire stream at the point of discharge above 93°F assuming complete mixing. The heat content of discharges may be increased or further limited where local conditions would be benefited thereby. Where downstream circumstances warrant, the area in which the temperature may be artificially raised above 93°F will be prescribed."

It was estimated by the Edison Electric Institute that, during 1959, about 26,813 billion gal of cooling water was circulated through the condensers in the steam-electric generating stations of investor-owned electric utilities. This amount was forecast to increase by 1980 to 106,409 billion gal yearly. Details of the development of these estimates are shown in Table I, taken from the 1960 report of the Edison Electric Institute to the Select Committee on National Water Resources, U. S. Senate.

Analysis of the cooling water requirements given in Table I indicates significant trends. Between 1959 and 1980, it is indicated that the combined increase in demand for river water, lake water, brackish, and sea water for cooling purposes will approximate 300%, whereas, for the same period of time, it is predicted that water circulated through cooling towers will increase almost 500% and the use of artificial cooling reservoirs and ponds will increase about 800%. As stated earlier in this chapter, substantially the entire water requirement of the power industry is one of water usage and not water consumption.

TABLE I

TOTAL WATER CIRCULATED THROUGH CONDENSERS

Year	Rivers	Lakes	Brackish and sea water	Cooling towers	Artificial reservoirs or ponds	Total
1959	12,428	3,254	7,820	2,755	556	26,813
1970	23,842	8,168	16,455	6,635	2,185	57,285
1980	42,754	15,260	28,015	15,487	4,893	106,409

Data presented as billions of gal circulated annually.

Another aspect of the over-all problem is the quantity of water available at a given location. Steam-electric generating stations and individual generating units therein have been increasing in capacity at a rapid rate. Figure 2, compiled from reports of the Association of Edison Illuminating Companies, indicates an increase in maximum unit size from 125,-000 kilowatts in 1946 to 1,000,000 kilowatts in 1962. This graph identifies the fiscal year in which the machine was purchased, as it requires about 3 years after date of purchase to design, construct, and place the unit in commercial operation. The rate of increase in the average size of steam generating units is also shown on the graph.

Looking ahead, the Generating Stations Special Technical Committee of the National Power Survey made the following predictions of future unit sizes for average use in large interconnected power systems:

Date	Typical unit size, kilowatts	Maximum unit size, kilowatts
1970	500,000–600,000	1,000,000
1975	600,000–750,000	1,250,000
1980	750,000–1,000,000	1,500,000

This same committee recognized that increasing the size of a power plant has been a natural step to take advantage of economies in capital cost, operation, and maintenance. Increasing power demand, the greater scarcity of satisfactory sites for power plants, and the availability of large size generating units and extra-high-voltage-transmission all combine to emphasize the probability of developing larger power plants. Figure 3 shows the 15 largest thermal power plants in 1952 and 1962. It can reasonably be concluded that power plants will reach a size of 3 to 5 million kilowatts by 1980, as compared to the largest power plant now in operation with a capacity of 1,600,000 kilowatts.

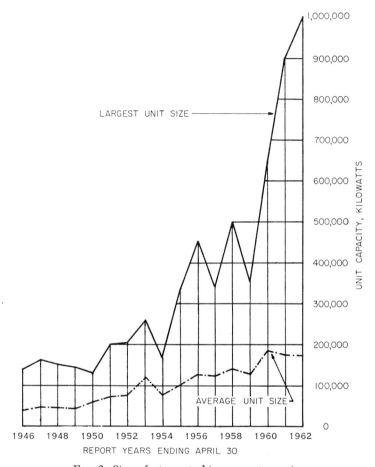

FIG. 2. Size of steam turbine-generator units.

These increases in individual unit sizes and in total plant capacity at a given site, both in the past and projected for the future, not only cause concern about heated water discharges from such installations but also raise the question of availability of an adequate quantity of cooling water. There is no question that the total generating capacity that can be installed at a given river site must be associated with the minimum flow of the river. The alternative is to reduce load on the generating station during the critical low flow period of the river in the summer.

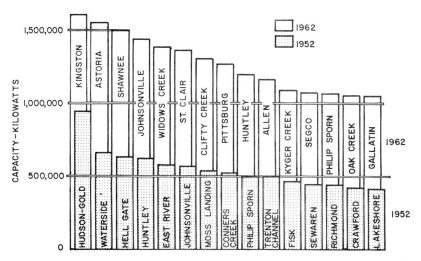

Fig. 3. Largest thermal power plants built 1953–1962 and existing in 1952.

HYDRAULIC MODEL STUDIES

Operating utilities with a heated water discharge problem, either actual or potential, are sponsoring hydraulic model studies of their particular water problems in order to develop adequate information for control.

Hitherto, the use of hydraulic model studies had been limited to hydroelectric and flood control problems. No doubt, the success of hydraulic models in developing satisfactory solutions to difficult problems in these areas had a great influence on their application to thermal pollution problems.

In recent years the Alden Hydraulic Laboratory of Worcester Polytechnic Institute has constructed and tested models of four conventional steam-electric generating stations where river water problems had to be studied. These were Elrama Station on the Monongahela River, Cromby Station on the Schuylkill River, Dickerson Station on the Potomac River, and Chalk Point Station on the Patuxent River.

The first three of these generating stations are in operation, and in each instance the model predictions were verified when the power plant was placed in operation. The Chalk Point Station is not yet in service although the model study has been completed. It is confidently believed that Chalk Point also will operate as the model indicates.

The Chalk Point model study is perhaps the most extensive river study ever undertaken in connection with a steam power plant site. The Patuxent River at this location is basically a wide, relatively shallow estuary. The river downstream, particularly below the Benedict Bridge, is an important area for oysters, clams, crabs, and fish. Because of this, the power company desired to take every reasonable precaution to assure that the Chalk Point Plant would operate without significant deleterious effect on the river or its abundant aquatic life.

FIG. 4. Scale model of Chalk Point Thermal Generating Station at Alden Hydraulic Laboratory of Worcester Polytechnic Institute.

The scale model of the Patuxent River in the vicinity of Chalk Point is shown in Fig. 4, with the power plant circled in white. This model duplicates, as accurately as possible, an 8-mile stretch of the river being studied. The model was constructed with a horizontal scale of 1 to 300 and a vertical scale of 1 to 30, resulting in a geometric distortion of ten. This distortion was necessary to achieve turbulent flow and to enable the model to be constructed economically. Tidal flows in the Patuxent River, and the required cooling water flows for condenser operation, were duplicated in the model.

The purposes of the investigation were twofold: to determine the best arrangement of plant intake and discharge canals for distribution of the condenser warm discharge water without recirculation of the warm water into the plant intake, and with minimum temperature elevation at the Benedict Bridge downstream; and to determine the magnitude and pattern of the temperature elevation of the waters of the estuary resulting from plant operations.

The model studies, which covered a period of 16 months, resulted in the development of a discharge canal extending 7000 ft upstream, with warm water re-entering the river via an outfall structure extending into the river; and the development of a diversion jetty near the plant intake to avoid recirculation of warm water. With this arrangement, temperature traverses with fixed and portable thermocouples indicated a satisfactory temperature pattern, with the temperature elevation at the Benedict Bridge not exceeding 1°F under critical summer conditions.

It is believed that similar hydraulic model studies will be of great value in the future in appraising thermal pollution problems at potential power plant sites prior to development of the site.

Model testing of power plant sites is particularly useful and important as no two bodies of water are alike. The dissimilarity of rivers, lakes, and estuaries, and their relative abilities to accommodate additional heat loads without serious detrimental effect, will be a constant challenge to the power industry in the location of power generating facilities.

CHEMICAL WASTES

There have been extremely rapid advances in the technology of steam-electric generating stations. Steam pressures have increased from the 1200 pound pressure level immediately following World War II to a fairly general acceptance of 3500 pounds in the year 1962. During this same period, steam temperatures have increased from 950°F to 1050°F, with occasional designs for operation at 1100°F or higher. Larger and still larger generating units have not only been accepted but have been aggressively promoted by the utility industry in a continuing effort to control costs in the face of inflation and rising material and labor prices. These advances, along with the necessity for high availability of equipment for service without breakdown, have resulted in many additions and complications to power plant chemistry.

Water conditioning for high pressure boilers has undergone revision to satisfy these new conditions imposed on all equipment in the steam-water cycle. At present, the acceptable purity of feedwater delivered to many steam boilers is measured in parts per billion, whereas at lower pressures and temperatures water of satisfactory quality was maintained with solids contents of several parts per million. These changed requirements in boiler water purity have been so radical as to challenge the ingenuity of the instrument manufacturer, who must develop instruments capable of measuring minute quantities.

Creation of chemical wastes from power stations has been influenced by these drastic trends. Demineralization of boiler feedwater by resins involves complex chemical reactions and requires the use of acids and alkalies, the disposal of which, while intermittent, must be controlled. In the normal operation of demineralizers, the units must be regenerated at intervals of a few days, depending on the chemical composition of the raw water. These processes require that the regenerants be disposed of, but in some locations they may not be discharged to waste without neutralization, and must then be released at controlled, low rates of disposal to the adjacent water sources.

The installation of very high pressure boilers, especially those in the supercritical range above 3200 pounds steam pressure, has necessitated the maintenance of internal surfaces meticulously free from all deposits. This, in turn, has imposed the need for internal chemical cleaning of the boilers and other associated equipment in the steam-water cycle. Such cleaning must be done prior to initial operation and at periodic intervals thereafter. The frequency of cleaning will vary considerably between plants but may average once per year for each boiler unit. The chemical solutions most commonly used as cleaning compounds are hydrochloric acid, citric acid, potassium bromate, ammonia, corrosion inhibitors, detergents, and phosphates. These chemical cleaning processes are still the subject of much study.

Where the discharge of these raw chemical wastes is prohibited, it is customary to deliver them to a central retention basin or elevated tank where they are neutralized as required. After adequate treatment, they may be discharged at a slow, controlled rate into the receiving body of water. It is general practice to discharge the neutralized wastes into the condenser cooling water as it leaves the station. In this manner further dilution is effected before final discharge to the main body of water.

Because chemicals for cleaning power station equipment are both alkaline and acidic, equipment for their collection and disposal must be carefully designed. The problem of collection and disposal is complicated further because they are usually hot. The lining of collecting tanks or reservoirs must be capable of standing up under these conditions. The most satisfactory retention basin or reservoir is one that is lined with acid-resistant brick of the type used in acid manufacturing plants. Such brick will also resist strong alkalies.

As an alternate to reservoirs, overhead steel tanks may be used, provided they are lined with a suitable material to withstand the action of the hot chemical solutions. Rubber lining is satisfactory if the proper type of rubber is used and if it is well bonded to the surface. It may be desirable, with either the retention reservoir or steel tank, to provide a mixing device. The admixture of alkali and acid wastes will save neutralizing chemicals and minimize secondary adjustment to meet any legal requirements.

Chapter 24

ATOMIC ENERGY

by WALTER G. BELTER

The atomic energy industry is unique in that the necessity for management of its effluents was realized from the beginning. Effluent control was an integral part of early atomic energy research and weapons production installations. Significant strides are presently being made in radioactive waste management and technology to reduce further the quantities of radioactive material discharged to our environment. The development of nuclear power technology and the utilization of radioisotopes and radiation for scientific, medical, agricultural, and industrial application have not been hindered by lack of waste management systems. These systems are characterized by complex chemical processes, sometimes under remote control, requiring sensitive analytical techniques and control procedures.

THE INDUSTRY

The nuclear energy industry in the United States has developed to its present state in a period of less than 20 years. At the core of the industry is the Atomic Energy Commission's (AEC) large nuclear enterprise. Of the operations involved, including mining and milling of uranium ore, chemical purification of fissionable materials, fabrication of fuel elements, operation of nuclear reactors, chemical reprocessing of spent fuel, and research and development activity associated with each of these steps, most are performed in an integrated industrial operation conducted under contract for the Atomic Energy Commission. While the AEC directly employs only approximately 7000 persons, research and production facilities such as Oak Ridge, the Savannah River Plant, the Hanford Works, the Los Alamos Scientific Laboratory, and the National Reactor Testing Station employ more than 100,000 persons.

Through 1963, the total cost before depreciation of AEC-owned plants and equipment was approximately $8.0 billion. This does not include investments and other assets such as stockpiled materials and weapons. Over $2.5 billion annually is required to conduct the Commission's operating program. A major portion of AEC research and development is conducted in government-owned laboratories and the investment in AEC-owned research and test reactors, accelerators, laboratory buildings, equipment, and research devices through 1963 was approximately $2.0 billion.

Peaceful use of the atom may be summarized as: to accelerate the use of radioisotopes and other radiation sources in industry and science; to develop civilian nuclear power plants economically competitive with plants fired by the fossil fuels; and to develop nuclear power for military and space application. Interrelated with these national objectives are the challenges for nuclear energy applications abroad. Industrial nations of the world face problems of rapidly diminishing sources of conventional fuels, or sources so difficult or expensive to recover that nuclear fuels are increasingly attractive. Countries with small fuel supplies are forced to import fuel at high cost. For these countries, early introduction of nuclear power is an imminent possibility and may be a necessary condition for growth and industrialization.

Mining. Uranium ore is mined mainly in the western part of the United States, with the principal source being the Colorado Plateau states of Colorado, Utah, Arizona, and New Mexico. Domestic ore production during 1962 amounted to 7 million tons, and large quantities of uranium ore were imported from such sources as Canada, South Africa, and the Congo. The ores average about 5 lb/ton or 0.25% of U_3O_8, the common natural oxide of uranium. During 1962, approximately 29,000 tons of U_3O_8 were procured, including about 17,000 tons from domestic sources.

Milling. Uranium is extracted from the ore by milling, which involves preparation steps such as crushing, blending, roasting, and acid or alkaline leaching. The final product, uranium oxide concentrate, is obtained by chemical operations such as ion exchange, solvent extraction, filtration, and precipitation. The oxide product averages about 75% U_3O_8 by weight. At the end of 1962, there were 24 operating uranium mills in the United States.

Refining. The uranium concentrate is shipped to refineries at Weldon Spring, Missouri, or Metropolis, Illinois, where the uranium is converted to metal or chemical products of acceptable purity for reactor fuel. In a series of processing steps, the concentrate is first refined to UO_3 of high purity, and this in turn is converted to green salt, UF_4. The UF_4 can be reduced to metal and cast into ingots as the starting point for metallic fuel elements, or it can be converted by fluorination to uranium hexafluoride, UF_6, which is feed material for gaseous diffusion plants at Oak Ridge, Tennessee, Paducah, Kentucky, and Portsmouth, Ohio. Gaseous UF_4 is passed through a series of diffusion cascades from which uranium-

235 can be removed at any desired degree of enrichment. Much of the output of the diffusion plants to date has been enriched U^{235} for weapons use, but the demand for U^{235} for reactor fuel elements increases. Reactor designs call for uranium of varying degrees of isotopic enrichment, ranging from natural uranium containing 0.7% U^{235} to enriched uranium in the neighborhood of 90% U^{235}.

Reactors and Fuel Reprocessing. In reactor operation, after a certain operating period, the fission reaction becomes inefficient and the fuel elements are removed with only a small part of their uranium having been consumed. After "cooling" for 90–120 days to reduce the extreme radioactivity, irradiated fuel is shipped to a chemical separations plant where plutonium and the unused uranium are recovered. During reactor operation, heat, radiation, and fission products are produced. In chemical processing by acid dissolution and solvent extraction, large quantities of radioactive waste are separated from plutonium and uranium and are subsequently concentrated and stored in underground tanks. Chemical separations plants are in operation at AEC sites in Washington, Idaho, and South Carolina. Radioisotopes with unique nuclear properties have been recovered from high level waste for beneficial use in industry, research, and medicine.

RADIOACTIVE WASTE

Radioactive wastes, in comparison with other industrial wastes, are unique in that radioactivity is not detectable by human senses, toxicity of certain radionuclides is greater than any other known industrial waste, and there is no known process for destroying radioactivity; thus, these wastes become inactive only by their own natural decay or disintegration.

It is desirable to define certain terms used in quantifying radioactive waste, in their relation to radiation protection standards used by the industry. The unit most frequently used in handling radioactivity is the curie (c), defined as the quantity of any radionuclide that produces 3.7×10^{10} disintegrations per second. It is approximately equivalent to the radiation emitted by 1 gm of radium. A millicurie (mc) is $\frac{1}{1000}$ of a curie, a microcurie (μc) is one-millionth of a curie. Liquid and gaseous concentrations of waste effluents are generally given in μc/ml. Solid waste is described by the external radiation delivered to a specific area or volume of receiving material. The most common term in this connection is the roentgen (r) or milliroentgen (mr), the roentgen being defined as the quantity of X- or gamma-radiation that produces

1 electrostatic unit of electricity in 1 cubic centimeter of dry air at 0°C, 760 mm pressure. The "rem" is the dose of any ionizing radiation that produces the same biological effect as that produced by one roentgen.

Radioactive wastes vary over a wide range of concentration. Liquid wastes may contain activity near natural background, about 10^{-16} c/ml, or more than 1 c/ml in high-level wastes. For radioactive effluent control, the Atomic Energy Commission uses radiation protection standards established by the National Committee on Radiation Protection and the Federal Radiation Council. These include a value of 10^{-7} μc/ml for unidentified mixed fission product waste. If the absence of especially hazardous radionuclides such as strontium and radium can be determined, a less stringent permissible concentration may be used. An additional safety factor of 10 is recommended for use beyond the atomic energy plant control area, on the supposition that the general public is not provided with the careful health monitoring programs used for nuclear workers. The maximum permissible concentrations (MPC) for radioactive materials are much lower than for chemically toxic elements such as arsenic, lead, and mercury; for example, the MPC for strontium-90 in water is equivalent to about 10^{-9} mg/liter by weight, whereas for arsenic it is 0.05 mg/liter, or many million times higher.

In waste management operations, waste is categorized as low, intermediate, or high level to determine the general handling or processing method that will be used. Table I defines these terms in a broad sense as they have been used throughout the industry.

TABLE I

RADIOACTIVE WASTE ACTIVITY LEVELS

Type of waste	Solid wastes, r/hour	Liquid wastes, μc/ml
High level	> 2	> 10^3
Intermediate level	0.05–2	10^{-3} to 10^3
Low level	< 0.05	< 10^{-3}

In general, low level wastes include all wastes generated in laboratory research, medical and industrial use, normal operation of nuclear reactors, and other parts of the nuclear fuel cycle such as uranium mining and milling, feed material purification, and fuel element fabrication. High activity wastes are produced only in the chemical reprocessing of spent reactor fuel elements for the recovery of plutonium and unburned uranium, i.e., the fission products contained in the first cycle raffinate in this process. Intermediate level wastes are derived from fuel decladding and from the second and third cycles of solvent extraction operations in the chemical reprocessing plant.

PREPARATION OF MATERIALS

In the mining of uranium ore, only naturally occurring radioactive elements are encountered, and the activity levels of the waste are low. Uranium-238 and its daughter products constitute the main radioactivity present. The total combined alpha and beta activity of the ore is 2.1 mc/lb of uranium. Radon gas and radioactive dust are of principal concern to uranium miners.

Uranium ores as delivered to the mills contain on the order of 0.25% uranium oxide (U_3O_8). Milling processes are designed to extract uranium from the ore, but the concentration is so low that practically all material fed to the mills is discarded as waste slimes and sands. Process waters, most of which are discharged as plant effluent to tailings ponds, contain most of the radioactivity delivered to the mills. Uranium, radium-226, and thorium-230 are the radioisotopes of most concern in tailings solutions.

In the next step of the fuel cycle, ore concentrates containing 70–90% U_3O_8 are chemically purified to produce uranium salts. These are fed to the gaseous diffusion cascades for the separation of uranium-235 from uranium-238, and reduced with calcium or magnesium to uranium metal or converted to uranium compounds such as UO_2 to be used as reactor fuel. Natural uranium and its decay daughters are the main constituents in the waste, and approximately 1000 gal of solvent extraction wastes are produced for each ton of uranium processed.

In fuel element fabrication, uranium, uranium alloys, and UO_2 are used. Plant processes include melting, casting, rolling, machining, and metal cleaning, and produce varying quantities of uranium-bearing wastes as scrap, liquids, contaminated metal and trash, and airborne dust. Wastes containing low concentrations of uranium are generated in these operations.

REACTORS

Many types of nuclear reactors are in operation at universities, medical research facilities, electric utility power stations, and AEC plutonium production and research sites. Distinguishing characteristics for each type of reactor include power level and the types of fuel element, cladding, and coolant used. Reactors are utilized for different purposes, such as research, teaching, and materials testing and for production of plutonium, electric power, process heat, and radioisotopes.

In research and teaching reactors, nuclear radiations are used as a tool
for basic or applied research, for instruction in reactor theory and performance, and for training in the operation and utilization of reactors. Thermal power levels vary from several kilowatts up to 1 megawatt. Test reactors have a thermal output of 10,000 kw or more, and include test loops
or experimental facilities within or in proximity to the core. Their major
function is the use of radiation for testing the life or performance of reactor components. Plutonium production reactors differ from power reactors
in that they operate at lower temperatures and have different fuel and
structural materials. The AEC-Hanford plant has a nonrecirculating single-pass water cooling system. Electric power and propulsion reactors
operate at higher temperatures, using uranium oxide or uranium metal alloys fuels clad in zirconium alloys or stainless steel, with primary coolant
recirculation and side-stream purification.

The nature and quantity of wastes from nuclear reactor operation depend on the reactor type. In general, wastes are produced by two processes: neutron activation of the coolant and its impurities, including corrosion scale; and nuclear fission, or the escape of fuel and fission products
into the coolant by fuel element failure. Reactor fuel elements are clad
with structural material such as aluminum, zirconium, or stainless steel,
which provide protection of the fuel from the cooling system, and contain
the fission products formed during reactor operation. Reactor coolants
used are water, liquid metal, organic liquids, and air, with water the most
common because of the advanced stage of pressured and boiling water
reactors.

The water cooling system may be single-pass or recirculating. The
Hanford production reactors are an example of the former, in that coolant is discharged after passing through the reactor once. More than 60
radioisotopes have been identified in the reactor liquid effluent. Recirculating water cooling systems, in which feed water is pretreated by ion exchange and a portion of the coolant is continuously treated by the same
method, result in the discharge of only low quantities of fission and corrosion product activity from the system. Table II summarizes some of the
specific radionuclides encountered in various kinds of reactor operation.
Gross concentrations of radionuclides in liquid waste effluent from all
types of water reactors vary from 10^{-5} to 10^{-1} $\mu c/ml$.

Fuel Reprocessing

The major waste management problem in the future nuclear energy
industry will be the ultimate disposal of high activity waste from the
chemical reprocessing of irradiated reactor fuel. This chemical plant
operation is necessary to recover unburned nuclear fuel and transmuta-

tion products, such as plutonium-239 and uranium-233, from mixtures of fission products and inert components of the fuel. Solid fuels, after removal from the reactor and after storage for 90–120 days for decay of short-lived fission product activity, are dissolved in nitric acid. The resulting solution is fed to a solvent extraction column, normally containing tributyl phosphate in a hydrocarbon diluent, which selectively ex-

TABLE II

PRINCIPAL RADIONUCLIDES IDENTIFIED IN WATER-COOLED
REACTOR EFFLUENTS

| Radionuclide | Research | Test | Plutonium production | | Electric power | Propulsion |
			Hanford	Savannah River		
Tritium—3	X	—	—	X	X	—
Nitrogen—16	X	X	—	X	X	X
Fluorine—18	—	X	—	—	X	X
Oxygen—19	X	—	—	X	—	—
Sodium—24	X	X	X	—	X	X
Aluminum—28	—	X	—	—	—	—
Silicon—31	—	—	X	—	—	—
Phosphorus—32	—	—	X	—	—	—
Argon—41	X	—	—	—	—	—
Chromium—51	—	X	X	—	X	X
Manganese—56	—	X	X	—	X	X
Cobalt—58	—	—	—	—	X	—
Iron—59	—	X	—	—	X	X
Cobalt—60	—	X	—	—	X	X
Copper—64	—	X	X	—	X	X
Zinc—65	—	X	X	—	—	—
Arsenic—76	—	—	X	—	—	—
Iodine—131	X	X	—	—	X	X
Tungsten—187	—	—	—	—	—	X
Plutonium—239	X	X	X	—	—	—

tracts uranium and plutonium. The resulting first-cycle waste, containing more than 99.9% of the total fission products, is characterized in Table III. These wastes are mainly solutions of fission products in nitric acid, with trace constituents of corrosion products such as iron, nickel, and chromium, and have radioactivity concentrations ranging from 80 to 5000 c/gal.

High activity wastes are evaporated to small volumes, 50–100 gal/ton of uranium processed, and are neutralized before being stored in underground concrete tanks. As higher fuel burnups are achieved in power reactor fuels, activity levels in reprocessing wastes will increase by factors of 10 to 15 times greater than those obtained from present-day plutonium production and test reactor fuels.

High level waste now in storage at major AEC reprocessing plants exceeds 70 million gal. These plants also produce larger volumes of low and intermediate level liquid waste, generated in second- and third-cycle

TABLE III

CHARACTERIZATION OF FIRST-CYCLE HIGH LEVEL AQUEOUS WASTES
FROM SELECTED SOLVENT PROCESSES[a]

Process	Waste volume,[b] gal/gm of U^{235} consumed	Approximate concentration of U in feed gm/liter	Waste activity[c]	
			c/gal	Total,[d] watts/gal
Redox	0.27	450	1720	8.6
Purex	0.34	300	1320	6.7
Thorex	0.34	350 (Th)	81	0.4
Hexone-"25"	0.13–0.31	2–5	1620–3940	8.1–20.2
TBP-"25"	0.11–0.22	3–6	2580–5160	12.9–26.0
Zirconium-HF for enriched U	1.50	0.3	350	1.75
Stainless steel-Darex with added H_2SO_4 for enriched U^{235}	0.35	2–3	1500	7.5

[a] Wastes are untreated; they are essentially as they leave the solvent extraction plant and are subject to further treatment by evaporation, neutralization, chemical treatment for fission product removal, etc.

[b] Waste volume per gram of U^{235} consumed is an inverse function of burnup; i.e., for hexone-25 at 20% burnup, the gal/gm $U^{235} = (53/20)$ (0.14). To obtain liters per gram multiply by 3.79.

[c] Waste activity varies approximately as the (irradiation level)$^{0.2}$. Basis for activity numbers: Irradiation period 4000 megawatt-days per ton for natural uranium; neutron flux 5×10^{13} n/(cm)^2(sec); 4000 gm U^{233} per ton of thorium; 53% burnup for U^{235} in enriched fuel elements; and 100-day decay cooling from time of reactor discharge.

[d] After 100-day decay, the distribution of energy is approximately 50% gamma and 50% beta.

solvent extraction operations, fuel decladding, laboratory and laundry operations, and cell decontamination. The radioactivity of second- and third-cycle raffinates has ranged from 1 to 10 c/gal.

When spent reactor fuel is dissolved, radioactive gases are formed; I^{131}, Ru^{103}, and Ru^{106} have been of major concern. Kr^{85}, with a 10.5 year halflife may require collection and storage in a large-scale nuclear energy industry.

RADIOISOTOPE USE

The quantity of radioactive wastes generated through the use of radioisotopes is small compared with other aspects of the nuclear energy program. Since 1946 the AEC has shipped approximately 1 million curies of reactor-produced radioisotopes to about 4500 institutions throughout the United States. About 98% of these isotopes are contained in sealed sources and have halflives greater than 30 days. On the basis of present rate of radioisotope use, it is estimated that the total amount of waste produced per year from all categories of use is in the range of 100–200c of material having a halflife greater than 30 days, and 400–500c of material having a halflife less than 30 days.

Within the Atomic Energy Commission complex there are numerous nuclear research and development laboratories, including Argonne, Brookhaven, Knolls, Los Alamos, and Oak Ridge. The types and quantities of radioactive wastes generated at these research centers are highly variable in nature. Included are wastes from fuel reprocessing research, development of fuel fabrication methods and irradiation testing of materials or fuels, basic chemical studies of radioactive materials, studies of radiation effects on biological systems, normal operation of test and power reactor prototypes, equipment decontamination, and such supporting facilities as shops and decontamination laundries. Liquid wastes from laboratory research and development operations generally range in concentration from 10^{-6} to 10^{-1} μc/ml of gross beta activity.

WASTE MANAGEMENT OBJECTIVES AND PRACTICES

The objective of waste management in atomic energy operations is control over the radiation hazard that might be produced by the wastes in storage or in nature. Strict effluent control is required during normal plant operations, and extensive surveillance activities are carried out to monitor the movement and distribution of radioactive wastes through the water, air, and land environments. As the industry has developed, three major waste management concepts have evolved:

Concentrate and Contain. This concept is used for high activity liquid wastes originating from chemical processing of irradiated reactor fuel. The radioactivity is concentrated by volume reduction, and is then confined or isolated in a controlled area such as an underground storage tank, away from man and his natural resources. Because even small volumes of high activity waste would require excessive amounts of environmental dilution capacity, it is essential that containment be utilized for these wastes.

Dilute and Disperse. In this waste management concept, radioactivity is reduced to acceptable levels by dilution in air or water. For example, certain laboratory liquid wastes in which the radioactivity concentration is only a few times greater than drinking water standards may be disposed of in streams, whereby dilution reduces the concentration to a permissible level. Stringent control is required to assure that the safe capacity of the environment is not exceeded.

Delay and Decay. This waste disposal approach has been used in the discharge of liquid wastes into the ground at suitable locations. Soil holdup or exchange capacity is utilized in this concept. Safe disposal is achieved either by direct discharge to the environment or by discharge after standard treatment.

With favorable environmental conditions, certain wastes containing quantities of activity many times above permissible long-term concentration limits have been dispersed into the atmosphere, surface waterways, and the ground. Rigorous control and surveillance are required in such direct dispersal, and extensive research and operational data are required for the safe conduct of these operations.

In the design of all nuclear waste disposal systems, three basic considerations are involved: the specific nature and quantity of radioactive waste being handled, the characteristics of the receiving environment, and basic radiation protection standards established by the Federal Radiation Council or the Atomic Energy Commission in its Standards for Protection against Radiation. These standards are based on recommendations of the National Committee on Radiation Protection and the International Commission on Radiological Protection, as derived from the best available medical information.

Uranium Mining and Milling

Most uranium mines of the Colorado plateau area are dry, and the pumping of mine water is negligible. However, other mines discharge hundreds of gallons of natural groundwater per minute, containing measurable amounts of uranium, radium, and thorium. These are naturally present in the water, but are of no health significance. Such waters are normally released to natural drainage systems which, in many areas, dry up within short distances during most of the year. Solid refuse or waste from mining operations, containing uranium concentrations below 0.05% U_3O_8, is usually piled near mine portals or adjacent to the open pit mines. Because the amount of radioactivity involved is small, these operations do not constitute a hazard. Air and gases discharged from mine ventilation systems may contain radon (Rn^{222}) and short-lived radon daughters. Mechanical ventilation is used to maintain acceptable air concentrations for these materials; the total quantity of radon discharged to the atmosphere from uranium mines is small compared with that naturally produced from the earth's surface.

Waste treatment and control practices in the uranium milling industry have improved greatly in recent years. Liquid wastes are discharged to tailings ponds or lagoons, at a rate of 300–500 gpm for the mill of average size. The radioisotope of principal concern in the ore, Ra^{226}, is mostly insoluble and remains in the impounded tailings solids. At uranium mills located adjacent to a watercourse, tailings pond effluents overflow to the river, carrying the dissolved radium, which is 1% or less of the total radium present. Dilution of the liquid effluents by receiving streams has generally been sufficient to maintain Ra^{226} concentrations below the AEC drinking water standard of 10 $\mu\mu c$/liter for effluents released to unrestricted areas. Where stream dilution factors are not adequate, neutralization and chemical treatment with barium sulfate have been successfully used for removal of dissolved radium. Good mechanical ventilation is required to keep toxic gases such as hydrogen sulfide, arsine, and acids, as well as uranium, within acceptable levels.

FEED MATERIALS AND DIFFUSION PLANT OPERATIONS

Chemical purification of U_3O_8 to produce uranium hexafluoride generates wastes similar to uranium mill wastes, containing natural uranium and its decay daughters. Wastes generated in the reduction of U_3O_8 to uranium metal or in its conversion to UO_2 are also similar to mill wastes. Gaseous chemical fumes and entrained uranium are removed by wet scrubbing. Solid wastes include small quantities of filter residues containing radium and large amounts of magnesium fluoride slags. The production of uranium metal generates solid waste which is sometimes leached to remove uranium; the leachate is subsequently treated by a solvent extraction purification cycle and ion exchange.

In the gaseous diffusion plants, essentially all liquid wastes are produced as a result of decontamination and recovery procedures. Uranium hexafluoride is removed from equipment surfaces with nitric acid; uranium is then separated by solvent extraction. Wastes from these operations consist of the aqueous column raffinate, spent acid, and rinsewater. These are discharged to settling basins, monitored, and released to local streams at permissible levels.

FUEL ELEMENT FABRICATION

The manufacture of fuel elements requires various machining and metal cleaning operations, and results in dilute wastes containing low concentrations of uranium. The wastes may be processed by ion exchange or by precipitation of uranium followed by filtration. In certain circumstances, it is possible to handle the waste by monitoring, dilution, and discharge to the environment. Waste volumes amount to only several thousands of gallons per year.

REACTOR OPERATIONS

Reactor wastes vary with the type of reactor involved. At present, water-cooled heterogeneous reactors (solid fuel elements) are predominate because this technology is most advanced. During reactor operation, short-lived radioisotopes are produced by nuclear reactions in the bulk coolant. After a relatively short period of operation, activation products are also formed in the coolant. Pinhole fuel element failures add fission product activities to these induced radioactivities.

The Hanford production reactors are of the low pressure, noncirculating, water-cooled type. Columbia River water, treated by conventional methods, is used for cooling. Reactor effluents are discharged to retention basins that provide from 1 to 3 hours holdup before release to the Columbia River. During this time, radioactive decay reduces the gross activity of the effluent by 50–70%, which is sufficient to keep river concentrations below Hanford at acceptable levels. The principal radioisotopes in the Hanford effluent, which are measured on a routine basis, are shown in Table II.

The Materials Testing Reactor at the National Reactor Testing Station in Idaho is provided with a recirculating water cooling system in which the feed water is pretreated by ion exchange. Total primary coolant flow through the core and reflector is about 22,000 gpm. Typical test reactor sources of waste include a continuous bleedoff of demineralized primary coolant, canal overflows, wastewater from test loops, waste streams from various laboratories, and primary coolant purges at the time of shutdown. Corrosion products and other activities encountered in the operation of the reactor are shown in Table II. During 10 years of reactor operation, including a series of fuel element ruptures in 1954, the bypass cation resin bed has been sufficient for handling all fission product activity generated in these operations.

Waste handling systems at the large nuclear power reactor sites consist of collection, treatment, storage, and disposal facilities. Waste treatment processes used include evaporation, ion exchange, steam stripping, catalytic recombination of hydrogen and oxygen, fixation of solids and liquids in concrete, and liquid and gas filtration. Table IV summarizes these waste plant processes and equipment for four nuclear power reactors of the pressurized and boiling water types now in operation.

As noted in Table IV, evaporators ranging in capacity from 0.7 to 12 gpm are used, with treatment by this method limited to wastes with high dissolved solids content. Ion exchange equipment is used for waste processing at most nuclear power stations, with the exception of the Rowe reactor which can use the primary coolant purification system ion exchangers for waste treatment if necessary. Ion exchange is used mostly for liquids with low total solids content, such as evaporator distillates and reactor plant liquid waste. Mixed bed ion exchange units are utilized, and a decontamination factor of 10^5 may be obtained depending on the initial feed activity, other water constituents, and condition of the resin. Provisions are made for either removing or replacing the whole resin column, or for sluicing the resin out for regeneration or disposal.

As further noted in Table IV, the nuclear power stations at Rowe, Indian Point, and Shippingport have drumming facilities for the fixation in concrete of spent ion exchange resins, incinerator ashes, evaporator concentrates, and contaminated noncombustibles, using standard 55-gal steel drums. Activities in these concrete-encased waste materials are normally low enough that they can be shipped under ICC regulations. Each drum contains less than 2.7 c, and the external dose rate is less than 0.2 rem per hour at the surface, and 0.01 rem per hour at 1 meter. Provisions are made for interim storage of these drums on site with final off-site disposal by either land or sea burial.

Table V summarizes waste management operating data for nuclear power reactor sites during 1962. In general, the quantities of radioactivity handled at these reactor plants have been considerably lower than conservative design estimates, while the waste volumes have been somewhat higher.

AEC Production and Laboratory Research Operations

The major portion of waste generated in the nuclear fuel cycle, including both total volume and inventory of radionuclides, is produced at the AEC plutonium production facilities, fuel reprocessing sites, and associated laboratory research and engineering test facilities. Plutonium production and fuel reprocessing operations are carried out at Hanford, Washington, and the Savannah River Plant in South Carolina; reactor research and development, along with fuel element reprocessing, are conducted at the National Reactor Testing Station in Idaho; and extensive nuclear research and development work is carried out at national laboratories such as Argonne, Illinois, Brookhaven, New York, Oak Ridge, Tennessee, and the Knolls Atomic Power Laboratory in New York. These installations produce over 99% of the radioactive waste material generated in the United States. The waste is either stored in suitable con-

TABLE IV

RADIOACTIVE WASTE TREATMENT PROCESSES AND EQUIPMENT, U. S. NUCLEAR POWER REACTORS, WATER TYPE

Waste treatment systems	Shippingport, Pa. (60,000 Kw)	Rowe, Mass. (134,000 Kw)	Indian Point, N. Y. (255,000 Kw)	Dresden, Ill. (180,000 Kw)
Evaporators	One 0.7 gpm stainless steel evaporator with Inconel steam heating basket	One 5 gpm stainless steel electrode evaporator	One 12 gpm Inconel evaporator with removable steam heating basket	One 2.5 gpm stainless steel natural circulation evaporator with removable steam coil
Gas strippers	One 3 gpm stainless steel gas stripper 16 ft high, 20-inch diameter with 12 ft bed of 1-inch ceramic Berl saddle packing	One 5 gpm stainless steel gas stripper, 27 ft high, 11-inch diameter, 14 ft section, with 20 corrugated bubble trays	One 12 gpm Inconel gas stripper, 31 ft high, 30-inch diameter, with about a 25 ft bed of ceramic Berl saddle packing	No
Ion exchangers	Four 20 gpm mixed bed, with 4 ft bed	No[a]	One 12 gpm mixed bed	One 200 gpm mixed bed
Catalytic hydrogen combiners	One 70 scfm carbon steel combiner, 30 inches high, 10-inch diameter, with 4-inch bed of Ni wire coated with Pd	No	Two 4 scfm carbon steel steel combiners with Pd catalyst[b]	No
Drumming station (waste fixation in concrete-filled drums)	Yes	Yes	Yes	Yes

Incinerators	One 20 lb/hour gas-fired incinerator[a]	One 20 lb/hour gas-fired incinerator[a]	Space left for future installation	No
Tank volume for gas	4900 scf	4340 scf	2750 scf	0
Tank volume for liquids and solids	180,000 gal	180,000 gal	350,000 gal	480,000 gal

[a] Resin in purification system can be used to treat waste.
[b] Another 25 scfm combiner is located in the sweep gas system.
[c] Burning rate is 40 lb/hour.

tainers or underground tanks, or discharged to the environment after satisfactory treatment and monitoring.

Low and intermediate level waste management in these operations, while less complex than high level waste management, is nevertheless important. These wastes are either directly discharged to the environ-

TABLE V

Waste Management Operating Data for Nuclear Power Plants, 1962

| Reactor site | Net power generation, millions of kw (electrical) | Liquid waste handled | | Gaseous activity discharged[a] curies |
		Volume, 10^6 gal	Radioactivity discharged, curies	
Shippingport	331	1.83	0.09	0.0012
Yankee	687	0.87	0.008	21.7
Dresden	1179	1.9	2.372	58,600[b]

[a] Quantities of gaseous radioactivity discharged vary widely, depending on type of water reactor (pressurized or boiling), treatment and decay storage systems provided, etc.

[b] Essentially all short-lived noble gases, which result in less than 1% of permissible dose at site boundary.

TABLE VI

Low and Intermediate Level Liquid Waste Discharge to Environment, 1962

Location	Volume handled, 10^6 gal/year	Activity discharged, curies
AEC Laboratories		
Argonne National Laboratory	214	0.20
Brookhaven National Laboratory	347	0.13
Los Alamos Scientific Laboratory	20	0.1
National Reactor Testing Station	660	7,546
Oak Ridge National Laboratory	160	1,435
Production Sites		
Hanford	5515	63,624[a]
Savannah River	70	227

[a] Ground disposal operations, radioactivity discharged to cribs, swamps, and trenches.

ment on a controlled basis, or processed by single or multiple stage treatment systems involving filtration, chemical precipitation, ion exchange, evaporation, concrete solidification, vermiculite adsorption, and tank storage. Table VI provides a summary of AEC laboratory and production site waste management operations during 1962.

Where suitable hydrologic conditions exist, ground disposal of low and intermediate level wastes is utilized. At Hanford, through careful control, it has been possible to dispose of large quantities of intermediate level waste to the ground. Before the liquids reach the groundwater table some 200–300 ft below the land surface, the significant radionuclides are effectively retained and decayed in the sediments through which the liquid percolates. In this sense, the operation is not disposal but ground storage, inasmuch as it utilizes the capacity of soil clay to retain the significant radioactive contaminants by ion exchange, adsorption, and holdup in pores. Wastes are processed by the method which provides, at that site, the required decontamination at the lowest cost, in accordance with acceptable health and safety standards.

Table VII presents data on AEC laboratory low activity liquid waste treatment facilities. Satisfactory flocculation and chemical treatment processes have been developed for decontamination of large volume, low activity waste at research installations such as Argonne and Oak Ridge. Treatment efficiencies up to 90% have been achieved for strontium and cesium, and up to 99% for alpha' activity, using single stage treatment. Multistage treatment is capable of achieving over-all decontamination factors as high as 1000 (treatment efficiencies of 99.9%), but complexity and cost increase considerably.

Improved decontamination processes using special ion exchange material have been developed and are in use in laboratory waste and power reactor station treatment systems. Extensive research in this area has been conducted at Argonne, Los Alamos, and Oak Ridge. Decontamination factors for cation exchange resins have ranged from 20 to 50 for mixed fission product waste with as high as 10^5 for mixed-bed units.

Liquid waste which cannot be processed by other methods or which requires greater decontamination for release is treated by evaporation. Since the early 1950's, several types of evaporators have been developed, ranging from small batch evaporators to multiple effect vapor compression distillation units. Decontamination factors as high as 10^6 have been obtained for this processing method, with volume reduction factors ranging from 15 to 400.

More than 15 years' experience in handling highly radioactive liquid waste from fuel reprocessing by storage in underground tanks has shown this to be a safe and practical means of interim handling. Because of the high radioactivity concentrations (500–10,000 c/gal), it has not been possible to discharge high level liquid waste into any part of man's environment. Over 70 million gal of radioactive solutions and sludges are being stored in nearly 200 underground tanks throughout the AEC complex. All major chemical processing sites are located in remote or

TABLE VII

AEC LABORATORY LOW ACTIVITY LIQUID WASTE TREATMENT FACILITIES

Site	Activity in waste, μc/ml	Volume of wastes, 10^6 gal/year	Treatment units	Chemicals employed	Plant efficiency, % Beta-gamma	Plant efficiency, % Other	Sludge treatment and disposal
Argonne National Laboratory	10^{-2} to 10^{-6}	203–237	Evaporation, ion exchange, flocculation, neutralization	NaOH	99.99 90–97 70–90		Vermiculite adsorption and concrete solidification; shipped to ORNL for land burial
Brookhaven National Laboratory	10^{-2}	2.4	Evaporation		99.99		Concrete solidification for sea disposal
Knolls Atomic Power Laboratory	$< 5 \times 10^{-2}$	1.8	In-plant dilution, controlled discharge to river				Spent resins and evaporator slurries shipped to ORNL
	$> 5 \times 10^{-2}$	0.9	Evaporation, ion exchange		99.99		
Oak Ridge National Laboratory (ORNL)	5×10^{-4}	132–273	Mixing, flocculation, settling	Ca(OH)$_2$, Na$_2$CO$_3$, clay	70–90	a, 90 Sr, 84 Cs, 86 Pm, 94 Co, 78 Ru, 76	Disposal to seepage pit

semiremote areas, such as Hanford, Savannah River, and the Idaho Chemical Processing Plant.

Major factors that influence design and operation of tank storage facilities for high level waste management are the radiochemical and chemical composition of the waste. These wastes are generally segregated into two categories, self-heating wastes in which enough heat is generated by radioactive decay to heat the liquid to boiling, and low heating wastes (0.1–0.5 BTU/hour/gal) which still contain enough radioactivity to require storage. Wastes generated at Hanford and Savannah River, essentially 6–7 M HNO_3, arise from the processing of aluminum-clad natural uranium fuels, and are neutralized prior to storage. The Idaho Chemical Processing Plant processes principally full enriched aluminum-clad, uranium-aluminum alloy fuels; the wastes are stored in acidic form.

Self-heating wastes contain more than 99% of the fission products. The rate of heat generation in typical high level waste decreases by a factor of 10 as the waste ages from 0.5 to 10 years from time of reactor discharge. After 10 years' storage, most of the heat comes from decay of Sr^{90} and Cs^{137}, which have halflives of 28 and 30 years, respectively. In neutralized high level waste containing iron, strontium is almost entirely found in the precipitated sludge, while cesium occurs in the supernatant solution.

Tanks used for the storage of high level wastes range in size from 300,000 to 1,330,000 gal capacity; they are 50–85 ft in diameter, and have an operable depth ranging from 18 to 32 ft. At Hanford, the wastes are stored in steel-lined, reinforced concrete tanks, equipped with external condensers for heat removal. At Savannah River, the storage tanks are of different construction because of more restrictive environmental conditions; these tanks consist of an outer steel-lined concrete shell and an inner steel tank. Monitoring equipment is provided between the shells for detection of any leakage that may occur. At the National Reactor Testing Station, first cycle wastes are stored in underground stainless steel water-cooled tanks. These wastes, containing dissolved stainless steel, aluminum, and zirconium, with fluoride and nitrate ions, are less amenable to neutralized tank storage than nitric acid wastes because of their corrosivity and chemical instability. Second and third cycle wastes are stored together in noncooled tanks.

New waste management techniques have recovered some storage space, so additional tank construction requirements have been reduced. During almost 20 years of Hanford operations, four different chemical separations processes have been utilized for the recovery of uranium and plutonium. Original processing methods resulted in several thousand gallons of wastes per ton of uranium processed. Extensive process development work has reduced these quantities of waste to the range of tens of gallons of waste per ton of uranium.

LAND BURIAL AND SEA DISPOSAL

After the processing of liquid low and intermediate level wastes, essentially all of the radioactivity has been transferred to a semisolid phase such as a chemical precipitate, evaporator slurry, or ion exchange resin. These wastes are solidified with concrete or absorbed in material such as vermiculite, in 55-gal drums for temporary on-site storage before ultimate disposal by sea or land burial. These wastes along with other low hazard wastes from laboratory and routine reactor operations, such as contaminated glassware and equipment, paper wipes, rags, animal carcasses, filters, and fuel element boxes, are disposed of by burial in shallow trenches at government-controlled Atomic Energy Commission installations. The disposal of solid or packaged radioactive waste material into the ocean at designated locations represents an equally safe and acceptable method.

Because of the growth of the atomic energy industry, a decision was made in 1959 that regional disposal sites other than the existing AEC sites could be established, as required, on state or federal land. From May 1960 to August 1963, the Atomic Energy Commission operated two interim land burial sites at Oak Ridge and the National Reactor Testing Station in Idaho for disposal of solid packaged waste from all radioactive material users (industry, hospitals, universities, and other government agencies). During the years 1961–1963, over 7 million cubic feet of solid waste materials was buried at principal AEC operating sites, of which only about 300,000 cubic feet came from outside AEC contractor operations, including other government agencies and AEC licensees. During 1963 two privately operated land burial facilities were placed in operation, near Beatty, Nevada, and Moorhead, Kentucky. The AEC, in accord with its policy of encouraging industrial participation, has withdrawn its land burial services.

Since 1946 the AEC has disposed of solid packaged waste material in the Atlantic and Pacific Oceans. Table VIII summarizes the extent of sea disposal operations.

In sea disposal operations, the Atomic Energy Commission has stressed that it is desirable, as an added safety factor, that packages be constructed to maintain their structural integrity while descending to the 1000 fathom depth. With the quantities and characteristics of radioactive materials involved, and with the diffusion and transport capabilities of the ocean environment, it is not considered necessary to assure continued containment of the radioactivity after the containers reach the required depth of 1000 fathoms. Although sea disposal is still licensed by the AEC, the existence of privately operated land burial sites, and the resulting economics of land disposal (approximately three-fourths of the volume of sea disposal containers is concrete ballast) no longer make ocean disposal an important service. This is evidenced by the fact that more than 95% of low level solid packaged wastes are now buried on land.

TABLE VIII

SUMMARY OF SEA DISPOSAL OPERATIONS, 1946 TO JULY 1962

Location	Number of containers, all types	Estimated activity, at time of disposal, curies
Atlantic Ocean		
AEC Contractors (1951–1962)	28,800	43,500
Licensees (1952–1962)	1,343	2,625
Total	30,143	46,125
Pacific Ocean		
AEC Contractors (1946–1962)	24,279[a]	14,162[a]
Licensees (1959–1962)	34,903	670
Total	59,182	14,832

[a] Includes licensee sea disposal operations to 1959.

GASEOUS EFFLUENTS

Air and gas cleaning for the nuclear energy industry differs in two major respects from general industrial air cleaning: the high degree of toxicity of the radioactive contaminants, and the contamination of the cleaning device itself. The latter creates a potential health hazard due to radiation or disposal of the collected materials.

Radioactive gases and particulate material are generated in most nuclear research laboratories, where a variety of chemical, metallurgical, and biological operations are carried out. Experimental work is done in hoods or hot caves that are provided with ventilation systems for the collection of gaseous effluents. Inlet air to each hood usually is conditioned and filtered through glass fiber prefilters that remove large particulate matter and dust; exhaust gases are discharged through high efficiency filters. These filters consist of cellulose-asbestos, or a noncombustible glass medium, and are capable of routinely removing 99.95% of particles 0.3 microns in diameter. In "hot" laboratories used for examining irradiated fuel, it is necessary to provide caustic scrubbers for removing volatile radioactive iodine and ruthenium released during the dissolving period.

In the gaseous effluents from fuel reprocessing operations, the predominating isotope is radioiodine, although ruthenium is also present. The discharge of iodine is controlled by a combination of aging the fuel elements for 90–120 days prior to processing to allow radioactive decay, and retention or removal of most of the volatilized iodine by activated charcoal or silver reactor systems. Ruthenium has been removed by caustic scrubbing. At Hanford, a fixed-bed glass fiber filter system has operated for several years at a collection efficiency of greater than 99.9% for submicron particles present in chemical separations plant process air streams. Silver nitrate packed columns have been developed which, in routine operation, remove over 99.5% of the radioiodine discharged in chemical processing waste gas streams.

Fission Product Utilization

The recovery and beneficial utilization of waste by-products has frequently been suggested as a solution to the waste disposal problems of the nuclear industry. The idea is attractive, but selective removal of specific fission products such as strontium and cesium from high level waste streams does not affect appreciably the waste disposal problem nor significantly aid in its solution. For fission product recovery, a 90% yield is usually satisfactory, whereas for waste disposal purposes, decontamination factors of 10^6 to 10^8 are required before the effluent can be satisfactorily discharged to the environment. Secondly, recovered fission products still require disposal when they are no longer usable. Therefore, from a waste disposal standpoint, there is little economic incentive for separating specific fission products from waste streams.

INDUSTRY TRENDS

The generation of electric power is, and will continue to be, the primary objective of nuclear development programs throughout the world. Major technological advances are being made also to extend and accelerate the beneficial applications of radioisotopes and radiation.

Our rapidly advancing industrial and technological society requires ample sources of energy. With an ever increasing rate of energy consumption, it is estimated that the readily available fossil fuel resources would be exhausted in 100 years or less if no other forms of energy were utilized. Therefore, development of economic nuclear energy will make an important and vital contribution toward meeting our long-term energy requirements. With this ultimate objective, it has been estimated that the installed nuclear electrical capacity in the country will rise to approximately 40% of the total installed electric capacity by the year 2000.

The use of nuclear energy for electric power and, less immediately, for industrial process heat and other purposes is now technically feasible and is becoming economically reasonable, especially in high fuel cost areas. Recent cost estimates on large nuclear power plant facilities have ranged from $135 to 150 per kilowatt of installed electrical capacity, which is approaching the construction costs for conventional power plants. The future use of nuclear power will be further enhanced by the successful development of "breeder" reactors, that produce more fissionable material than they consume.

The beneficial use of radioisotopes as sources of nuclear radiation for scientific, medical, agricultural, and industrial application continues to increase. Certain radionuclides serve as sources of heat to generate small amounts of electric power for space use or in remote unattended devices such as buoys and automatic weather stations that transmit their data by radio. Considerable research and development is being carried out on new radioisotope applications and on packaging methods, the latter being related to similar developments for ultimate waste disposal purposes.

As the atomic energy industry develops, commercial chemical reprocessing of irradiated reactor fuels will become increasingly important. The first commercial facility of this type is now under construction in western New York State, at an estimated cost of $30 million, and is expected to become operational in late 1965.

WASTE MANAGEMENT RESEARCH AND DEVELOPMENT

Two major problems will assume growing importance in a developing atomic industry: the treatment and disposal of large volume, low activity wastes, and the permanent storage or disposal of concentrated high level wastes.

During the past 20 years, with relatively small nuclear activities, it has been satisfactory to discharge large volumes of low activity wastes to the environment on a controlled basis and to assure that the safe capacity of the environment was not exceeded. This will become increasingly difficult in the future because of the larger quantities of radioactivity being handled and the more stringent radiation protection standards being established. Therefore, the waste management research and development program for low and intermediate level waste is directed at developing improved and more efficient methods for decontaminating and disposing of large volumes. Process treatment efficiencies of 99.9% are now being routinely obtained in pilot plant operations with low level waste streams. In connection with these engineering development studies, continued environmental research is being conducted to determine the ultimate fate of specific residual radionuclides discharged to the air, land, or water environments, and to establish reasonable technical criteria for safe disposal of low level radioactive effluents into the environment.

A vigorous research and development program is now in progress to develop methods for safe ultimate storage or disposal of concentrated high level wastes. There are two general approaches: conversion to an inert, water-insoluble solid, with subsequent packaging in suitable containers; and storage or disposal in dry geologic formations such as salt structures or other safe containing media. Both of these phases of the high level waste development programs are approaching the pilot plant and field demonstration phase, and it is expected that results will be available when industrial reprocessing of spent reactor fuels becomes a reality.

The economy of nuclear power depends in part on developing safe and economic methods for disposal of the industry's waste. It has been reported that over $200 million has been spent in the Atomic Energy Commission complex for capital facilities involving the collection, handling, treatment, and disposal of radioactive wastes. A major portion of the capital cost is associated with the handling and storage of high activity liquid wastes. Annual operating costs of these facilities are estimated at $6 million. The fraction of nuclear power costs allowable for waste disposal has not been established and, because of the preliminary status of the development program, no realistic cost estimate for the ultimate disposal of high level wastes is available at the present time. Present engineering cost studies indicate that waste disposal operations should account for less than 1% of the cost of nuclear power in a 0.6 cent/kwh economy. Based on an expected successful field demonstration and testing program with high activity waste, it is believed that waste management operations will not constitute a major obstacle in the development of the nuclear energy industry.

REFERENCES

1. American Standards Association Working Committee, "Report on Uranium Mining and Milling Wastes," 1964.
2. Civilian Nuclear Power—A Report to the President, 1962.
3. Edison Electric Institute, "Radioactive Waste Handling in the Nuclear Power Industry," 1960.
4. Rodger, W. A., "Radioactive Waste Disposal," U. S. Atomic Energy Commission ANL-6233, 1960.
5. U. S. Atomic Energy Commission, "Atomic Energy Facts: A Summary of Atomic Activities of Interest to Industry," 1957.
6. U. S. Congressional Joint Committee on Atomic Energy, "Industrial Radioactive Waste Disposal," Hearings before the Special Subcommittee on Radiation, 1959.

Chapter 25

TRANSPORTATION

by A. R. BALDEN

The automobile industry contains within its complex many operations that often, by themselves, constitute complete businesses. For example, many automobile manufacturers have their own stamping, casting, metal finishing, and electroplating divisions, and a large number of smaller enterprises center around the casting or forming, finishing and electroplating, anodizing, or painting of parts such as bumpers, door handles, grilles, and moldings. The chapter on Metal Finishing Products deals in detail with the treatment of wastes from the electroplating and allied industries. Discussions of this waste are limited in this chapter to its treatment in combination with other wastes.

Oily wastes are common to all plants in which machining is part of the sequence of operations. Although the problem is complicated by the presence of emulsifiers, there is still much in common with the disposal of oily wastes from refineries, which are dealt with in the chapter on Petroleum. This chapter treats the disposal of oily wastes in the automobile industry.

Because the manufacturing of all transportation vehicles, whether passenger cars, tractors, trucks, buses, boats, trains, or aircraft, involves stamping, forging, casting, machining, electroplating, anodizing, chemical surface treatment, and painting, these manufacturing facilities are faced with the same problems in the treatment and disposal of industrial process wastes. There are differences between various manufacturing operations depending on the end product, for example, buses and aircraft use more aluminum; but much greater differences exist due to the location of the plant. A plant located in a large metropolitan complex is allowed greater freedom in the composition of industrial waste effluent than one located in a rural area and dependent on a small stream to carry away its treated wastes.

THE AUTOMOBILE INDUSTRY

The automobile industry uses 20% of all steel produced in the United States. Of all radios currently made, 32% are for automobiles. Car and truck production during the decade 1950–1960 averaged 7 million units per year, at an average value of $11,557,000,000 per year. There is one passenger car for every three persons in the country.

The automobile industry starts with basic raw materials and performs, in one or another of its various plants, all the operations necessary to produce the completed vehicle. Steel sheets are cut to size and formed into the various components such as roof panels, doors, and deck lids. To obtain a piece free from wrinkles, distortions, or scored or torn metal, drawing compounds are used to enable the die to move freely over the metal in the forming operation. This drawing compound may be any of several types, ranging from mineral oils with fatty oil additives to pigmented soluble soaps. It may be in an aqueous, oil, or emulsified medium.

The component parts, so formed, are next welded into the finished assembly. The drawing compounds previously applied must now be removed so that an adherent phosphate coating can be applied to serve as a base for paint. The drawing compound, applied to the car body components for a necessary purpose, now becomes an organic contaminant that must be removed before the effluent is released to a public waterway. The cleaning medium is normally an aqueous solution of an alkaline detergent, and requires neutralization before discharge. Often the acid wastes from the phosphating compound are adequate to accomplish this.

The final rinse in the phosphate process is usually a dilute chromic acid solution. Restrictions on hexavalent chromium discharges are strict, and this waste requires reduction to trivalent chromium and precipitation as hydroxide to rid it of this poisonous material. However, the concentration of chromic acid is low, and often other contaminants are present in sufficient quantity and are sufficiently oxidizable to accomplish the reduction of hexavalent to trivalent chromium. Because the pH of the waste from cleaning and phosphating is normally on the alkaline side, this effluent is often an item requiring only monitoring.

After phosphating and oven drying, unitized bodies having the structural members welded to the other body components are, in some installations, dipped in a water-dispersible paint to protect the inner surfaces of the structural members. This paint is removed, by means of a water rinse, from those exterior decorative surfaces that are to receive the final color coat of paint. Because this paint owes certain of its critical properties to emulsifiers, the means of treating such wastes depend upon destruction of the emulsifiers. This is a distinctly different operation from treating organic paint wastes, and requires a separate system.

Exterior surfaces are spray painted with the primer and surfacer, cured, wet sanded to improve the surface finish, dried, spray painted with the chosen color, and cured. The booths are maintained free from airborne dust by filtration. The air stream is brought from the atmosphere, filtered through a glass fiber filter, and, carrying the paint overspray and solvent, leaves the spray booth through a water curtain that washes the air clean before it is again released to the atmosphere.

Effective removal of paint from the exhaust air is aided by means of an additive to the water curtain. This is alkaline in nature and normally contains materials such as finely divided clays or chalks around which the suspended paints can collect and which facilitate flotation for subsequent removal.

Engines, power steering units, transmissions, brake systems, and other components made of cast iron or aluminum are normally produced in plants other than the assembly plants described above. Iron or aluminum castings are machined to size before assembly.

Cutting oils are used to obtain lubricity of the tool-to-metal surface, to remove metal dust and particles from the surface, and to cool the cutting edges. Water has a high cooling capacity, and where dimensional tolerances are critical this capacity is needed. To prevent the metal from corroding and to provide some lubricity for improved cutting tool life, an oil-in-water emlulsion or "soluble oil" is added.

Because of increased horsepower demands on engines, and because cars are generally expected to travel more comfortably, more economically, and longer than ever before, the parts assembled into the various units must be machined to much closer tolerances than were previously required. This calls for frequent gauging. Because accurate gauging requires clean parts, washing must be done before each inspection. As dirt or metal particles can cause malfunctioning of moving parts, by obstructing such motion, the components of a mechanical unit must be carefully cleaned before assembly. Such cleaning is occasionally accomplished by immersion in the cleaning solution, but more often a high pressure power spray washing machine is used. The cleaning solution may be prepared using an emulsion of oil in water, or it may be a solution of alkaline compounds such as silicates, phosphates, carbonates, and hydroxides, plus soaps or synthetic detergents, or both.

The plating department of an automobile manufacturing plant is called upon to plate, anodize, or phosphate many different parts with a variety of processes. Wastes from these processes, of course, vary considerably. Cadmium, zinc, copper, nickel, and chromium metals are present in the rinsewaters. Complex alkali cyanides are normally used to prepare the plating solutions to electroplate cadmium, zinc, and copper. Sulfuric acid is used to prepare the solution in which an anodized coating is formed on aluminum. Either sulfuric acid or hydrochloric acid is used to chemically activate or renew the surface of a part prior to electroplating. A solution of sodium stannate is used to tin coat by chemical displacement aluminum parts subject to reciprocal motion. Zinc phosphate solutions are used to form a coating on steel to hold oil and thus resist corrosion; this is common on such parts as nuts and bolts. Manganese phosphate solutions are used to produce a similar coating on parts such as gears, which are subject to wear.

AUTOMOBILE MANUFACTURING WASTE CHARACTERISTICS

Although the metered water intake in the automobile industry is approximately 10,000 gal per car produced, much of this water is affected only in that its temperature is increased and the dissolved gases including oxygen are correspondingly decreased. Other portions of this water may be partially or seriously contaminated during use by one or more of the manufacturing operations. The exact characteristic of the waste is a function of the operation performed, such as cleaning, processing, and painting, modified by the material used in the operation.

The characteristics of rinsewaters, constantly overflowing to waste from washing operations, and of washing solutions themselves, which periodically become contaminated to the extent that they must be sent to the treatment plant, are many and varied. Of particular interest to the engineer responsible for prevention of water degradation are alkalinity or, on occasion, acidity, oil content of the waste, and the oxygen-consuming capacity. An extreme pH, either acid or alkaline, kills fish, and less than lethal dosages may drive them away. The aquatic life that serves as food for game fish and is an important link in the life cycle of a healthy stream is often more sensitive to contaminants than are the game fish.

Waters of low pH corrode and destroy steel or concrete sewer pipe. A less obvious effect is retardation of bacterial action, seriously interfering with a stream's ability to cleanse itself. Often a shock dosage can completely disrupt a municipal sewage treatment plant because of bactericidal action of acidic effluents. Depending on the extent of deviation from an acceptable pH between 5.5 and 9.0, the effect may vary from incomplete treatment to no treatment of the municipal sewage.

Organic wastes are a serious pollutant to water. The presence of wastes such as oils and greases is readily apparent; they appear in small concentrations as an iridescent film and in large quantities as unsightly floating masses or slicks. In addition to the obviously undesirable esthetic qualities of water polluted with organic soils, including oils, greases, waxes, paint solids, and solvents, there is other evidence of degradation. Slightly contaminated water has the ability to purify itself. Bacteria in the water consume reasonable amounts of organic materials, using up a certain amount of dissolved oxygen in the process. The oxygen thus consumed is quickly replaced by absorption from the atmosphere, especially in a moving stream. If, however, an oil film has eliminated the air-water interface, adequate replenishment of oxygen by this method is impossible. If penetration of light to the stream has been reduced by an opaque or semitranslucent film, replenishment of the oxygen supply by means of photosynthesis is also eliminated or seriously impaired.

The presence of game fish in a stream is a good indication of the high quality of the water, as their oxygen requirements are considerably higher than those of scavengers or bottom feeders. When game fish begin to leave a stream, it usually indicates that the quality of the water has deteriorated. Organics such as alcohols, which are soluble, and emulsified soils that are well dispersed deplete the oxygen supply by rapid bacteriological action.

Solid matter emptied into a stream has on occasion built sludge banks to the point that they have interfered with navigation. In some rivers frequent and expensive dredging is necessary to maintain channels for deep draft boats. Matter sufficiently fine that turbulence and the forces of Brownian movement prevent early precipitation acts to reduce light penetration. Whether this matter be liquid in nature, as the emulsified oils, or solid like silt, the result is the same, as photosynthesis is essential to a healthy water environment. If the solid matter is oxidizable, bacteriological action consumes it, and so uses oxygen. If the rate of oxygen consumption is no greater than the rate of replenishment, the water quality is maintained. If, however, the rate of consumption is excessive, an inferior, polluted waterway results. Solid matter can also interfere with a live, healthy stream by covering bottom aquatic life and cutting off its supply of food and oxygen.

Certain other pollutants, mostly organics, are serious not only because of their poisonous nature but because even in extremely small quantities they have a serious effect on taste. Good examples of these are the phenols and their derivatives. Chemicals of this group of benzene ring compounds are used in emulsified oils as bacteriostats. It is possible, of course, for a high concentration of phenols to overwhelm a sewage treatment plant and completely knock out the bacteria. However, we are usually conscious of phenols in much lower concentrations because of their distinctive medicinal taste. Concentrations of 5 parts per billion are considered the maximum by most ordinances. Chlorinating the water supply does not destroy phenols but attaches a chlorine atom to the ring and makes the medicinal taste more noticeable than before.

Many metals are lethal to aquatic life in small concentrations. Chromium, copper, cadmium, and lead are examples. Many ordinances pertaining to industrial waste effluents limit the concentration of these metals to 1 mg/liter.

Certain of the wetting agents used in power spray washing are synthetic detergents of the foaming type. These could contribute to the troublesome froths encountered in sewage treatment plants. However, foaming-type wetting agents are being engineered out of industrial application because of the high pressures used in power spray washers. To prevent the washing compound from foaming excessively, nonfoaming wetting agents were developed.

In general, the objectionable waste characteristics resulting from automobile manufacturing include disagreeable taste effects of the phenols, esthetically unacceptable oils on water and the more serious killing of ducks and fish as well as other forms of aquatic life, and the poisonous effects of certain of the heavy metals. Fortunately, techniques for separating these materials from water are generally available and, where the technique is not sure, it is often feasible to operate without use of the troublesome material.

AUTOMOBILE INDUSTRY WASTE DISPOSAL

ENGINEERING CONSIDERATIONS

The engineering of disposal methods for industrial process wastes must include the broader and more inclusive concept of water engineering and process engineering. In water engineering, the costs and feasibility of conditioning cooling water for recirculation have to be evaluated and compared with the costs and feasibility of using the water once and disposing of it to the sewer or waste treatment facilities. Included in these considerations is the cost of water, adequacy of the water supply, quality of the water for cooling and recirculating purposes, and the cost of treating the water to prevent corrosion of the circulating system or bacterial attack on wood in the cooling towers. Information on these points helps establish the amount of water available to dilute the plant effluent before it is discharged to the city sewer or elsewhere.

Radioactive materials are seldom found in the automobile industry; when they are present, disposal is by burial. After a series of atom bomb tests, the soil removed from high flying airplanes is often found to be radioactive. This soil must be collected and buried.

There is often considerable flexibility in the operations required of a plant within the general framework of manufacturing a given item. As an example, corrosion protection may be required for certain parts such as nuts and bolts but the option is frequently allowed to obtain this protection by means of an electrodeposit such as zinc or cadmium or through the use of an oiled phosphate coating. If zinc or cadmium plate is chosen, the deposit is obtained from a complex sodium zinc cyanide or a sodium cadmium cyanide solution. This requires accumulation of the electroplating rinse solutions in holding tanks and destruction of the cyanide ions by an oxidizing agent such as sodium hypochlorite. If a phosphate coating is chosen for the part in question, no poisonous contamination results. Furthermore, the limit on phosphate concentration in the effluent is high because its only significant effect on the receiving waterway is to encourage the growth of algae. Because the oil is applied as a final coating that remains on the part as it is shipped, proper precautions to prevent loss of oil to the sewer eliminate any necessity for treating oily wastes.

Rinsewaters used prior to electroplating must be kept clean or contamination from the rinse will, by carry-over, affect the plating solution and cause the electrodeposit to be of poor quality. Oily contamination can also, by adsorption on the part to be plated, interfere with adhesion of the deposit. To avoid electroplated metal of poor quality, the plater has often resorted to a high rate of water flow through the rinse tanks. This is not only wasteful of water, which is expensive, but is sometimes impossible because, during periods of drought, water may be rationed. Some interesting approaches to the problem of conserving water and yet having an adequate supply of sufficient purity to maintain a high quality deposit have proved effective. In one, a counterflow of water is used in multiple rinses. For example, two or more rinses are often used prior to nickel plating. Instead of each of these rinse tanks having an independent water intake and overflow, all are connected; fresh water enters the last rinse, which must be kept cleanest, and flows counter to the direction of the work as it passes through the tanks in series. This reuse of water has proved practical in many plants. Another means of obtaining best use from a given volume of water utilizes the property that water following an acid dip has greater electrical conductivity than clean water because of the presence of acidity. Flow of makeup water into a rinse tank can, accordingly, be automatically controlled by a conductivity actuated valve.

At one time, cleaning tanks were emptied frequently to prevent accumulation of fine soils and machining dust in the solution and possible redeposition of the soil onto the part being cleaned. This technique was satisfactory as long as replacement of the cleaner was on a sufficiently frequent cycle. Its weakness lay in the fact that parts were being cleaned in a washing solution that varied from one newly prepared to one ready for disposal and often already redepositing soil. When the quality requirements became such that redeposited metal fines were considered entirely unacceptable, a new approach to the problem became imperative. Cleaner compounders developed detergent materials with enhanced soil-carrying capacity. Equipment manufacturers designed baffles into the reservoirs of their washing machines to permit better settling of suspended soils. The most effective way to provide good quality work also relieved some of the load on the waste treatment facilities. A filter medium was developed so that much of the suspended solid soils could be removed by high rate filtration. Cleaning solutions thus stay clean for longer periods, and better results are obtained at reduced chemical costs and with a decreased volume of wastes to be treated.

Another example of choice of type of waste involves the engineer's control of specifications. An illustration of this relates to the use of phenols. These chemicals have for years been used as bacteriostats in soluble oil coolants and as additives in paint stripping preparations. However, phenols are difficult to destroy, and even a trace is sufficient to impart objectionable taste and odor to water. For this reason, work was done to eliminate the use of phenols in any metal finishing preparations. It was found after exhaustive tests that soluble oil coolants could be maintained free from bacterial decomposition by proper aeration and filtration. This technique has been placed in operation in central systems large enough to hold the coolant from many machines, and it has been found possible to rewrite specifications for soluble oil coolants to eliminate the use of phenols. After this was accomplished, the problem of paint strippers was investigated to determine if an additive could be discovered or formulated that, in the highly alkaline medium, would encourage penetration and removal of the paint film as well as the phenol compounds previously used. This also was found to be possible and was put into effect.

DISPOSAL PROCEDURES

The wastes resulting from making an automobile are, in the main, capable of treatment by known means. Soluble oils, emulsified cleaners, and water soluble paints are capable of clarification by chemical treatment followed by precipitation or air flotation. The overspray resulting from use of enamels and lacquers can be modified by strong alkalies and the float readily removed. Chemical poisons such as cadmium, chromium, copper, and cyanide can be destroyed or effectively removed from water. The use of certain materials, such as phenols, at the present state of technology, is best avoided. However, there are units in operation that use specially adapted bacteria which can metabolize the phenols.

Free oil is readily removed from waste waters by gravity separation. It is seldom the cause of stream pollution because any waste treatment facility should have a catch basin or equalization tank provided with skimmers or other means for removal of free oil before treating the wastewater.

There are many electrolytes that can be used for breaking emulsions, with varying degrees of effectiveness. Selection of the most suitable method for treatment requires study of the conditions in the specific plant under consideration. This includes knowledge of the other pollutants present, as well as the concentration of the emulsion present and the type of emulsifier used. Laboratory tests are essential to establish the most suitable type and concentration of emulsion breaker.

An oil-in-water emulsion consists of many small particles of oil held in suspension in the water medium by the effect of the ionic atmosphere. The particles are isolated because their like charges cause them to repel each other. This prevents them from joining with other particles of like material, forming agglomerates large enough to allow gravitational forces to overcome the dispersive forces associated with Brownian movement. Most emulsions are of the oil-in-water type. Examples are soils emulsified by an alkaline detergent, most soluble oils, and emulsion cleaners. These carry a negative charge in their ionic protective layer and are thus destroyed by the neutralizing effects of cations. Salts such as calcium chloride, ferrous chloride, ferrous sulfate, ferric chloride, ferric sulfate, and aluminum sulfate have been used alone and in various mixtures to destroy emulsified wastes. Because the hydroxides of these metals are insoluble, the pH of the solution must be adjusted to 7 or below to obtain maximum benefit from the multivalent cations. Lowering of the pH often in itself introduces a sufficient number of cations to break the emulsion. The concentration of oil in the emulsified wastes and the amount and types of emulsifiers used determine the amount of acid and emulsion breaker needed, as well as the exact choice of chemicals to be used for this purpose. In some cases, the use of ferrous salts is preferable; in others, ferric salts are superior. Aluminum salts have certain obvious advantages; for example, they form a floc at a slightly acidic pH and, when the matter adhered to the floc has been released by further acid treatment, a soluble and reusable aluminum salt is formed as a by-product. Many times, best results are obtained by mixtures of salts, the exact mixture and proportion varying from day to day and often within a given work shift. It is unfortunate that more is not known of this phase of chemical engineering, but the possible combinations are so numerous and changing, with new and improved oils and cleaners, that the empirical approach has considerable merit.

Normally, room temperature is appropriate for treatment but, as with most reactions involving organic chemicals, heat accelerates the reaction. In certain wastes difficult to treat, the use of heat has proved to be extremely beneficial. The time required to destroy the emulsion and to accomplish complete separation varies from a few minutes to several hours. However, a few minutes is adequate for treatment of most emulsified wastes.

Although occasional difficulties may be encountered in treating a waste, it should be admitted that the most frequent cause for difficulty is that the particular waste was not anticipated in the concentration encountered. Often, dilution alone reduces the waste to one that can be handled. Such difficulties also are minimized if a thorough survey of the kinds and quantities of all wastes that may be encountered is made before design and installation of the waste treatment equipment.

After chemical separation of the oil-in-water or paint-in-water has been accomplished by destruction or modification of the emulsifying or solubilizing agent, the remaining problem is to effect physical separation. If the density of the released organic material is less than that of water, separation is achieved by flotation. If the difference in densities can be increased by attaching air bubbles to the matter being removed, separation can be achieved much faster and the size of the required equipment can be reduced.

Water-dispersible paint can be treated by many of the same procedures as are used for emulsion cleaners and soluble oil wastes. In the present state of development of water-dispersible paints, a number of approaches are used to accomplish dispersion of paint materials in the aqueous phase. Thus there is considerably more variation in the treatment used for specific paints than there is in the treatment of emulsified oils.

Alum is used successfully in air flotation units to purify water-dispersible paint wastes. In certain installations, activated silica has been used advantageously with alum to obtain increased clarity. In other installations, in which paint of a different manufacturer may be used, the employment of activated silica has no apparent advantage. Elsewhere, ferric chloride has produced a waste that lends itself extremely well to treatment by air flotation.

Some success has been achieved in precipitating water-dispersible paint wastes mixed with other process wastes by using ferric chloride to destroy any emulsifiers present and then adjusting the pH to 9.5–9.8 to form the floc and obtain precipitation. Experience has shown that the pH should be brought to 5.5 or below to obtain good action of the ferric ion on the emulsifier. The relative amounts of ferric chloride and sulfuric acid used to bring the pH to the proper reaction range depend on a number of factors, most important being the total alkalinity of the solution and the amount of oil present in the waste. It is essential, in the operation of batch treatment followed by lagoon settling, that jar tests be used: first, to determine the proper concentration of chemicals to obtain clarification, and, after the chemicals have been added to the large mixing tanks and a retention time of approximately ½ hour has been allowed, a second test to determine that clarification has been accomplished or, if not, what further chemical adjustment is required.

Because the chemical requirements for the sedimentation process are somewhat greater than the requirement in flotation, and the high solids from this procedure cause a heavy load on the lagoons, a combination of air flotation followed by lagoon settling has been tried with some success. Air flotation removes the solids from the paint waste effluent to a concentration of 25–50 mg/liter. The solids are pumped directly to a drying bed. The clarified effluent is then mixed with the remainder of the plant waste in large reaction tanks, and precipitated as previously described.

Paint spray-booth water wash compounds used to prevent adhesion of overspray of enamel or lacquer to the surface of the booth and to wash the overspray from the ventilating air stream are highly alkaline. These materials are used in a closed system and require treatment only when they lose effectiveness to the point that it cannot be restored by additions of fresh chemical. The alkaline material to be treated has some suspended paint pigment and vehicle. The mass of the overspray paint, which by chemical reaction, occlusion, or absorption loses its original tacky nature, is so altered that it can be floated and skimmed, or in certain instances, depending on the paint and the wash compound, settled and removed as sludge after emptying the tank. The water wash compound requires pH adjustment and a few hours retention time for the solids to settle before it can be emptied to the sewer or other public waterway.

Passenger carrying vehicles such as buses, airplanes, and boats have an added problem of disposal of sanitary wastes accumulated en route in service. Deodorizing chemicals are added to the receiving receptacles and the wastes are transferred to sewerage systems at terminals.

EQUIPMENT

Figure 1 shows a typical air flotation unit. Waste liquid to be treated is mixed with the chemical combination designed to break the emulsion and form the floc. The liquid is then pumped to an air saturation tank in which it is retained for a period of approximately 3 minutes at a pressure of about 35 psig. In a typical installation, an emulsified oily waste is treated with a 5% solution of alum (aluminum sulfate) plus sufficient sulfuric acid to adjust the pH to a range of 5.5 to 6.0.

A. R. BALDEN

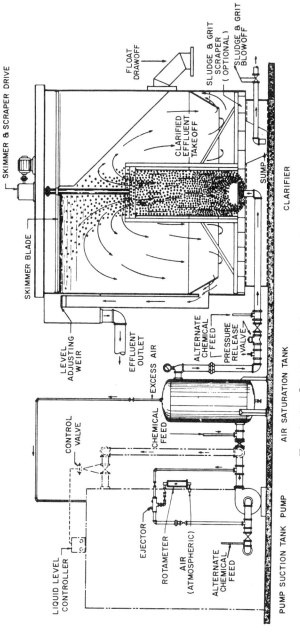

FIG. 1. Air flotation unit for separating oil and water.

Figure 2 is a schematic drawing indicating the flexibility possible in operation of an air flotation unit. The liquid waste from the manufacturing operation enters a flash mix tank, into which the treating chemicals are metered at a predetermined rate. The waste next enters a flocculation tank where, by the action of gentle agitation, the floc is caused to grow and the waste material becomes occluded and adsorbed onto the growing floc. The waste is next mixed with a certain percentage of its volume of clarified effluent, which had been retained in an air saturation tank for a period of time, as indicated above, to saturate the liquid with air. As this mixture now reaches the clarifier and the pressure drops to that of the atmosphere, the air is released in many small bubbles that, on rising to the surface, take the floc and occluded waste in the manner of minute balloons. Sweeps remove the risen float to a storage tank for further separation.

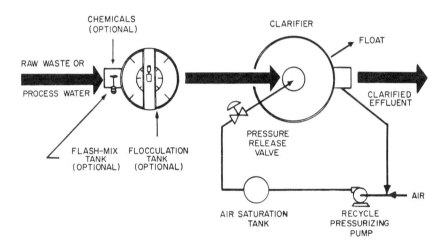

FIG. 2. Air flotation unit illustrating its versatility.

In the instance just given, a preclarified effluent is pressurized and then mixed with the incoming waste. This procedure is used where the floc is sensitive to agitation, and air bubbling in the saturation tank could disperse it. It has the evident shortcoming that a portion of the capacity of the unit is used by the effluent being recycled. In many instances it is possible and preferable to use direct flotation, where the chemically treated waste is itself saturated with air.

Certain flocs formed have the unfortunate tendency to become denser under the influence of prolonged agitation. Then, the agitation time is reduced and, if necessary, restricted to the flash mix. It may be noted, in Fig. 1, that an alternate chemical feed may be made after the air saturation. In this procedure, floc is forming at the same instant that air is released, which has very definite advantages at times.

Figure 3 shows a reactor-clarifier. A unit of this type is based on the observation that if an insoluble substance is formed in the presence of other particulate matter, the crystals grow at an accelerated rate. Controlled recirculation of slurry permits separation of the solids and production of a high purity water. To add weight to the precipitate, lime is normally used for pH adjustment.

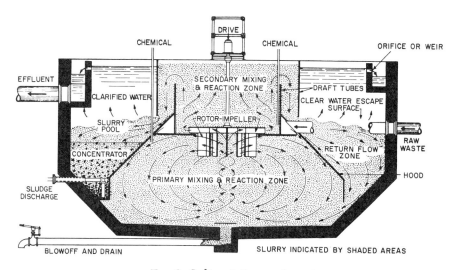

Fig. 3. Sedimentation equipment.

Various combinations of these processes have been used. Although it is not possible to make a hard and fast rule, it is generally true that the precipitation processes are considerably more time consuming than flotation. This means that to handle a given flow of a certain type of waste, the equipment required to precipitate it will be larger and more expensive than that required for flotation. Generally speaking, flotation will not produce as pure a water as precipitation. A combination of floatation to remove the gross soil and sedimentation for final clarification is becoming more generally employed as more rigorous control is required. After the solids have been concentrated and accumulated, the sludge handling problem does not differ from that discussed in the first section of this chapter.

TRENDS

The growth of suburban living has given rise to the multicar family. Modern mechanical aids have largely freed the housewife from the routines which have been her lot through the memory of mankind. With the newly released time, she is able to follow a career of her own or become active in community projects, either of which make the owning of a second family car important. A higher standard of living is reflected in more travel by land, air, and water.

A larger population with more wealth will increase the demand for goods. More and larger cities and factories will require more water or greater reuse of water for their existence. To make greater reuse of water possible, more stringent requirements on the quality of the effluent to the nation's waterways will be enforced on cities and industries. Some relief will be accomplished by better water planning, for instance, by storing of water from periods of high precipitation. Research will be required to develop improved methods of treating sanitary wastes. Economical means are required to remove a higher percentage of pollutants. However, if the techniques now available were applied, a vast improvement in the nation's waterways would result.

SUBJECT INDEX